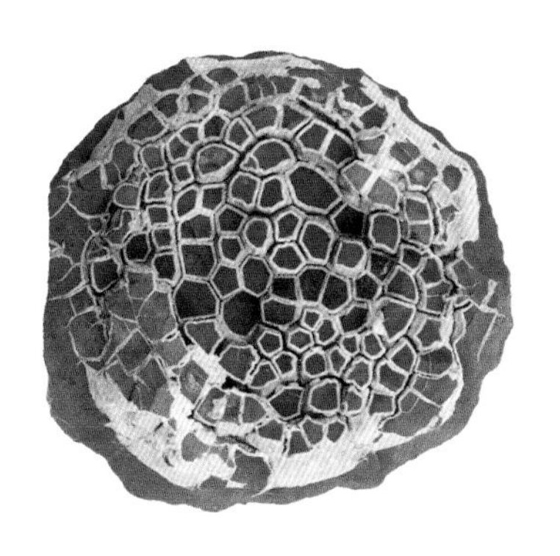

James Hutton

THE FOUNDER OF MODERN GEOLOGY

Alan McKirdy

James Hutton

Art historian Dr David Mackie dates this portrait of James Hutton by Sir Henry Raeburn as having been completed around 1790. On the table, to Hutton's left, are specimens from his geological collection, including shells, mineral veins and a section through a septarian nodule.

Sir Henry Raeburn: *Portrait of James Hutton 1726–79. Geologist* [detail]. PG 2686: National Galleries of Scotland. Purchased with the aid of the Art Fund and the National Heritage Memorial Fund 1986.

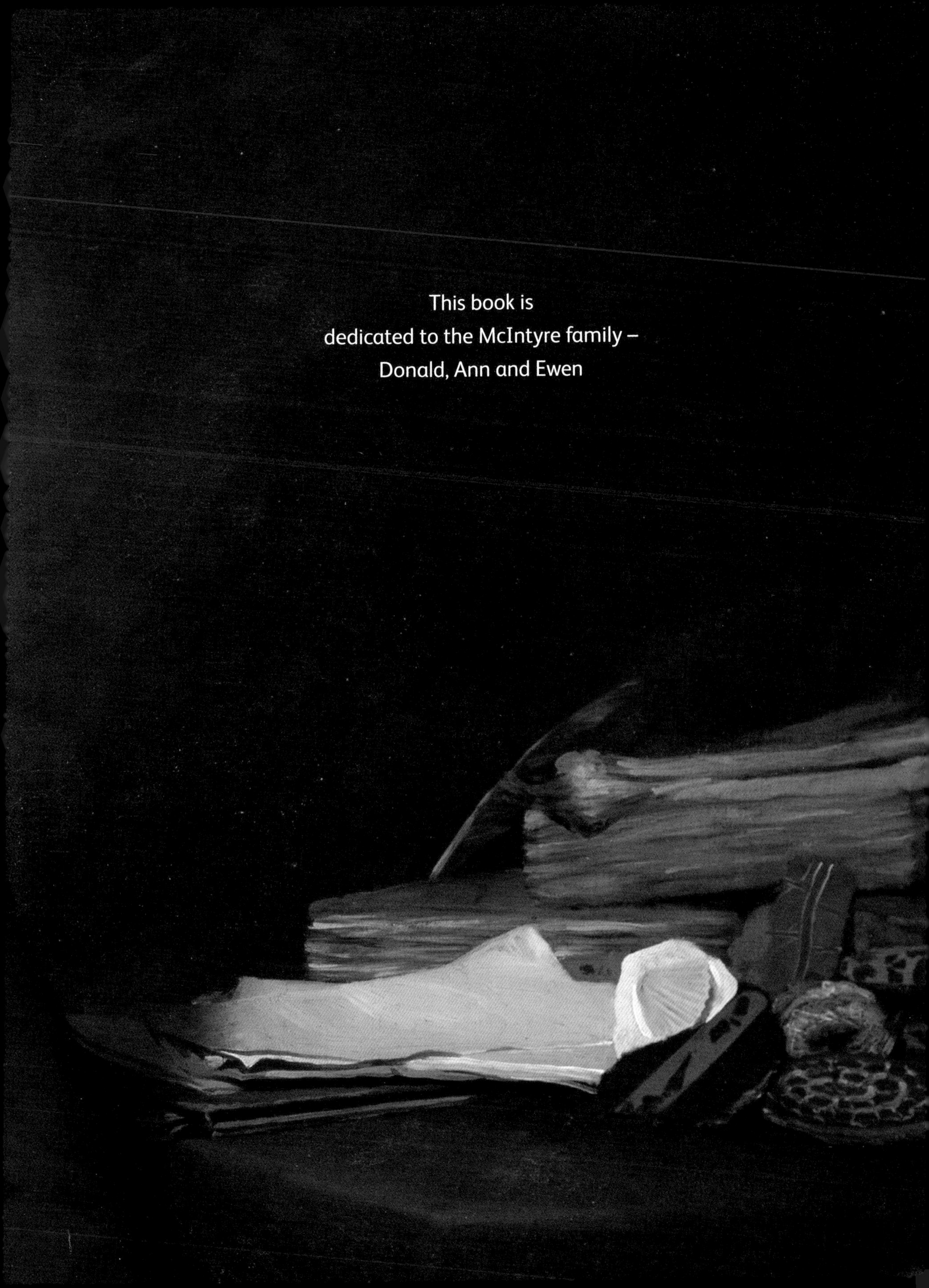

This book is
dedicated to the McIntyre family –
Donald, Ann and Ewen

James Hutton

THE FOUNDER OF MODERN GEOLOGY

National Museums Scotland would like to thank
The James Hutton Foundation
for their generous donation towards this publication.

The James Hutton Institute
Invergowrie, Dundee, DD2 5DA

This book first published in 1997 by The Stationery Office Limited.
Revised and amended edition published in 2001 by National Museums Scotland Publishing Limited.
Further revised and updated edition published in 2012 by NMS Enterprises Limited – Publishing.

This revised and expanded edition first published in Great Britain in 2022 by

NMS Enterprises Limited – Publishing
National Museums Scotland
Chambers Street
Edinburgh EH1 1JF

Reprinted in 2024.

(see also page 153)

British Library Cataloguing in Publication Data
A catalogue record of this book is available from the British Library.

ISBN: 978 1 910682 44 9

Cover design by Mark Blackadder.
Cover images: front: Siccar Point (Alan McKirdy);
James Hutton by James Tassie, 1739–99
(Image © National Museums Scotland)
Internal text design by
NMS Enterprises Ltd – Publishing.

Printed and bound in Great Britain by
Bell & Bain Ltd, Glasgow.

This product is made of material from well-managed, FSC®-certified forests and other controlled sources.

For a full listing of NMS Enterprises Ltd – Publishing titles and related merchandise visit:

www.nms.ac.uk/books

Contents

JAMES HUTTON TIMELINE

1726 BORN 3 JUNE IN EDINBURGH
James Hutton was one of five children.

1731 Began his education at the Royal High School of Edinburgh.

1740 Studied Latin, logic, rhetoric and mathematics at University of Edinburgh.

1743 Apprentice to lawyer, George Chalmers WS.

1744 Start of his medical studies at University of Edinburgh.

1745–46 Jacobite Rising took place, which interrupted Hutton's medical studies.

1747 Fathered an illegitimate son.

1747 Attended university in Paris to continue his medical studies.

1749 Qualified as Medical Doctor (MD) at the University of Leiden.

1749 Stayed briefly in London whilst he considered his future.

1750 Returned to Edinburgh. Started a manufacturing business making *sal ammoniac* from soot.

1752 Travelled to East Anglia to learn more about farming. Also travelled widely across England.

1754 Toured northern France and parts of Holland, studying agriculture.

1754 Settled at Slighhouses Farm, Berwickshire.

1764 Made his trip to the Highlands and Caithness to study geology.

1767 Moved back permanently to Edinburgh and found employment working on the Forth and Clyde Canal project.

1774 Travelled to Cheshire and Wales with James Watt to study geology.

1777 Published *Considerations on the Nature, Quality, and Distinctions of Coal and Culm*. Started to gain recognition for his work on geology.

1778 Rented out Slighhouses Farm, earning Hutton a good income.

1783 Royal Society of Edinburgh received its Royal Charter.

1788 Hutton elected as a Member of the Royal Society of Agriculture at Paris.

1788 First of Hutton's many papers published in the *Transactions of the Royal Society of Edinburgh*.

1794 Published his version of 'natural selection' in *Principles of Knowledge*.

1795 Hutton's *Theory of the Earth* is published in two volumes.

1797 DIED 26 MARCH, AGED SEVENTY

1802 John Playfair published *Illustrations of the Huttonion Theory of the Earth.*

1830–33 Charles Lyell's *Principles of Geology* published. Lyell reworked many of Hutton's ideas and concepts.

1831 Charles Darwin set sail on HMS *Beagle*. Reading Lyell's *Principles of Geology* helped Darwin develop his ideas on natural selection.

1899 Third volume of Hutton's *Theory of the Earth* published by The Geological Society of London.

1978 *The Lost Drawings* that were designed to illustrate Hutton's *Theory of the Earth* finally came to light and were published.

Dedication

Professor Donald Bertram McIntyre and family

by Alan McKirdy

Donald McIntyre (1923–2009) devoted much of his life to the study of James Hutton and The Scottish Enlightenment. He was the consummate Hutton scholar and is recognised the world over as the foremost authority on the founding father of geology. In an obituary prepared by the late Professor Gordon Craig and Dr Charles Waterston, themselves both granite pillars of the Royal Society of Edinburgh, they wrote that 'Donald was not merely a scholar of the Enlightenment, but a product and embodiment of it'.

In the first edition of the 'little book' we wrote together on James Hutton, Donald acknowledged his considerable debt of gratitude to the late Professor S. I. Tomkeieff for his stimulating lecture in March 1947 on the commemoration of the 150th anniversary of Hutton's death. He also thanked Professors F. J. Turner and Herbert M. Evans for inviting him as a speaker at the History of Science Club in Berkeley in 1957. Donald's interest in Hutton has very deep roots.

Donald was a 'son of the manse', educated at George Watson's College, Edinburgh and, during the early years of the Second World War, at Grantown Grammar School in Speyside. After his degree and PhD studies at the University of Edinburgh, he spent a formative year in Switzerland for his DSc degree on Alpine geology and was greatly stimulated by studying under Professor Eugene Wegmann in Neuchatel, Switzerland. At the early age of 30 he was elected a Fellow of the Royal Society of Edinburgh in the same month that I was born – March 1953.

In 1954, after teaching under Professor Arthur Holmes at the Grant Institute, University of Edinburgh, Donald was appointed to lead the Geology Department at the prestigious Pomona College, Claremont, a liberal arts college in the earthquake country and sunnier climes of southern California. Quickly recognised as a brilliant speaker and inspirational teacher, perhaps his crowning glory came in 1985 when, from a potential pool of 5000 eligible candidates, he was voted 'Professor of the Year' of the state of California.

Opposite: Timeline

The timeline of James Hutton's life and times.

Adapted from a graphic produced by The James Hutton Institute.

Donald at Glen Tilt

Donald is pointing to the exposures that Hutton used to prove his idea that granite was introduced in liquid form to the surrounding, and therefore, older rocks. Hutton worked hard to get the point accepted that granite was not the oldest rock of all, and also that it had once existed in liquid form as molten magma. This place provided the conclusive evidence on both issues for which he had long searched.

Courtesy of the McIntyre family

Donald was also a pioneer in computing, particularly in the furtherance of geological studies. After Pomona College purchased a (then) state-of-the-art IBM 360, Donald adapted it for use in various aspects of geology including plotting contour maps, crystallography and geochronology. He went on to become the first Director of the Pomona College Computer Centre.

In January 1958, Donald was joined in Claremont after a brief end of term visit back to Edinburgh where he had tied the knot in marriage with a former neighbour and friend Ann Alexander. Thanks to a set of unusual circumstances, Ann had spent a memorable and beautiful summer as a house-help/guest/'daughter' in Professor Wegmanns' home in Neuchatel; and to her immeasurable pleasure these summer months included a fine field trip along with the Professor, his wife and some of his students to the Swiss Alps above Sion. As a result of this unique shared friendship, Professor and Madame Wegmann were with Donald and Ann on their wedding day in Edinburgh when Wegmann delivered – in French – a delightful and witty address to the newly wedded couple and their guests.

In 1969–70, Donald, Ann and their son, Ewen, spent a sabbatical year in Edinburgh, and for many summers (1962–87) they returned to the United Kingdom to allow Donald to pursue his research on Hutton, but also to enable Ewen, who is greatly challenged by living with cerebral palsy, to receive Bobath therapy in London.

Over the years, Donald was instrumental in rediscovering the geological drawings that Hutton's field companion, John Clerk of Eldin, had made during their forays into the field. Although these had come to be known as *The Lost Drawings*, they saw the light of day again in 1978, along with an account published by Scottish Academic Press in association with the Royal Society of Edinburgh and Geological Society of London.

On Donald's retirement from Pomona College in 1989, the family returned to live in Scotland, choosing to settle in Perthshire close to Capability Scotland's care centre. They quickly reintegrated into community life, evidenced by Donald's election as Chairman of Perth Civic Trust. He was also an accomplished piper and joined the Piobaireachd Society – indeed there is a pipe tune composed in his honour.

The McIntyre family

Ann and Donald with Ewen.

Courtesy of the McIntyre family

Now back in Scotland, Donald's interest in Hutton's work intensified and, in 1997, we wrote the first edition of *James Hutton: Founder of Modern Geology* together which was published to celebrate the 200th anniversary of Hutton's death. Donald gave a brilliant keynote address at the conference convened by the Royal Society of Edinburgh to celebrate this important anniversary.

I dedicate this book to the entire McIntyre family. Ann supported Donald so ably and has continued to give me help, guidance and access to his books and papers as I embark on this latest venture. With Donald's passing in 2009, I now pick up the baton he handed to me as we celebrate the tercentenary of Hutton's birth in 2026.

Foreword

Professor Colin D. Campbell

James Hutton is truly a rich source of inspiration. The epitome of a polymath he was remarkable for the diversity of approaches to science. His tremendous ability to observe, think theoretically, and test his theories through further observation and experiment led to insights that changed our view of the world. Digging ditches on his farm led him to ponder on soil formation, loss and renewal processes and the time needed to accommodate them. This, with his observations of rock formations, led to his greatest work on *Theory of the Earth* and the epithet 'Founder of Modern Geology'. But equally staggering are his scarcely recognised prescience and insights around meteorology such as the *The Theory of Rain*, and in his conscientious rationalisation of how useful observation, theory and experiment was he helped to develop and define what we now call the scientific method. His *Principles of Knowledge* is perhaps one of his most understudied texts.

Although Hutton was academic and capable of great thinking, he was at the same time driven to translate this into useful knowledge. He was one of the first to understand how the environment selects variation in crops and animals, and pondered how plants use sunlight to grow and how crops might grow faster with nutrients and lime. The knowledge that he developed about rock formations was applied to help survey the route for the Forth and Clyde Canal and he brought back many ideas from his travels to solve practical problems around ploughing and agronomy. He was more than just pragmatic and in fact was an entrepreneur at the age of 24, developing a process to recycle chimney soot into a valuable industrial chemical.

As a polymath interested in all things, Hutton was also one of the first to think of the world as a system that evolved and adapted, and we are only now realising how important that is in relation to climate change. Not content with dealing with the biophysical world, he also thought about and observed on land economy and the role of women in society, including 'lamenting their lost talents'.

So, for many, James Hutton sits alongside James Clerk Maxwell as one of the greatest scientists that Scotland has ever produced. Yet he is far less well known. Partly for this reason, The James Hutton Institute has created a Foundation to help celebrate the man and his work as a scientist and to create a campaign to celebrate his 300th birthday in 2026.

Alan's engaging and insightful book expands our appreciation of James Hutton the polymath and his much wider contributions. It reflects good research by Alan and Moira and an ability to tell a interesting story so that more people can appreciate Hutton's many contributions. We are very grateful to them.

Professor Colin D. Campbell
Chief Executive,
The James Hutton Institute

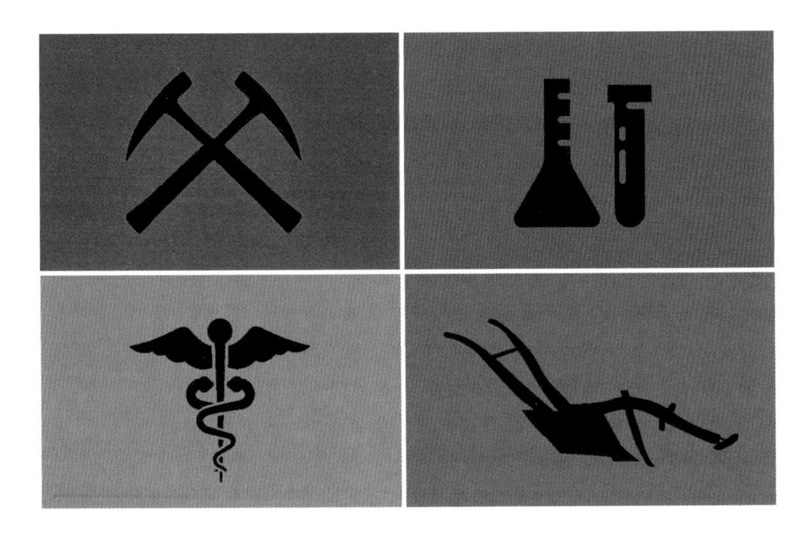

Foreword

Dr Rebekah Widdowfield

A founding member of the Royal Society of Edinburgh, Scotland's National Academy, in many ways James Hutton can be seen as an embodiment of the Society. A polymath, whose formal training took in everything from Logic to Latin, Mathematics to Medicine, and with a wider knowledge founded upon his experience working the land on the family farms and running a chemical business, Hutton encapsulated the diversity of thought and breadth of expertise which has been at the heart of RSE since its inception in 1783. This span of expertise continues to distinguish the Society from many other national academies with a membership that embraces the breadth of academia but also reaches into business and public service. At the same time, Hutton's work to improve agricultural practices and animal husbandry aligned perfectly with the Society's founding mission of the advancement of learning and useful knowledge or, as we express it today, 'knowledge made useful'.

RSE was born out of the Scottish Enlightenment – a time of unprecedented intellectual endeavour and innovation, of pushing the boundaries of knowledge and practice. As a founding member of the RSE, Hutton sat alongside other leading scientists and thinkers of the day, including Joseph Black, Adam Smith and John Playfair, as one of the members of the first Council – the Society's governing body. RSE was to play an important role in the development of his thinking. Many of Hutton's ideas were first aired at meetings of the RSE and disseminated in the pages of the Society's journal, *The Transactions of the Royal Society of Edinburgh*. This includes of course, work for which he is better known, most notably his almost 100-page treatise on the *Theory of the Earth* (later translated by Playfair for a wider audience), but also contributions on a raft of topics which were testament to the intellectual heft and curiosity he brought to the Society and its discussions.

While Hutton has a room named after him at RSE's home on George Street in Edinburgh, his name is undoubtedly less familiar than many of the names that adorn other rooms in the building, including Sir Walter

Scott, Lord Kelvin and James Clerk Maxwell. Yet his contributions should not be underestimated. As we approach the 300th anniversary of Hutton's birth, it is right that we should take the opportunity to reflect on and celebrate his contribution to both thinking and practice, and we welcome Alan McKirdy's book in supporting that endeavour and giving greater visibility to the 'Founder of Modern Geology'.

Dr Rebekah Widdowfield
Chief Executive
The Royal Society of Edinburgh

Foreword

Professor T. C. Smout

CBE, FRSE, FBA, FSA (Scot)

James Hutton was a genius, a star of the Scottish Enlightenment, that constellation of friends and kin that gave the world modern philosophy, modern economics and much of modern science. In that great age of eighteenth-century intellect, none made more of an original contribution than Hutton to our understanding of the planet. He simply gave us a true sense of time. It was the investigations of this enormously vigorous, brilliant and sociable man, travelling the length of Scotland and England to scan the strata and poke amongst the rock that began to show how very ancient the Earth really was. In doing so, Hutton laid the foundation of geological science.

Geology is a marvellous part of Scotland's natural heritage: no land has more varied rocks and soil, or a more exciting history of their discovery. To read this story of James Hutton is an ideal way to begin to understand it all.

Professor T. C. Smout
Historiographer Royal in Scotland

Opposite page: James Hutton and his contemporaries

In a frieze at the Scottish National Portrait Gallery in Edinburgh, painted by William Hole RSA, James Hutton (middle, side view) stands with Sir Henry Raeburn (painter), Lord Jeffrey (judge), Sir Walter Scott (writer), John Hunter (surgeon), Robert Burns (poet), Thomas Telford (civil engineer), James Watt (mechanical engineer) and Charles Adam (architect)

William Brassey Hole: *Processional Frieze in the Great Hall of the Scottish National Portrait Gallery*. UPG.039: National Galleries of Scotland

Introduction

James Hutton (1726–97) came to prominence during an extraordinary period of intellectual curiosity and exploration that has come to be known as 'The Scottish Enlightenment.' During the second half of the eighteenth century, Edinburgh was set ablaze by men of unrivalled intellect and insight who developed ideas across an unparalleled span of subjects. Economics, architecture, literature, medicine, chemistry and, of course, geology were just a few of the areas touched by this prolific flowering of creativity and discovery.

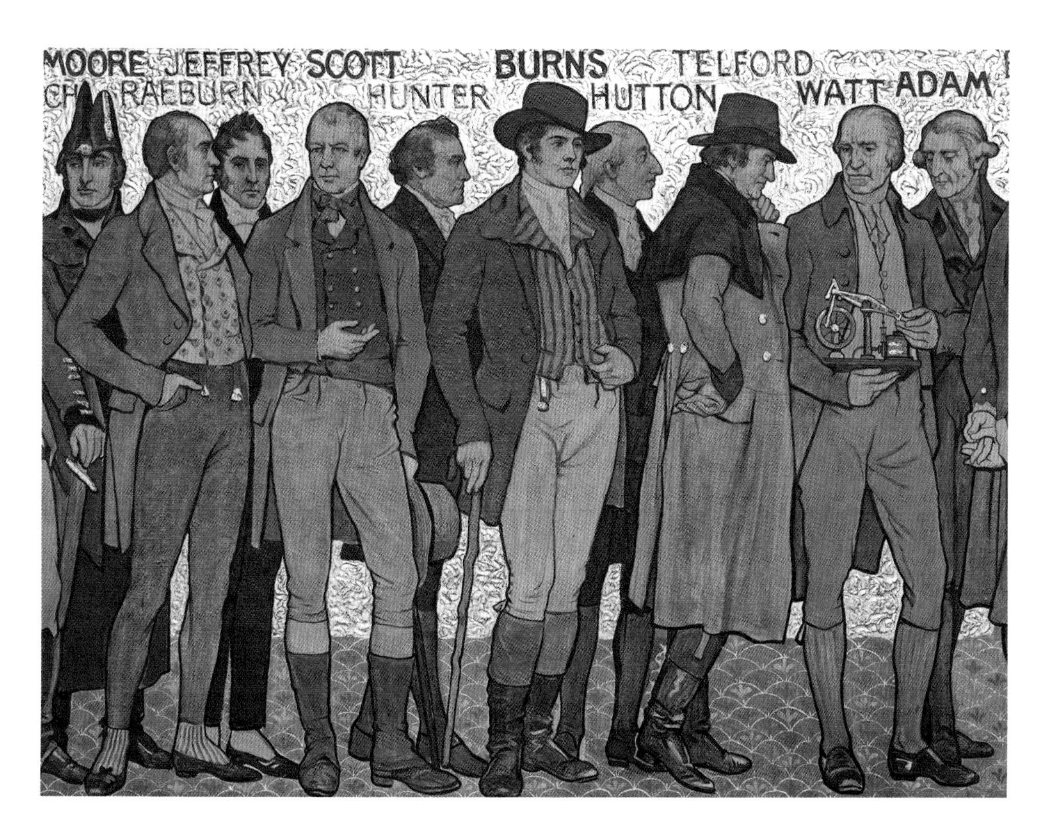

James Hutton's achievements during this period stand comparison with other scientific giants this country has nurtured, such as James Watt and Dr Joseph Black. Since those heady days in the late eighteenth century, Hutton's achievements in understanding the antiquity and workings of Planet Earth have largely been forgotten. He is better known abroad than in his homeland, particularly in America, although the naming of Scotland's premier environmental and agricultural research institute in his honour has helped greatly.

Ask Google who the 'Founder of Modern Geology?' is and the answer is always 'James Hutton'. The same inquiry randomly made of most citizens of Scotland, young or old, is likely to be met with a shrug of the shoulders or a puzzled look. He deserves much greater recognition for all that he achieved in so many areas. This book has been written to share the story of James Hutton with a wider audience and to enable interested readers to rediscover a largely forgotten Scottish genius.

Scotland had always been a country that boasted people of intellectual achievement. Three universities were founded in the fifteenth century in the most advanced cultural centres of the time: St Andrews in 1413, Glasgow in 1451 and King's College Aberdeen in 1495. The University of Edinburgh followed in 1582, Aberdeen's Marischal College in 1593, and the short-lived University of Fraserburgh in 1595.

This placed Scotland at the forefront of academic achievement in Europe during these times. These institutions had strong links across the continent

Below: Hutton statue, Scottish National Portrait Gallery

Only the great and good of Scottish society are immortalised on the exterior walls of the Scottish National Portrait Gallery in Edinburgh. In this sculpture by David Watson Stevenson, Hutton stands tall, hammer in one hand, rock specimen in the other.

Mike Browne

Below, right: Bust of James Hutton

Bust of James Hutton displayed in the Royal Society of Edinburgh. This plaster bust is by Patric Park, based on the Henry Raeburn portrait and the medallion by James Tassie.

Donald B. McIntyre

St Salvator's Chapel

The University of St Andrews' oldest building.

Wikimedia Commons

and many scholars from Scotland worked in universities across Europe including Leiden, Paris, Frankfurt, Padua and Bologna.

By the sixteenth century, Scotland had an academic class that was vigorous, outward looking and well connected. The interchange of people and ideas between these institutions ensured that the *literati*, as they styled themselves, were leaders in their respective fields. This knowledge and burgeoning of new ideas was passed on to their students and all who came after them. The subjects studied in these earlier times included logic, theology, philosophy, medicine and Roman Law.

By the 1750s, around half of the male population of Scotland could read and write and most larger towns had access to a library. Education has been valued since that time as a fundamental way of improving the quality of life of the population. Schools existed in almost every parish across the land and were available, by and large, free of charge. It was the church that provided these educational facilities. Their motivation was simple. Only those who were literate were able to read the Bible. The knock-on effect of this wider population of engaged citizens meant that they could also read for themselves the new ideas as they emerged from the pens of the *literati*.

Against this backdrop of centuries of academic achievement, what made the activities of those who contributed to the Scottish Enlightenment worthy of the name? A period of 'enlightenment' almost presupposes that what went before was shrouded in darkness. There was, however, more than a grain of truth in that assumption. Up until that point, the moral authority of the Bible was thought to be unassailable. But an age of critical analysis and reason had dawned with the Scottish Enlightenment. The tramlines that religion and other forms of authority had laid down were now subject

Blackfriars Monastery

Home to the Royal High School of Edinburgh from 1578 until 1777 when it moved to High School Yards.

Cassell's *Old and New Edinburgh*

to rigorous re-examination. No matter how exalted the source, if ideas were found wanting, they were challenged by this new generation of thinkers.

The reformed Presbyterian Church in Scotland had form in persecuting and even executing religious disbelievers as recently as 1697, just 29 years before Hutton was born. Thomas Aitkenhead matriculated as a student at the University of Edinburgh in 1693 and later, after studying theology, said that a belief in God was 'a rapsodie of feigned and ill-invented nonsense'. He was indicted on two counts, the first and most important of which was that he 'railed upon or cursed God'. Five witnesses were called who heard these profanities and no defence witnesses were allowed. For his challenge to accepted beliefs and norms, the Church 'vigorously' petitioned the King for Aitkenhead to be executed. His trial was quickly concluded and he was duly sentenced to death, a judgement carried out on 8 January 1697. Apparently, he clutched a bible in his hand when the hangman's noose was placed around his neck. This was the last execution to be carried out anywhere in Britain for this 'crime'.

It clearly demonstrates the iron grip that religion had in Scotland during the late seventeenth and early part of the eighteenth century and the difficulties that the emerging generation of *literati* and intellectuals would have in challenging years of religious dogma. This applied particularly to James Hutton as his new ideas on geology would challenge a literal interpretation of the Bible. As he looked at the world around him, he observed that nature and natural processes were the dominant forces which had, and continued to, shape the landscape. Although he was a man of strong

Sunday service

John Kay's portrait of a typical Sunday service demonstrates the power of the Kirk, with not a seat to be had as it was an obligation to attend the Sunday service. Fire and brimstone rained down from the pulpit on the congregation below.

John Kay

Christian faith, it seems most likely he rejected a literal interpretation of the Bible. This meant that he had to play his hand very cleverly in negotiating sensitive issues of science and religion.

A very special aspect of Scotland's version of enlightenment thinking was that many of the new ideas which emerged during this golden age were more of a collaborative effort than just the product of one mind. The new breed of intellectuals who inhabited the ale houses and coffee shops of late-eighteenth-century Edinburgh did so in a highly socialised manner. Small groups of men, often with disparate cultural or scientific interests, met on a weekly basis. They shared ideas in a spirit of openness and candour. To illustrate the point, John Playfair, Hutton's first and most celebrated biographer, said that John Clerk of Eldin, who was Hutton's 'great friend and coadjutor … through the unreserved intercourse of friendship and the adjustments produced by mutual suggestion, might render those parts indistinguishable even by the authors themselves'.

These men were geographically distant from the seat of power. With the accession of James VI and I to the throne of Great Britain and Ireland

Adam Smith by John Kay

Adam Smith was one of the most influential writers and thinkers of the Scottish Enlightenment. He often joined Hutton on his walks on Arthur's Seat and Salisbury Crags. According to Smith's biographer, James Buchan (2006), 'Smith seldom uttered a word, but walked on moving his lips and muttering to himself'. As we'll hear later, he joined Hutton on Friday evenings for dinner with a collection of other intellectuals. They styled themselves as members of the 'Oyster Club'.

John Kay

in 1603, the Royal Court had departed for London. After the Union of the Parliaments in 1707 Scottish Members of Parliament left for the same destination. However, as suggested in a recent biography of Adam Smith, author of the *Wealth of Nations*, these Enlightenment figures were certainly not without influence. It is said that, 'when Smith entered the room in which the Prime Minister of the day William Pitt the Younger, William Wilberforce and others were sitting, they all rose'. Pitt reportedly said on that occasion, 'No, we will all stand until you are first seated, for we are all your scholars' (Buchan 2006).

It was into this tumultuous intellectual world that James Hutton was hurled. He pursued medical studies at the University of Edinburgh, later became a successful entrepreneur in the city, travelled extensively across England and northern Europe and endured a self-imposed exile in the Scottish Borders whilst, for 14 years, he exercised his passion for farming and agricultural improvements. But before we describe the Hutton who returned to Edinburgh from these adventures aged 41, let's rewind to the beginning of his life.

Glen Feshie

Although Hutton may not have visited Glen Feshie in the Cairngorms (illustrated here), these are the natural forces Hutton grasped that were responsible for shaping the landscapes.

Lorne Gill/NatureScot

Edinburgh from Arthur's Seat

This is a view of Edinburgh from Arthur's Seat as it would have been in the early eighteenth century. It illustrates the rural nature of the city that would have been familiar to Hutton in his formative years.

John Kay

Chapter 1
Hutton's early life and studies

Early years

James Hutton was born in Edinburgh on 3 June 1726 into a life of relative privilege. He was one of five children born to William Hutton and Sarah Balfour. William was a merchant and a man highly respected for his good sense and integrity, who went on to become the Edinburgh City Treasurer. His father's influence was short-lived as he died in 1729 when James was three years old and as a result, the women in Hutton's life played a pivotal role; his life bookended by a dependency on female members of his family. In his youth his mother was the sole homemaker, and his rock. His elder brother, John, died before Hutton was born, so he shared his earliest years with his mother and three sisters – Isabella, Jean and Sarah. His school days, brief sojourn as a legal apprentice, and his subsequent medical studies in Edinburgh were all supported by his female family network. However, the family were left well provided for. Throughout his life, because of the inheritance his father left and also his own entrepreneurial skills, Hutton never had to worry about financial matters. This was a crucial factor in his intellectual and scientific development as he could devote his time exclusively to his twin passions of geology and farming, without the distraction of having to earn money.

It was the inheritance of two working farms from his father that allowed Hutton to develop his ideas on agriculture. Although we know him primarily as the 'Founder of Modern Geology', for many, his contribution to improvements in agricultural practice and animal husbandry is Hutton's equally important legacy. We will return to his pioneering work in farming in due course.

Hutton's formal education began when he attended the High School of Edinburgh. His early interests were known to be science-related, particularly chemistry, which would be an enduring passion for the rest of his life. His achievements at school were sufficient for him to attend lectures at the University of Edinburgh from 1740 onwards: he was just 14 years of age when he started. Initially, Hutton studied Latin and humanities but, as was commonly the case, he didn't matriculate for this course of study. He just turned up and attended the lectures that took his fancy. Neither did he graduate with any qualification. As he himself probably realised at the time, this was not to be his final academic calling. Nonetheless, during this initial period of study he received instruction in Latin, logic, rhetoric and mathematics and was fortunate to be taught by Professor Colin Maclaurin, who was one of Scotland's most eminent mathematicians of the day.

In order that he might develop a respectable professional career, Hutton was then apprenticed to a legal firm. At this time, Edinburgh was a city bursting at the seams with lawyers, so it seemed a prudent career move. But Hutton had little interest in the dull legal work he encountered in the offices of George Chalmers WS (Writer to the Signet). Furthermore, he frittered away some of his time by undertaking chemical experiments with fellow legal apprentices when his attention should have been directed elsewhere. Clearly it was an apprenticeship that was doomed to failure and he left soon after by mutual consent. According to a contemporary account, 'Mr Chalmers, with much good sense and kindness, advised him to think of some employment better suited to his turn of mind and released him from his obligations'. In today's parlance, he was sacked.

Medical studies

Hutton's interest remained focused on the emerging science of chemistry. As the University of Edinburgh did not offer any formal course on this subject, he chose to study medicine instead, the subject most closely aligned to his primary interests. This time, there is a record of his matriculation. His name also appears in the class list of students beginning their medical studies in 1744. The University enjoyed a fine reputation for medical studies and Hutton enrolled just a few months after he left his position in the lawyer's office.

Hutton would soon encounter a fellow medical student, John Clerk of Eldin, forming a friendship that would endure for the rest of his life. In fact, he became close to a number of members of that family. The Clerks were substantial landowners in the area just to the south of Edinburgh and some of their holdings yielded large quantities of coal. To exploit this rich resource required a detailed knowledge of geology, and it was here, at only 18 years of age, that James Hutton had his first encounter with the subject that would come to dominate much of his life.

John Clerk of Eldin (1728–1812) by Archibald Skirving

Hutton's friendship with John Clerk of Eldin was arguably the most significant collaboration he had with any of the Enlightenment figures. They met as medical students at the University of Edinburgh, but went their separate ways for almost the next two decades. They became reacquainted when Hutton returned to live permanently in Edinburgh in 1767. Hutton and Clerk made many geological expeditions together, particularly between 1785 and 1788. Their lively debates and discussions about what they saw helped Hutton to formulate some of his most incisive ideas. Clerk was also a talented artist and he recorded geological features from some of the most significant places they visited as pen and ink drawings. Most of these invaluable scientific documents were lost for almost 200 years, only to emerge in the late 1970s, when they were published as *The Lost Drawings*. Clerk married Susanna, sister of the celebrated architect William Adam, with whom he had seven children. His son, also John, accompanied Hutton on his visit to Arran in 1787, where he produced geological sketches and cross-sections of a quality equal to that of his father. Son John was raised to the bench as a judge in 1823.

Adam Collection; photographed by Stephen Kearny

Hutton the man

Recent biographers have had thin pickings to research 'Hutton the man'. His published and some of his unpublished reports survive, as do some of the letters he exchanged with close friends and acquaintances, but little else. So it is to John Playfair and his biographical account that we must turn for a first hand contemporary account of the man. He helps us greatly to understand Hutton's character and general demeanour. The following description by Playfair is the closest we get to an illumination of Hutton's true nature. John Playfair wrote of Hutton:

> His figure was slender, but indicated activity; while a thin countenance, high forehead, and a nose somewhat aquiline, bespoke extraordinary acuteness and vigour of mind. His eye was penetrating and keen, but full of gentleness and benignity.
>
> His conversation was inestimable; as great talent, the most perfect candour, and the utmost simplicity of character and manners, all united to stamp a value upon it. He had that genuine simplicity, originating in the absence of all selfishness and vanity, by which a man loses sight of himself altogether, and neither conceals what is, nor affects what is not .... His conversation was

Playfair's Memorial, Calton Hill

The monument was designed by William Henry Playfair, one of Scotland's most distinguished architects, and nephew of John Playfair. The inscription on the podium translates as:

JOHN PLAYFAIR
HIS FRIENDS PIETY SPURRED ON BY
CONSTANT LONGINGS IN THE PLACE
WHERE HE HIMSELF HAD ONCE DEDICATED
A TEMPLE TO HIS URANIA PLACED THIS
MONUMENT 1826,
BORN 10TH MARCH 1748.
DIED 19TH JULY 1819.

Wikimedia Commons
Translation courtesy of
Historic Environment Scotland

John Playfair (1748–1819)

Playfair was one of Hutton's closest friends. He was 22 years younger than Hutton, but he played a vital role in making *Theory of the Earth* and other Huttonian musings more accessible to a wider audience. Playfair's *Illustrations of the Huttonian Theory* was published in 1802. It provided a readily understandable insight into Hutton's ideas that Hutton's own published works did not. He also presented a *Biographical Account* of the late Dr James Hutton to the Royal Society of Edinburgh on 10 January 1803 which was published in the Society's *Transactions* two years later. Observations from this affectionate and revealing work are peppered throughout this book. He adds considerable colour and perspective to our understanding of Hutton the man. There are no other reliable contemporary accounts of Hutton's life and times, so we must treasure Playfair's many observations on the actions and achievements of his great friend. He also provides reliable dates for the important events in Hutton's life – a chronological structure that all biographers who came after have followed, including this one!

John Playfair himself was a man of considerable achievements. Born in the parish of Liff and Benvie near Dundee, he studied theology at the University of St Andrews. He was later appointed Professor of Mathematics at the University of Edinburgh in 1781 and subsequently held a Chair of Natural Philosophy from 1805. With James Hutton, he was also a co-founder of the Royal Society of Edinburgh and became its General Secretary in 1791. His tenure of this post came to a close with his death in 1819.

> extremely animated and forcible, and, whether serious or gay, full of ingenious and original observations. Great information, and an excellent memory, supplied an inexhaustible fund of illustration, always happily introduced, and in which, when the subject admitted of it, the witty and the ludicrous never failed to occupy a considerable place.
>
> A brighter tint of gaiety and cheerfulness spread itself over every countenance when the good Doctor entered the room …

Playfair's language is high-flown and certainly of its time, but the warmth, affection and admiration he feels for the 'good Doctor Hutton' clearly permeates every word of his observation.

For the first time, Hutton had stumbled across an academic course that fired his interest. John Playfair declared that the young James 'pursued his studies in chemistry and anatomy with great ardour'; and presumably with considerable success as he completed the first part of his medical studies in Edinburgh. Hutton's lecturers and mentors were some of the leading academics of the age, including the pioneering surgeon, Dr George Young.

The '45 Rising

As Hutton was earnestly engaged in his medical studies, Scotland descended into political turmoil. An unsuccessful attempt to wrest back the British throne for the Catholic Stuarts from the Protestant Hanoverian succession was made in 1715. A second more concerted effort was made in 1745 and into the following year by the charismatic Prince Charles Edward Stuart, or 'Bonnie Prince Charlie' as he was popularly known. It was a romantic notion, which was ultimately doomed to failure but, at its height, the Jacobite Rising was a disruptive and bloody affair.

Though Scotland prospered in terms of academic accomplishments and literacy in the enlightened towns and cities, large parts of the rural countryside were mired in grinding poverty. For them, talk in learned books about the age of the Earth or theories about supply and demand economics were a world away from their everyday existence. It was therefore no surprise that the possibility of a change in their prospects and circumstances brought about by this rising was long overdue and much welcomed. The romantic idea of the return of the 'king over the water', a reference to the deposed Catholic Stuart line now in exile in France and Rome, was the spark that set the Highland heather on fire. Most of the clans in the north of Scotland followed Rome, with 'outliers' of Episcopalianism in north-east Scotland. In contrast, their lowland cousins favoured Presbyterianism. This source of religious tension had existed since the Reformation and considerably energised the '45 Rising.

Prince Charles Edward Stuart

Better remembered as 'Bonnie Prince Charlie', Prince Charles Edward Stuart was born in Rome and died in the same city some sixty-seven years later. He was the last Stuart claimant to the British throne. His hopes, and those of his Jacobite supporters, of achieving that objective, were finally crushed at the Battle of Culloden on 16 April 1746.

Cassell's *Old and New Edinburgh*

The Jacobite army gathered in strength as they marched down from the Highlands of Scotland from where they drew most of their support. Edinburgh was a staging post for their long march south to England to claim their prize, but no preparations had been made to defend the city against such an incursion. After a brief sojourn in Linlithgow, the Highland men sauntered the final ten miles towards Edinburgh to enter the city unopposed.

The role that James Hutton played during these extraordinary times of crisis is unknown. He may have commented on these events, and his part in them, in letters to friends, but no record remains. However, Professor Colin Maclaurin, Hutton's former maths tutor, took an active part in the

Cannonball House

Cannonball House on Castelhill has two cannonballs lodged in the walls that date back to the time of the '45 Rising. One can clearly be seen in the inset.

Lynne Reilly

defence of the city. He was supported by the High Constables of Edinburgh who had a key role in guarding the streets of the city. Maclaurin also tried to rally the population to defend themselves and their homes. The permanent garrison at Edinburgh Castle had previously been significantly reduced in numbers and it was left to a bunch of untrained but enthusiastic students and other assorted volunteers to try to block the path of the wild Highland men soon to cross their threshold. The motley crew of defenders marched to meet the invaders, but as good sense prevailed they melted away like snow off a dyke into the wynds and side streets of the Old Town as they sensed the approach of Jacobite soldiers. It was a good call, as the Highlanders were armed to the teeth.

The army spent just over a month in Edinburgh, with the Prince and his officers quartered in the Palace of Holyroodhouse and other ranks camped in the adjacent Holyrood Park. To the great relief of the Edinburgh residents, the Prince and his troops left on their quest without visiting too much damage on their reluctant hosts.

After this rather terrifying interlude, Hutton returned to his books and lectures. He was studying in one of the finest medical institutes in the world which had developed a reputation for its pioneering work in surgery. Despite these advances in medical sciences, the subject remained rudimentary. Most of what we take for granted today, in terms of treatments and medicines, had yet to be discovered and developed. Hutton showed the first signs of disillusionment with his adopted profession when he later wrote: 'The more medical knowledge we acquire, the more we know how little efficacious that art is' (Playfair 1805). Despite such misgivings, he finished his studies at Edinburgh in 1747. As was the practice for some students, Hutton did not formally graduate, although his studies had been successfully completed. His name does not appear among the many who did graduate from the medical faculty. He then followed the accepted convention that his medical education should be completed in Europe.

But before he left Edinburgh, Hutton fathered a child. Research suggests that he met a young woman called Mary Eidington. The birth of a girl by that name is recorded in the parish records of Aberlady in East Lothian in 1732. Mary was 15 years old at the time they met; Hutton was 21. Their brief acquaintance led to Mary becoming pregnant, her condition a considerable embarrassment to her family. Although they did not marry, Hutton agreed to support Mary financially, and their son James who was born in 1747.

Dr Joseph Black (1728–99), who later became one of Hutton's closest friends, wrote to James Watt, another trusted acquaintance:

> We have become acquainted with a natural son of the Doctor [Hutton] whom he educated and supplied with money from time to time and to whom he intended some time past to leave a legacy. He is not unlike the Dr in person and bald like him but not like him in the face, having more of the features of his mother.

James Junior outlived his father by just five years. He married one Alice Smeaton and they had seven children, the last of whom died in 1880.

This episode seemed to have a profound effect on Hutton. It appears that he did not form any further long-term romantic relationships throughout the rest of his life. He certainly never married and, as far as we know, had no further issue. Alternatively, it may have been that he just never met a suitable partner who could accommodate his frenetic pace of life and wide-ranging interests.

Paris was Hutton's first port of call after Edinburgh. He stayed there for two years to further his medical studies and most likely greatly enjoyed the bohemian lifestyle that the city provided. Hutton may also have attended Professor Rouelle's popular chemistry course that included lectures on mineralogy and geology. This was to be Hutton's only formal instruction in geology. From this point onwards, he was entirely self-taught in the subject.

After Paris, Hutton enrolled at Leiden University in Holland, which was also a well-renowned medical school at this time. He graduated from Leiden as a Doctor of Medicine [MD] in 1749 after presenting his doctoral thesis on the circulation of the blood, a 34-page thesis entitled *Dissertatio Physico-medico inauguralis de sanguine et circulatione microcosmi*. Latin was the universal language of the scientist in the eighteenth century and even some of Hutton's lectures would have been delivered thus. The translation of the title of his thesis reads *Inaugural Physio-medical dissertation*

Leiden University

It was at Leiden that Hutton completed his medical studies. It was a centre of excellence for medicine during his time there; today it specialises more in the arts.

Graeme McKirdy

on the blood and the circulation of the microcosm. This topic echoed one of Hutton's most important geological ideas that he described some 40 years later, namely that there is circularity in the way that some rocks are formed, then eroded and re-formed as new layers. Perhaps his medical thesis at Leiden on the manner in which the blood is circulated around the human body prompted him to see the making and destruction of rock strata in a similar light.

Hutton the entrepreneur

After leaving Leiden, Hutton amused himself in London for a few months and the first serious doubts about a career in medicine set in. As ever, John Playfair has the inside story. It appears that Hutton felt the practice of medicine in Edinburgh at that time was a bit of a closed shop. Playfair wrote in 1805 that Hutton felt 'his native city afforded no very flattering prospect for his establishment as a physician'. When Hutton gravitated back to Edinburgh in the summer of 1750, he inevitably considered other career options. It was, of course, two centuries before the establishment of the National Health Service. Medical interventions, advice and treatment were services that only the wealthy could afford.

As his enthusiasm for the practice of medicine declined, Hutton's interest in putting his knowledge of chemistry to work sparkled more brightly than ever. At the age of 23, he became reacquainted with James Davie, an old friend, with whom he shared an interest in chemistry. They experimented together on one subject in particular, the production of a highly prized substance known as *sal ammoniac*, with the chemical name of ammonium chloride. From their experiments, they established that this substance could be made from soot, a commodity in plentiful supply in eighteenth-century Edinburgh. They knew that *sal ammoniac* could be sold for use in the dyeing industry and it also had a use in working with tin and brass. It had previously only been available as an imported naturally occurring material from the Middle East – presumably at considerable expense. Hutton and Davie's enterprise is thought to be the first time anywhere in the world that *sal ammoniac* was manufactured.

Although history does not record their reaction to the discovery that a much sought-after commodity could be recovered from a waste material like soot, we can perhaps guess that it would be one of surprise and elation. Again, we can only speculate in the absence of documentary evidence from Playfair or other reliable sources but, between them, Hutton and Davie must have had a considerable command of entrepreneurship and commercial drive. It is one thing to have a good idea, but entirely different to turn it into a lucrative and sustained commercial proposition. As it happened, once production started, their *sal ammoniac* was sold to the households and merchants of Edinburgh and further afield for a pretty penny.

Edinburgh itself was a soot-stained city, with chimneys belching black smoke day and night. It was known as 'Auld Reekie', a clear reference to

Below, left: Tronmen

It was the job of the tronmen or chimney sweeps to keep the 'lums' (chimneys) of Edinburgh clear of soot. John Kay's cartoon captures two tronmen at work.

John Kay

Below: 'Auld Reekie'

Eighteenth-century Edinburgh was aptly named as 'Auld Reekie'. Thousands of chimneys belched smoke and soot that poisoned the atmosphere but provided rich-pickings for the tronmen or chimney sweeps. The soot provided the raw material for Hutton's *sal ammoniac* business.

H. V. Morton, *In Search of Scotland* (1929)

the air quality or, more precisely, the lack of it. With a ready supply of soot as a raw material, their business model was secure.

Premises were found at a location just off Nicholson Street, close to the Old College, now known as Davie Street in recognition of Hutton's partner's contribution to the enterprise. The factory had a footprint of around half an acre and housed a furnace that contained rows of green glass flasks with protruding necks. The flasks were charged with soot 'within a few inches of their mouth' that were then heated as the furnace was fired up. Ammonium chloride or *sal ammoniac* was driven from the soot by the intense heat and the vapour condensed on the neck of the glass vessels. It is estimated that 26 kg of soot yielded around 6 kg of *sal ammoniac*. Considerable quantities of soot were therefore required to maintain this industrial process and it is said that they took all the black stuff the Edinburgh's chimney sweeps could supply. To produce this commercially valuable product in Edinburgh from soot, essentially a waste material, proved to be an enduring money-spinner. Today we would call this enterprise a fine example of the circular economy.

Hutton became a partner in this profitable enterprise with Davie and drew an income from it for much of the rest of his life. It is difficult to overstate the value of this income stream to Hutton. It freed him from the drudgery and anxiety of funding his lifestyle when, in later life, he would become one of Edinburgh's *literati*. Unlike many of his contemporaries, Hutton never held a salaried position at a university or other institution that generated a regular income for him. The *sal ammoniac* business was therefore crucial, as it allowed him the freedom to think, write, travel, experiment, collaborate with other intellectuals and observe the natural world in a manner that would have been impossible without this income support. It was also a great achievement for Hutton and Davie to deliver massive and enduring commercial success at such a young age, like upwardly mobile 'yuppies' of their day, admired and perhaps even envied by their peers.

And so by 1778, Hutton had become a respected businessman, with an interest in many properties across the city. In fact, so large had his empire become that he appointed a factor to collect the 'rents, mails and duties ... of the houses, shops and others in the Town of Edinburgh pertaining and belonging to me'. Records of his financial interests in properties across the city are held in the National Records of Scotland to this day.

The *sal ammoniac* business remained viable until at least 1783 when this commodity became available from another local source, namely as a by-product from the manufacture of tar. Hutton and Davie's company started to buy quantities of *sal ammoniac* from tar works at Culross, but the fortunes of their manufacturing enterprise started to decline thereafter.

Chapter 2
Hutton the traveller

A life beyond Edinburgh

Hutton decided to leave the city in 1752 for reasons that are not absolutely clear. He had established a thriving business with James Davie that would provide him with a healthy income for the rest of his life; his connection with the *literati* of Edinburgh had yet to be fully established and was free to go wherever the fancy took him; and he had already experienced travel on the continent and perhaps developed a taste for adventures in new places.

During the next two years, from 1752 until 1754, learning more about agricultural improvement was Hutton's main preoccupation. He inherited two farms from his father at Slighhouses and Nether Monynut in Berwickshire and clearly wished to take the role of farmer and agricultural improver more seriously. At the age of 26, the youthful James Hutton began his travels to England and later across the channel to Holland, Flanders and northern France with the purpose of studying farming techniques in other parts of the world.

At the beginning of the eighteenth century, farming in Scotland was a subsistence affair that yielded little profit or comfort. The harsh climate was partly to blame, but there was an appreciation that a more experimental approach would help to make Scotland's farmland much more productive. Three years before Hutton's birth, the Honourable Society of Improvers in the Knowledge of Agriculture was established in Scotland. Its purpose was to look at new ways of tilling the soil and experimenting with new crop rotations to raise standards across the board. It was in the context of this desire for agricultural improvement that Hutton began his new quest.

Travels in East Anglia and across England

One of Hutton's acquaintances in Edinburgh was John Dybold, a Norfolk farmer, who seemed to embody the agricultural innovation that he sought. Hutton was asked by Dybold to visit his farm in East Anglia, an invitation he was happy to accept. Although a long and uncomfortable journey from Edinburgh to Yarmouth on the East Anglian coast, the effort paid off as Hutton was about to get first hand experience of animal husbandry and crop management. He immersed himself in local life and customs and was clearly enjoying his new existence away from Edinburgh. Playfair tells us that, by this stage of his trip to East Anglia, Hutton

> ... lived in the house of a farmer, who served both for his landlord and his instructor. I have often heard him mention, with great respect, the name of John Dybold, at whose house he had lived with much comfort, and whole practical lessons in husbandry he highly valued. He appears, indeed, to have enjoyed this situation very much: the simple and plain character of the society with which he mingled, suited well with his own, and the peasants of Norfolk would find nothing in the stranger to set them at a distance from him, or to make them treat him with reserve.

After one year in this rural idyll, Hutton moved on to Suffolk where different agricultural challenges were posed by the need to cultivate a much heavier clay soil. Management of a herd of dairy cattle was also on the agenda at his new location. His sojourn to the east of England paid dividends as he served his farming apprenticeship here and gained hugely

valuable experience that would be put to good use on his return to Scotland. Hutton mentioned to Playfair on many occasions the great respect he had for his East Anglian mentors in agriculture, and he was introduced to new farming equipment, particularly the 'High Suffolk' plough, which he later used on his Berwickshire farm.

Hutton's travels were far from over. Travelling on horseback and occasionally on foot, he continued his agricultural education with visits to many parts of England, including the Isle of Wight, Cambridgeshire, Oxfordshire, Derbyshire, Yorkshire and Northumberland. Later he considered visiting Cornwall, but said 'my money won't hold out'. Nevertheless, his tour of rural England was impressive.

Although his primary focus was still on crop and animal husbandry, he started slowly, and almost imperceptibly, to notice the rocks around him as he made his way across the country. Travelling by 'Shanks' pony', as well as on horseback, would have been the perfect way to start his geological investigations. Apparently he poked his nose into every ditch and riverbed to see the rocks that built the land over which he travelled. It was clearly an uncomfortable mode of transport. He famously said: 'My arse, it is evident, is now a part of much greater consequence ... than my head ... lord pity the arse that's clagged to a head that will hunt stones ...'. A recent geology book entitled *Hutton's Arse* was named in recognition of this quote and the discomfort he suffered.

In his short life, Hutton had already demonstrated an insatiable intellectual curiosity for subjects he had studied at school and university. Now we can add geology to that list.

Norfolk

Changeless rural scene of the Norfolk countryside that Hutton would have experienced during his visit to East Anglia.

Shutterstock

Above: Isle of Wight

Hutton described the Needles on the Isle of Wight as 'remaining still undemolished by the waves' in an account written after his visit there. The role of the destructive forces of erosion acting on the land was beginning to dawn on Hutton. He also saw the effects of erosion on the sea cliffs at Yarmouth. Clearly some key elements of *Theory of the Earth* were starting to formulate in his mind.

Shutterstock

Right: Hutton on the move

Hutton travelled the highways and byways on horseback as he moved around the English shires. It was a slow and stately mode of transport, but it allowed him to appreciate the landscape both from an agricultural and geological point of view.

Shutterstock

To the continent

After two years travelling far and wide throughout England and learning his agricultural craft, in 1754 Hutton decided to once again cross the English Channel and travelled from Rotterdam through Holland, Brabant, Flanders and Picardy. Hutton held the Low Countries in high regard as farmers from that part of the world were deemed to be the main source of agricultural innovation at that time. What he had observed in Norfolk in particular stood favourable comparison with any practices observed abroad. After his extensive travels, observations and networking in England and in the Low Countries, it was time to return home to put what he had learned into practice. Playfair (1805) tells us:

> Though his principal object in this excursion was to acquire information in the practice of husbandry, he appears to have bestowed a good deal of attention on the mineralogy of the countries through which he passed, and has taken notice in his *Theory of the Earth* of several observations which he made at that time.

Picardy, France

Hutton saw the best agricultural practices during his visit to Northern Europe. Here in the Picardy Region of Northern France, he would have seen well-tended fields of wheat and other illustrations of good farming technique.

Shutterstock

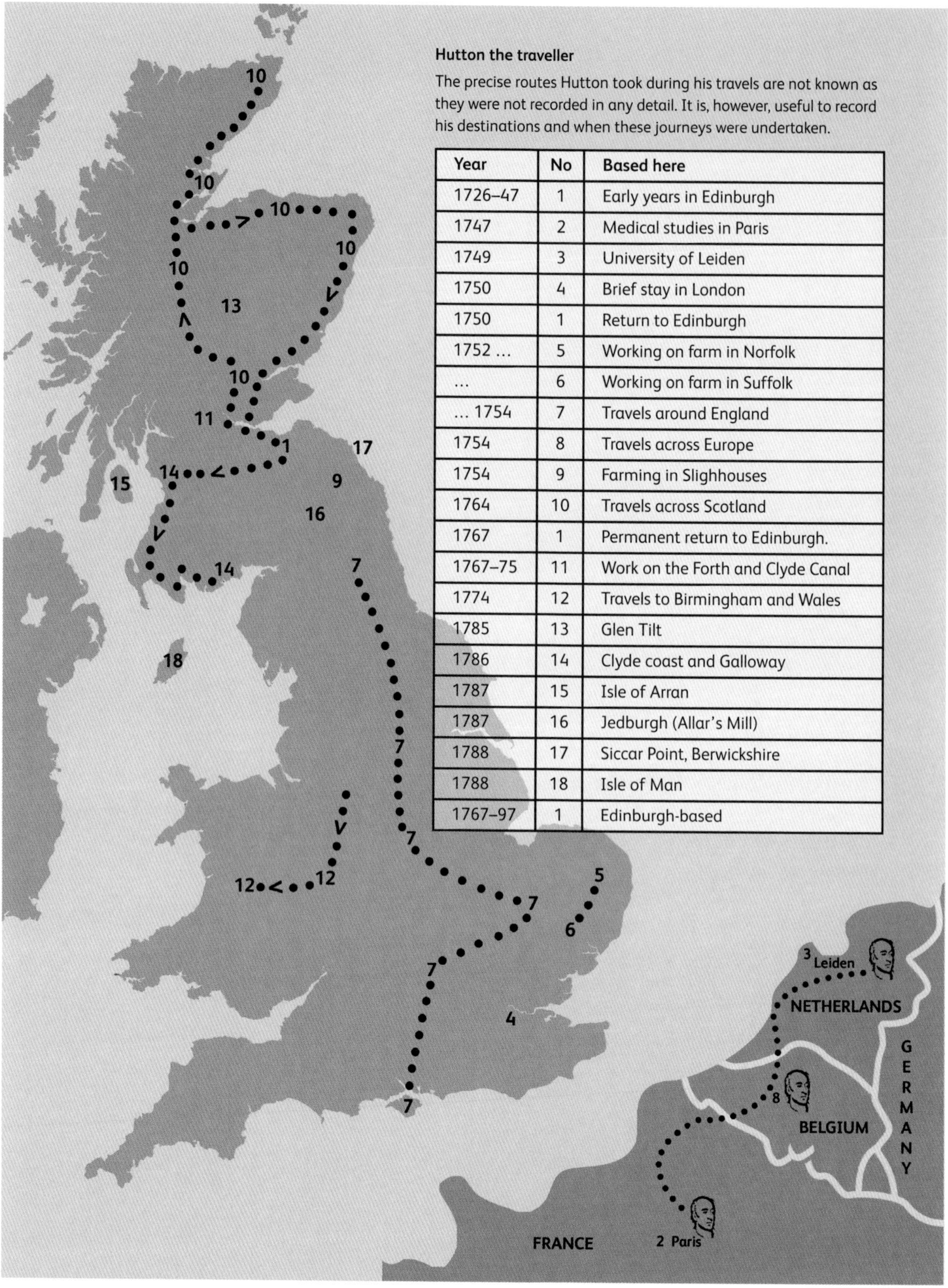

Hutton the traveller

The precise routes Hutton took during his travels are not known as they were not recorded in any detail. It is, however, useful to record his destinations and when these journeys were undertaken.

Year	No	Based here
1726–47	1	Early years in Edinburgh
1747	2	Medical studies in Paris
1749	3	University of Leiden
1750	4	Brief stay in London
1750	1	Return to Edinburgh
1752 …	5	Working on farm in Norfolk
…	6	Working on farm in Suffolk
… 1754	7	Travels around England
1754	8	Travels across Europe
1754	9	Farming in Slighhouses
1764	10	Travels across Scotland
1767	1	Permanent return to Edinburgh.
1767–75	11	Work on the Forth and Clyde Canal
1774	12	Travels to Birmingham and Wales
1785	13	Glen Tilt
1786	14	Clyde coast and Galloway
1787	15	Isle of Arran
1787	16	Jedburgh (Allar's Mill)
1788	17	Siccar Point, Berwickshire
1788	18	Isle of Man
1767–97	1	Edinburgh-based

Chapter 3
Hutton the farmer

Taming Slighhouses

Later in the same year, 1754, Hutton returned from Holland to his farm at Slighhouses near Duns to the south-east of Edinburgh. The farm is located in the typical rolling countryside of Berwickshire and had been in his family for two generations before Hutton fell heir to it. It must have been a rude awakening for a man who had seen the very best of contemporary agricultural practice. The land at Slighhouses was unkempt and uncared for, wild with weeds, poorly drained and littered with heavy rocks and stones. The land which Hutton inherited had never been cultivated for crops or been drained. Extensive areas of marsh were fed by streams and burns that ran off the nearby Lammermuir Hills.

With the rough moorland of the Lammermuir Hills almost within touching distance, Hutton's latest challenge must have looked a monumental one. Here he would stay for the next 14 years of his life, working the land with his own hands and trying to implement, as best he could, the key agricultural principles of crop rotation and animal husbandry observed in England and on the continent.

Life was hard for the young Hutton, toiling in the fields all day, removing stones and draining the land. It had been shaped into long ridges by previous owners in an effort

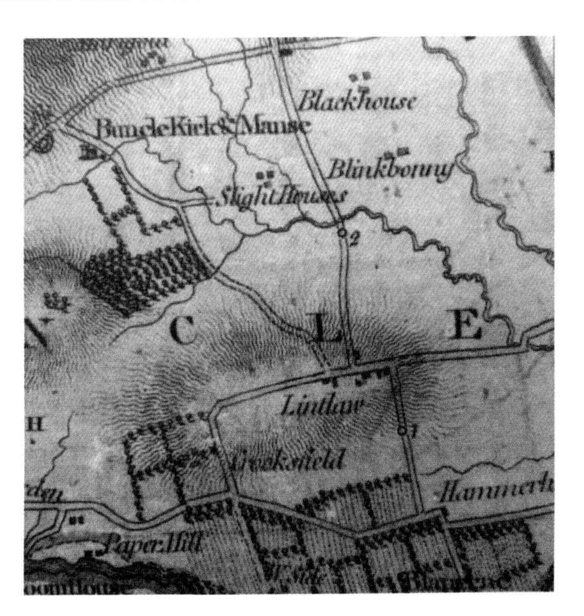

Map of Slighhouses, 1797

Hutton spent fourteen years of his life here. He managed the land and, through back-breaking work, turned it into a productive farm.

Reproduced with the permission of the National Library of Scotland

Nether Monynut today

This is the rough land that Hutton also farmed at the nearby Nether Monynut.

Mike Browne

Inset: Nether Monynut in Hutton's day

The inset panel reconstructs what the land would have looked like when Hutton farmed the land.

Mike Browne

to enhance the drainage, but it just made the ground more difficult and laborious to plough. Excess surface water was carried away from the pastures by ditches he dug around the perimeter of the enclosed fields. At the start of his Herculean labours, Hutton felt ground down by the scale of the challenge that faced him in transforming his land into a productive farming unit. Famously he wrote of the task ahead, '… I find myself already more than half transformed into a brute'.

The other farm Hutton inherited from his father was close by at Nether Monynut, just five miles away and deeper into the Lammermuirs. Bought by William Hutton in 1710, it occupied even higher ground than at Slighhouses and the land was equally rough and stony – far from a perfect place to implement modern agricultural practices. In those days, it was unremarkable to own two farms that would be run as one business. The function of the higher farm was to rear lambs that would be fattened on the sweeter pastures of his improving lowland farm below. It seems that this is how James Hutton ran this small estate.

The main innovation introduced from his travels was to till the soil on his farm with a smaller, lighter metal plough that he had brought back

'High Suffolk' plough

Hutton brought the 'High Suffolk' plough back from his travels in East Anglia. It greatly improved his efficiency in tilling the soil on his Slighhouses farm.

Adapted from a graphic supplied by The James Hutton Institute

from East Anglia. Hutton referred to this new bit of kit as a 'High Suffolk' plough. It was easy to manoeuvre and could be pulled by only two horses. The Scots plough, by comparison, was cumbersome to use and required up to six heavy horses to manoeuvre it effectively. This new implement was therefore a welcome innovation. Over an acre per day could be tilled using the new equipment; it also required less feed for the draught animals and less manpower was required to steer the plough.

His hard work in draining the land, clearing stones and tilling the soil with his new plough was beginning to pay off. He also brought an experienced ploughman from Norfolk to help him with the heavy burden of working the land. Together they eventually tamed the rough pastures of his Berwickshire home and the land became more productive. He grew turnips and cultivated grass to feed the cattle he reared in addition to the sheep bred on his other farm. The cattle were used equally for meat and milk production. Hutton was particularly partial to butter and cheese, which he made for his own consumption. He also understood the need for crop rotation and soil fertility and discussed these subjects at length in *Elements of Agriculture*. This manuscript, written in later life, summarised his encyclopaedic knowledge of farming and agricultural practice.

It is Playfair's opinion that 'Dr Hutton' had 'the credit of being one of those who introduced new husbandry into the country where it has since made more rapid advances than in any other part of the country'. High praise indeed.

Observations and experiments

An interesting aspect of Hutton's preoccupation with agricultural improvement was his focus on climate and its effect on plant growth in particular. He took regular temperature readings whilst on his Berwickshire farm and measured other parameters of the changeable weather, including rainfall. This was the start of a lifelong interest in observing and recording aspects of the great outdoors, and his interest in temperature variation with altitude and rainfall was to continue even after his move back to Edinburgh. Hutton later recalled how, following repeated measurements of the temperature at the base and on the summit of Arthur's Seat, he was able to calculate the decline in temperature with altitude. His results were remarkably accurate when compared with measurements made today. Given the rudimentary nature of thermometers at this time, the accuracy of Hutton's calculations are even more impressive. We call this phenomenon the 'dry adiabatic rate.'

This was all part of his fascination with how the world works and the interplay between its component parts. It could even be described as an early form of environmentalism where natural forces and phenomena were observed, measured and evaluated to understand the working of Earth systems as a whole.

Hutton's interest in climate was also evident when he made the trip to East Anglia. He connected temperature with the latitude of the place where the measurement was made and estimated that there was a drop in temperature of 1° Fahrenheit for each degree of latitude: alas the actual tables he constructed of these temperature variations are now lost. He also took regular readings with his thermometer as he walked across his farm, with the purpose of establishing a relationship between air temperature and the growth of the crops he had planted. Hutton had hoped to help other farmers to establish which crops would grow best in their local area. It is not clear, however, that this ambition was ever fully realised.

Hutton also tried to calculate the length of the growing season in the years between 1774 and 1777. He tabulated average summer temperatures with total grain production for the whole country in those particular years. He also plotted average temperatures against the dates that the harvests started. A drop in temperature of 1° Fahrenheit meant that the harvest was delayed by around ten days. Unfortunately, none of his tabulations or graphs has survived.

In later years Hutton presented a paper on *The Theory of Rain* to the Royal Society of Edinburgh. Around 150 pages of his epic tome on *Elements of Agriculture* were devoted to the effects of climate, particularly heat on plant growth. Once again he demonstrated a dogged pursuit of reliable evidence in support of his new ideas.

In addition to climate studies, Hutton also experimented with the crops that he planted and the conditions under which they were cultivated. He was keen to explore the relationship between light, temperature and the chemistry of the soil. Bizarrely he grew carrots and radishes in the dark, observing that the resultant crop had little taste, colour or smell. He concluded that light was the critical factor, noting in *Elements of Agriculture*: '... it is the leaf that we can trace a chemical process operating upon the proper juices of the plant ... its colour is the effect of a combination of the solar system with the other chemical elements of the plant.'

What Hutton was describing, in a very rudimentary manner, is what we now understand as photosynthesis. This is the process by which plants convert energy from the sun, in combination with carbon dioxide and water, into life-sustaining food for the plant. The first scientist to describe this process in some detail was Jan Ingenhousz (1730–99), a Dutch-born scientist. He undertook a series of elaborate experiments in 1779 that were designed to understand how photosynthesis worked. Much of this experimental work was undertaken in England, with his findings published in a book entitled *Experiments with Vegetables*. This work would have been of great interest and relevance to Hutton, but he made no reference to the book in his writings on agriculture. Although widely read and familiar with continental literature, he may have seen it but chose, as was the practice in those times, not to refer to it.

A second experiment looked at soil fertility. Hutton planted seeds in both fertile and poorer quality soils to assess the effect the substrate had on the health and productivity of the resulting plants. Perhaps unsurprisingly he observed that seeds planted in poorer quality soils produced fewer ears of barley and wheat. The length of the plant stalks was also shorter. His two experiments allowed him to conclude that climate influenced the quality of the produce and soil fertility influenced the quantity of the yield.

He also considered the benefits of adding fertilisers to the soil to improve its natural productivity. Marl, coal ash, animal dung, seaweed and salt were all trialled under controlled conditions. Marl, a calcium carbonate rich deposit with clay and silt, was readily to hand on his farm. He dug a pit to extract the mineral and this excavation is still evident to this day. Hutton spread quantities across part of a field that was then planted with barley. Towards harvest time, he observed his farm from a high vantage point near a spot known as Buncle Edge: from there he could observe the areas that had been treated with marl and those that had not. He wrote in *Elements of Agriculture*:

> I saw the field chequered with the deepest and palest green .... all the other circumstances being the same, producing so great an effect in the operation ... and making a luxuriant crop from soil which otherwise gave the most scanty.

Plant disease was also of concern to Hutton, particularly a fungal blight that was visited on cereal crops. Known as 'smut' it caused a blackening of the ears of wheat which rendered them useless as seed for next year's crop

Marl pit

Hutton dug a small pit on his farm to recover marl that he applied to his fields. He hoped this would make his soil more fertile and increase crop yields.

Mike Browne

or for bread making. Hutton experimented by treating the seeds so that they became more resistant to this scourge. He tried immersing the seeds in cold water and also in urine. Today, sophisticated chemical treatments are available to protect the seeds against smut and other diseases that affect crop yield, so it is unlikely that Hutton's homespun approach would have been particularly effective. But, as ever, his intellectual curiosity and desire for improvement were very much in evidence.

A first draft of the Rock Cycle

Hutton also noticed that the ditches that he dug to achieve better drainage filled in after heavy rain. Topsoil from the adjacent fields was regularly swept away during rainstorms from these drainage ditches into streams and carried towards the sea. He had already seen erosion at work on a grander scale in East Anglia: in 1753 he observed the River Yare in flood, emptying into the North Sea, where it had carried away 'part of our land, to be sunk at the bottom of the sea'.

We can surmise that these observations triggered one of Hutton's big ideas. Rock, sands and gravels that swept from the land, built up on the sea floor and would, at some future time, form new lands. These new lands would themselves be eroded by wind and water and worn down. Hutton later found evidence of many cycles of formation and destruction of the land in his geological expeditions across the country. However, this initial series of observations, while undertaking the back-breaking task of clearing the drainage ditches at Slighhouses, may have started a train of thought that led to the first draft of what we now recognise as the Rock Cycle. Hutton was beginning to think like a geologist.

Experimental plots

Hutton scientists have recreated the same effect that Hutton saw from the hills high above his farm. A patchwork of different yields and crop health is the result of the application of a range of fertilisers and soil conditioners.

Intelligent Growth Solutions / James Hutton Ltd

Rural life

It was Hutton's social isolation that was his sorest personal trial. He missed the companionship experienced during his previous years in East Anglia and spent many lonely nights on the farm at Slighhouses. Two letters survive from this period that provide an insight into Hutton's state of mind. He wrote to one of his close friends, George Clerk Maxwell, intimating that he felt quite alone, bereft of company, and somewhat at odds with his social environment. These gloomy feelings, however, may have been an unfortunate snapshot of his mood at the time of writing: he stuck to this life 'in an outpost of civilisation' for 14 years, so he must have gained some comfort from farming and his isolated rural existence.

Sir John Hall of Dunglass, a near neighbour, turned out to be a fellow scientist and this was a great comfort to Hutton. They would remain firm friends for the remainder of his life. The friendship would continue into the next generation as Sir John's son, James, also an accomplished scientist, later accompanied Hutton on some of his geological forays.

Benjamin Franklin, the eminent American figure, who was a signatory to the Declaration of Independence and the American Constitution, was a visitor to Edinburgh in 1759. He met with Adam Smith and David Hume and there is the tantalising possibility that Hutton may have also been a house guest at Hume's family home where the visit was hosted; it was only ten miles distance from Slighhouses. Hutton was best known at that time for his interests in agricultural improvement, which was also a deeply held passion for Mr Franklin. The latter's connections with Scotland were further cemented with the presentation of an LLD degree from the University of St Andrews. He was thereafter known as Dr Franklin.

Benjamin Franklin

A portrait by Joseph Duplessis (1725–1802), oil-on-canvas painting, *c.*1785.
Wikimedia Commons

Another farming connection with America has recently been unearthed from archive of the University of Edinburgh. Handwritten letters from George Washington, first president of the United States, to David Erskine, the 11th Earl of Buchan, said how impressed he was with Scottish farmers in comparison to those working in America, calling his country men 'slovenly'. He could not poach Scottish farming families, which was illegal at the time, but stressed that the hand of friendship would be extended to any Scots 'considering emigrating anyway'. Scotland's reputation as a nation of efficient farmers and land managers was beginning to be established. One of the letters is dated 20 February 1796, and is part of a set of 18 exchanged between the two men during the 1790s.

Hutton's first geological foray

In 1764, Hutton took a break from farming to pursue his awakening interest in geology, leaving the farm in the care of his Norfolk ploughman. He travelled with his friend George Clerk Maxwell on foot and by horseback to Crieff, onwards through the Grampian Mountains to Dalwhinnie, then along the shores of Loch Ness to Inverness. It was a dangerous trip to attempt as the country, after the '45 Rising had been crushed, was still in the grip of what amounted to martial law. One saving grace was that the military, under the supervision of the British Army's commander General Wade, had constructed new roads and bridges to facilitate more efficient troop movements which were of considerable assistance to travel.

Sadly, neither Hutton nor Clerk Maxwell had much sympathy for the 'wyld men' of the Highlands occasionally glimpsed as they made their way cross-country. Hutton was much more interested in studying the rocks and rugged landscapes and appeared to have little concern for the defeated Highlander people. That was the brutal reality. The landed gentry, and Hutton was one of their number, had most to lose if the Rebellion had succeeded, so they favoured the victorious Government side. They were not exceptional in holding these opinions, as the *literati* generally tended to ignore the issues that afflicted the rural population.

Five-arched bridge

This elegant five-arched bridge was constructed in 1733 as part of General Wade's infrastructure programme. It crosses the River Tay at Aberfeldy in Highland Perthshire and carries traffic to this day and lies on the route that Hutton and Clerk Maxwell may have taken during their route march northwards to the Highlands.

Shutterstock

From this point onwards, Hutton's travels always had a geological purpose. As John Playfair (1805) reported, he 'never ceased to study the natural history of the globe, with a view to ascertaining the changes that have taken place on its surface, and of discovering the causes by which they have been produced'. And so, Hutton and Clerk Maxwell visited Cromarty and ventured as far north as Caithness, all the while studying the red sandstones of the area. Hutton observed of the coastal landscapes he saw,

> The East Coast of Caithness is a perpendicular cliff of sandstone, lying in a horizontal position, and thus forming a flat country above the shore. But along this coast there are small islands, pillars, and peninsulas, of the same strata, corresponding perfectly with that which forms the greater mass. Now, shall we suppose those strata of sandstone to have been formed in their place, and to have reached no farther eastward into the sea? In following this connection of things, we cannot refuse to acknowledge that Ireland had formerly been in one mass of land with Britain, in like manner as the Orkneys had been with Scotland. (*The Theory of the Earth*)

He was beginning to see change as a constant where geological processes are concerned.

Half a century later, Hugh Miller (1802–56), a stonemason, self-taught geologist and prolific writer from the village of Cromarty, made his name studying these rocks and the fossils they yielded. The date of Hutton's death and Miller's birth were separated by only five years. The paths of two of Scotland's most famous geologists so very nearly crossed.

Hutton and Clerk Maxwell now returned along the Moray coast by way of Portsoy and Peterhead and then southwards towards Aberdeen, noting granite outcrops and other igneous (rocks that were once molten) rocks on their homeward journey. Hutton was yet to realise what a prominent role granite would play in his later expeditions and researches.

This trip marked a turning point in Hutton's thinking and outlook. A better understanding of geology and the processes that affected the surface of the Earth became the main focus of his enquiries. Yet agriculture remained an enduring passion and he would return to that subject during the final years of his life, and he continued to wear the plain brown worsted dress of a farmer, as portrayed in the formal portrait by the artist Henry Raeburn (see page 132). As he wrote in *Elements of Agriculture* later, 'farming was the story of my life'. Geology may by now have captured his intellectual curiosity, but farming ran through his veins.

Hutton was about to move back to live in his native Edinburgh on a permanent basis.

Opposite: Caithness

Hutton ventured as far north as Caithness on this trip and would have seen the spectacular red sandstone sea cliffs of the area.

Shutterstock

Chapter 4
Permanent return to Edinburgh

Work on the Forth and Clyde Canal

James Hutton had lived quietly on his Berwickshire farm for 14 years. With his farming operations now running smoothly, it was time for a change. He was also becoming more confident as a self-taught geologist and, with a growing reputation as a 'mineralogist and collector', felt able to advise others on such matters. James Watt (1736–1819), the soon-to-be engineer of great fame, described him as a 'famous fossil philosopher'.

Fortuitously, a major civil engineering endeavour was about to begin right on Hutton's doorstep, namely the Forth and Clyde Canal project. Those managing it were in need of geological expertise and Hutton was able to provide some of the required input. It also had an unforeseen benefit of acting as a bridge between the relative isolation of Hutton's humdrum farming existence in Duns to his reintegration into the hurly-burly of intellectual life in Enlightenment Edinburgh.

The eighteenth century saw the start of the canal-building revolution in Britain. Inland waterways criss-crossed the country to transport raw materials and manufactured goods across the land. Scotland may have had less need of such arterial routes with distances more modest than, for example, the Midlands, the manufacturing heart of England, to London; nevertheless, work began in 1767 to link the main population centres of Edinburgh and Glasgow.

The idea of a canal across the central belt of Scotland had been discussed since the reign of Charles II over a century earlier. Large infrastructure projects, regardless of the historic period in which they are proposed, usually have an extraordinary gestation period from conception to implementation. The canal linking the Forth estuary in the east to the Clyde in the west was no exception.

The task of surveying the possible routes the canal might take was undertaken by Robert Mackell in 1762, augmented two years later by the work of John Smeaton, the well-known designer of the Eddystone Lighthouse.

Maryhill Locks on the Forth and Clyde Canal

The Forth & Clyde Canal is approximately 57 km in length with forty locks to negotiate.

Shutterstock

Four years of acrimonious debate followed, particularly on the route the canal should take. Playfair tells us that two camps quickly emerged. The first plan, proposed by Glasgow merchants, stipulated a deep canal, accessible to ocean-going vessels. Edinburgh-based backers, in favour of a 'small canal', advanced a second proposal. Ultimately, east triumphed over west and the more modest proposal was adopted.

Hutton was an active participant in this dialogue that quickly descended into a shouting match. The pages of the *Scots Magazine*, *Edinburgh Advertiser* and *Edinburgh Courant* were crammed with articles from all sides of the debate expounding their impassioned views. The articles were all anonymous, so it is not possible to see who said what, but it is known that Hutton backed the 'small canal'. This was the first time Hutton had used his rapidly developing expertise in geology for the public good.

The canal proved to be a complex civil engineering undertaking, with 20 locks to the west of the highest point of the route around 50 m above sea level. To the east, another 19 locks were required, each one designed to lift the vessels using the canal almost 3 m higher than the previous level. A large new reservoir was also needed to keep the water levels topped up.

Hutton's biographer John Playfair informs us that Hutton returned to live in Edinburgh 'about 1768', although other authorities place his return at a year earlier in 1767. This was convenient, for most of the meetings of the canal management committee of the Forth and Clyde Navigation Company took place in Edinburgh. Historical records are silent on whether Hutton was elected or co-opted onto the committee but, regardless, he was a regular attendee at meetings until 1775. In all, he attended 84 general, special and quarterly meetings over a seven-year period in relation to the canal project – usually held at the Exchange Coffee House in the High Street or alternatively at a vintner's premises in Old Ship Close.

Excavations started in June 1768 and the project was finally completed in 1790. Hutton was closely involved in the construction process, assisted in determining the canal route and helped to source the building stone used to line the walls of the canal structure. And with five £100 shares in the enterprise, he could be said to have invested physically, intellectually, managerially and financially in one of Scotland's biggest infrastructure projects of the age.

The project became a major employer in central Scotland. At the peak of activity, over 1000 men laboured along the route of the canal as it inched its way across the landscape. This figure diminished significantly at harvest time as the men and their labour were required elsewhere.

The land traversed by the new waterway was difficult terrain for the canal builders to navigate. The route was largely constructed on sedimentary strata of Carboniferous age with associated volcanic rocks of various types. Boggy land was also crossed and these areas proved to be amongst the most challenging conditions to manage. Traversing Dullator Bog was particularly problematic as the canal sunk steadily as construction proceeded. Even though Mr Mackell's survey report was most thorough, with 'the qualities of the soil for twelve feet deep' explored 'by boring', the project was bedevilled by unforeseen engineering problems. This led to increased costs and an evermore elastic completion date was required to accommodate every new challenge. The section of the route near Carron was particularly contentious, with land ownership issues, and the matter ended in litigation.

The project overran financially to a significant degree and ended up costing a great deal more than the initial £148,000 estimate. But although the project faced many setbacks, the success of the venture was eventually assured. Company records show that in 1800 the canal carried 129,480 tons of cargo consisting mainly of coal, but also quantities of herring, salt, timber, grain and iron. By the mid nineteenth century, trade on the canal was at its height with almost three million tons making its way back and forth along the waterway.

With the construction of a railway line that tracked a similar route, the canal went into a gradual decline and eventually closed for business on 31 December 1962. However, in recent times it has enjoyed a new lease of life as pleasure craft now glide along its waters on most days of the week. Parts of the canal that had fallen into disrepair have now been restored and its former glory recaptured, but for an entirely different purpose. Hutton's legacy lives on for the benefit of Sunday sailors and other recreational users who sail the Forth and Clyde Canal to relax and unwind.

Boats at Kirkintilloch

The Forth and Clyde Canal is now much used by pleasure craft carrying tourists.

Scottish Canals/Photograph © Peter Sandground

Hutton's correspondence with John Strange

Little remains of Hutton's copious writings that flowed from his loquacious pen. We know of his major works and frequent papers in the *Transactions of the Royal Society of Edinburgh* that were written in the latter part of his life, but informal communications with friends and other geology enthusiasts are rare. Nonetheless, four letters written by Hutton found their way to the Department of Manuscripts in the British Museum and were 'discovered' and published in 1951. These were originally penned about the time Hutton was engaged in his travails on the Forth and Clyde Canal project. They are particularly interesting as they provide an understanding of his knowledge of the emerging science of geology at the time. They also illuminate aspects of Hutton's personality, as he appears in these letters to be generous, helpful and witty in his correspondence, demonstrated by the remark, 'I shall hand you down any piece of stuff you desire'. Other warm words convey similar sentiments.

All four letters were written to John Strange FRS, described as a diplomat, naturalist and antiquarian. The pair were introduced to each other by the naturalist Thomas Pennant who met Hutton whilst the latter was on his travels across Scotland. Strange counted geology amongst his many hobbies and interests.

Hutton begins his first letter with characteristic modesty, noting on the subject of shells that, 'As I have never made [them] my study I cannot tell the names of the different fossil shells found in Scotland ....' – although this significantly underplays the obvious understanding of fossils that emerges in his next three published letters. He also demonstrates his knowledge of the geology of England with the comment, 'I know of no such limestone in Scotland as that of Portland, Bath, Oxford or Catton .... Our limestones are in general like those of Derbyshire, Yorkshire and Northumberland'. Hutton had travelled widely, so was able to draw on his extensive knowledge of the geology of the English regions. He also comments on the thickness of individual beds of limestone in Scotland as 'various, from a few inches to 10, 20 or 30 feet', and also their inclination which he describes as 'extremely irregular from flat to the perpendicular'.

These undated letters were estimated to have been written by Hutton between 1768 and 1774. They provide an early insight into his thoughts on geology. As such, he is clearly aware of the presence of fossils in the strata he was beginning to study and they played a key role in the development of his ideas later published in *Theory of the Earth*. He was confident that the fossil remains he saw of 'shells and madrepores' (a type of coral) originally flourished on the sea floor, only to be raised out of the ocean to locations high above, forming dry land. We now understand how this happens through the operation of plate tectonics. Hutton, however, was only able to talk in terms of the Earth as a heat engine which consolidated loose sediments and raised them up from the deep in some, as yet, to be discovered manner. Nonetheless, his version of events was a good estimation of a process only to be fully unravelled and understood around 200 years later.

Hutton's Edinburgh

The Edinburgh that Hutton returned to in 1767 was an insanitary and soot-stained city of around 70,000 souls. One of its most eminent chroniclers was Robert Chambers, later to be the publisher of an encyclopaedia and other literary works, who described it thus: 'Edinburgh was, at the beginning of George III's reign in 1760, a picturesque, odorous, old-fashioned town.' The population had swelled dramatically from around 40,000 inhabitants in 1720 to around 85,000 by the time of Hutton's death in 1797. Changes to agricultural practice had prompted this shift from country to the city.

Work on Edinburgh's elegant New Town had just started in 1767 and would take fifty years to complete. As such, the inhabitants were tightly squeezed into the Medieval Old Town that consisted of the High Street and the closes and wynds that ran off this central spine. The city had grown into an unplanned muddle of rickety, insanitary buildings and dark, foreboding backstreets and closes.

This was the haunt of many notorious criminals and ne'er-do-wells such as Deacon Brodie, the prolific housebreaker and thief who, incredibly, was also a city councillor. There is no evidence that Hutton was a victim of crime or an assault, but it must have been an ever-present threat to those who walked the streets, particularly after dark.

The city was a melting pot of social classes, of all professions and none, families and those living alone. The High Street had towering tenements of six stories or more housing this tumult of humanity. Writers rubbed shoulders with titled nobility, surgeons, lawyers, bakers, excise men, painters, schoolmasters, leather workers and merchants who all inhabited the same building. The interiors of those high-rise tenements that have survived and have not been renovated during later years are surprisingly commodious – a relatively generous living space with decorated walls and ceilings. The windows, however, were small. During the winter months, when the rooms were only illuminated by candlelight, they must have been dark and dingy places.

Risk of fire was huge and lethal blazes ripped through these tenement buildings from time to time causing considerable loss of life. No organised fire brigade existed at this time, so everyone took their chance of survival. Waking up the next day alive and unscorched was probably considered a blessing.

Deacon Brodie

Drawing by John Kay of Deacon Brodie in the Tollbooth before his execution.

John Kay

Sanitation was rudimentary at best, with the well-known cry of 'gardyloo' and the unspeakable unpleasantness that followed it from the upper floors of the tenement buildings. A visitor said that 'every street shows the nastiness of its inhabitants; the excrement lies in heaps'. To add to this melee, the streets thronged with people, pigs, sheep, carts and detritus of all descriptions.

However, leaving such insanitary matters, let us consider the social and intellectual world that James Hutton was about to enter. In fact, his address was not on the High Street at all; he had moved in with his three sisters, Isabella, Jean and Sarah, to a house on St John's Hill overlooking Arthur's Seat. Its precise location was established relatively recently by the Hutton sleuth, Norman Butcher. Butcher unearthed a book written by Sir James Crichton-Browne (1840–1938) who revealed that his grandfather had inherited a house on St John's Hill from a great-uncle, James Hutton. Hutton's abode for the final 30 years of his life was thus determined.

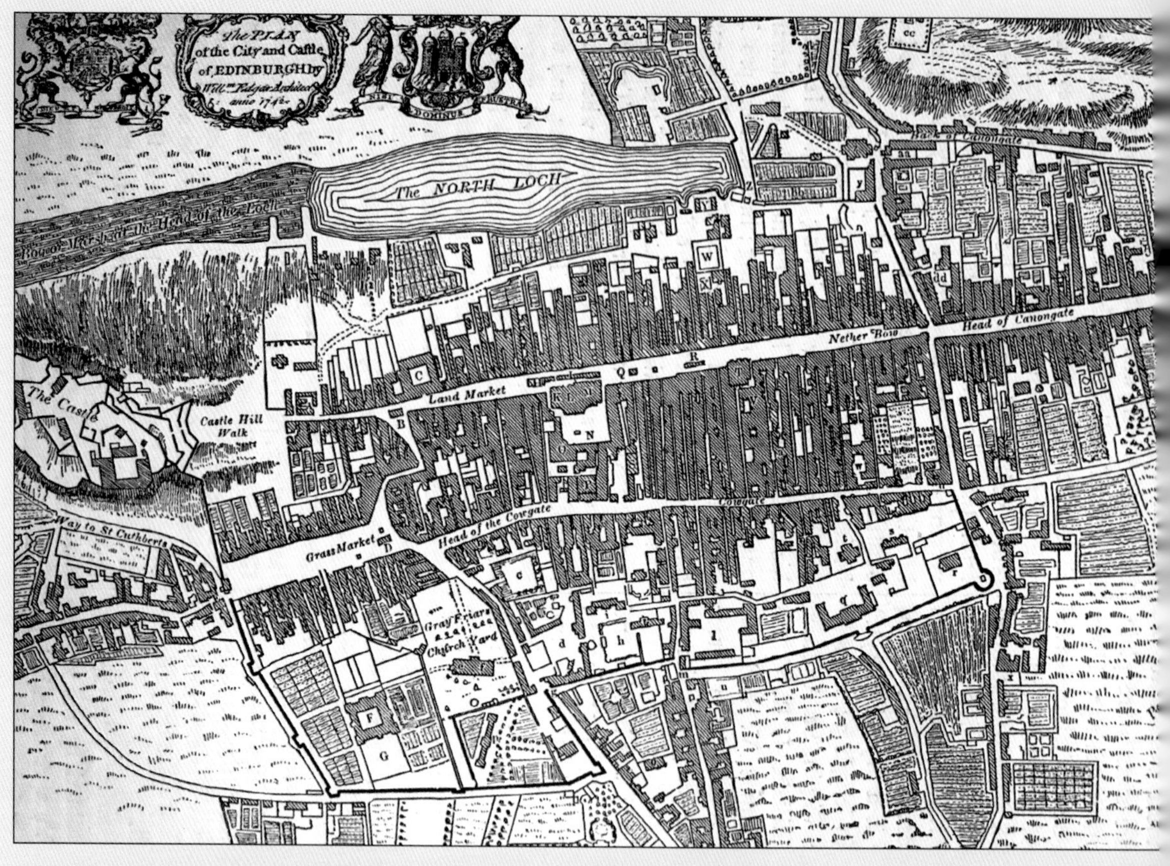

The PLAN of the City and Castle of EDINBURGH by
Willm. Edgar Architect anno 1742
The NORTH LOCH
Bog or Marsh at the Head of the Loch
The Castle
Castle Hill Walk
Land Market
Nether Bow
Head of Canongate
Cowgate
Grass Market
Head of the Cowgate
Gray Friars Church Yard
Way to St Cuthberts

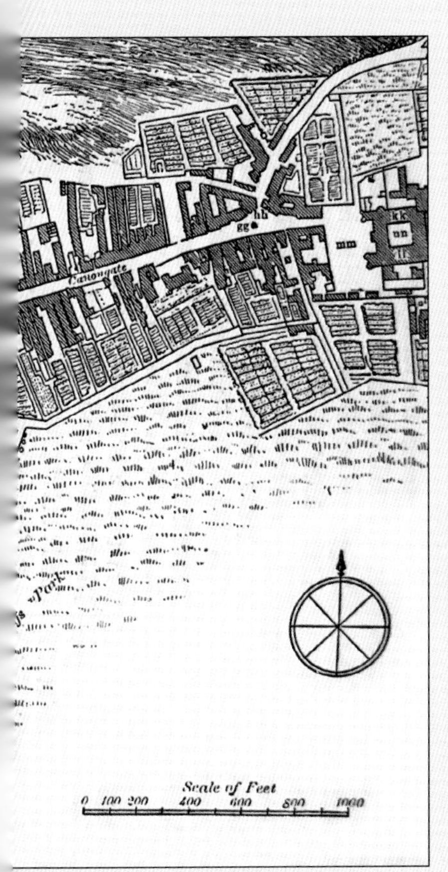

Left: Edinburgh, 1742

Eighteenth-century Edinburgh showing the High Street with wynds and closes running off the main thoroughfare.

Cassell's *Old and New Edinburgh*

Above: Gladstone's Land then and now

Thomas Gladstone was a wealthy merchant who owned this building during Hutton's time. He lived on the fifth floor and rented out the second and third floors that were considered to be the main real estate and revenue earner. On the ground floor, particularly the rooms facing the High Street, would have been occupied by merchants selling all manner of produce. It is more than likely that Hutton would have purchased food, perhaps bread or fruit, from these premises. Situated at 477B Lawnmarket, it was restored and furnished by the National Trust for Scotland.

Cassell's *Old and New Edinburgh* and Alan McKirdy

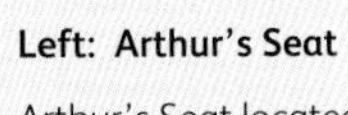

Left: Arthur's Seat

Arthur's Seat located in the east of Edinburgh was one of Hutton's regular haunts. This tranquil spot lay close to his house on St John's Hill.

Shutterstock

As he had never held a university post of any kind, all of Hutton's writing had to be done from home. As he noted in his correspondence with John Strange, 'Having no home, I am obliged to make one chamber serve me for laboratory, library and repository for self and minerals, of which I have grown so avaricious, my friends allege that I shall soon gather as many stones as will build me a house'. John Playfair also confirmed the clutter of rock specimens and chemical equipment in Hutton's study, which presumably increased as the years went by.

The house survived until the 1960s when it was pulled down as part of a redevelopment project. Edinburgh Geological Society placed a memorial plaque at the site of the Hutton's house in the 1990s.

Hutton on exploration, observations and oceanography

Three of Hutton's unpublished letters, penned five years after his return to Edinburgh, have found their way to the Fitzwilliam Museum in Cambridge. They were written to scientists and adventurers who were involved

Hutton's house

This peaceful spot marks the site of Hutton's house, high on St John's Hill. The boulder on the (top) right is from Glen Tilt close to the spot where Hutton made the seminal discovery that granite once existed in liquid form. The boulder on the (top) left is made from conglomerate that comprise many rounded fragments of older rocks. This also illustrates another idea developed by Hutton that 'the ruins of older worlds are visible in the present structures of the planet'.
Alan McKirdy

with Captain Cook's voyages to the South Seas. Hutton was therefore actively involved in the preparations for Cook's second voyage, and gave advice on geological and marine research that the mariners could undertake on their travels. The letters were to the botanist Joseph Banks (1743–1820) and his assistant James Lind (1716–94), who were to accompany Cook on his voyage. Lind had graduated in medicine in 1768 from the University of Edinburgh, some years after Hutton. The tone of the correspondence clearly indicates they were on friendly terms, which is unsurprising as Lind was one of the first people Hutton met on his return to Edinburgh from Duns. Banks, as it happened, would withdraw from the expedition because of the unsatisfactory nature of the accommodation offered on the ship.

The letters were written in 1772 and early the following year. Hutton was particularly anxious that geological surveys should be undertaken of these faraway places. He also advised on meteorological and oceanographic research that would add to the scant contemporary knowledge of these subjects. His suggestions on the nature of the scientific observations to be undertaken were very specific and, in places, in Hutton's own version of shorthand:

> It is your business to make observations of every subject. At sea, you have (1st) astron: obs (secondly) meteor: observations of the sea, its colour, depth, temperature streams and tides regularly recorded … (4thly) you should have a place for any other kind of observation that may not appear to fall immediately under the others. The coast observations should include nautical, geogra; veget; and anim–. The mineral observations consist both in a history both of soil and loose parts and of the solid parts of rocks and beds.

He also gave advice on the way in which the samples of rock should be packed and labelled. There was much more besides in terms of specific measurements that Hutton felt should be recorded, including measurement of air and sea temperatures near the surface of the water and evaporation rates of the seawater. More bizarrely, Hutton sent Lind two boxes containing 'diving machines'. It is not known whether Lind requested them or Hutton sent them on his own initiative. They were possibly sampling devices, like bottom grabs, to collect solid material from the ocean floor or maybe a way of collecting water samples from depth to assess their salinity.

The most significant message we can take from these letters is that Hutton was the driving force behind a myriad of scientific investigations that were undertaken during Cook's second voyage. Hutton was to be firmly rooted in his Edinburgh bubble with his kith and kin for the rest of his life, but these letters clearly show that he also had a keen interest in environmental and scientific issues that pertained to lands and seas on the other side of the globe.

James Lind by Sir George Chalmers

Portrait of James Lind – pioneer of naval hygiene and discoverer of the link between dietary deficiencies and scurvy.

With kind permission of John Hepner

James Hutton's friend and correspondent on these matters, James Lind, was a scientist of note in his own right. He is perhaps best known as the doctor who did much to improve the health of able seamen. In the eighteenth century, scurvy was a major cause of illness and death amongst seafarers. We now know this debilitating disease is caused by a lack of Vitamin C, but it was Lind who recognised a possible link. Later, the Royal Navy issued an order for lemon juice to be supplied to all on board. Lind also demonstrated that fresh water could be obtained through the distillation of seawater and campaigned for greater cleanliness of the sailors themselves as well as their quarters below deck. He is, therefore, remembered as a doctor who did much to improve the general living conditions and diet of seafarers in the eighteenth century. This resulted in fitter and healthier Royal Navy personnel thereafter.

Travels with James Watt

Before Hutton gave Enlightenment Edinburgh his full attention, he was off on his travels again. In 1774, Hutton headed south to tour the English Midlands and also parts of Wales. Playfair could find no 'memorandum whatsoever amongst Hutton's papers' for this visit, but we are certain it took place, as he refers in *Theory of the Earth* to the salt mines in Cheshire that he visited. The famous engineer James Watt was his travelling companion on this expedition.

After he reached Birmingham, Hutton set out for a tour of Wales. Playfair tells us:

> One of the objects of this tour, as I learned from himself, was to discover the origin of the hard gravel of granulated quartz, which is found in such vast abundance in the soils around Birmingham, and indeed over a great tract of the central part of England.' The Welsh leg of the journey was undertaken to find out whether 'amongst the primitive mountains of Wales, there were any that might be supposed to have furnished the materials of it.'

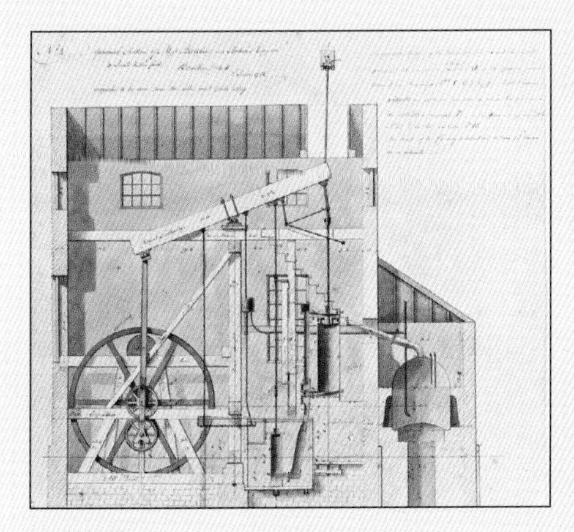

James Watt

Right: James Watt and Hutton became close friends. Watt had spent seven years working on the Forth and Clyde Canal project as a land surveyor, so it seems likely that they met when they were jointly employed on that endeavour. Watt's first prototype steam engine was built at Burn Pitt colliery near Kinneil and Hutton was mightily impressed with what he saw. They corresponded regularly as their friendship grew, exchanging ideas on engineering and scientific topics.

Above: Photograph of drawing number 4 depicting the general section of Barclay and Perkins engine original illustration by Watt, 2 June 1786.

Hutton had developed a remarkable knowledge of British geology with his criss-crossing of the country either on foot or by horseback. He wrote of this burgeoning ability:

> I can undertake to tell from whence had come a specimen of gravel taken up anywhere, at least upon the east side of this island. Nor will this appear in any way difficult, when it is considered, that, from Portland to the Orkneys, there are at least ten different productions of hard stone in the solid land ... with all of which I am well acquainted.

Although his enduring interest in agricultural improvement had not been entirely forgotten, his primary purpose was now the study of geology.

Chapter 5
Hutton and the Scottish Enlightenment

The Scottish Enlightenment

The Scottish Enlightenment differed in character from what had gone before in England and on the continent. Here, acquisition of knowledge and new ways of looking at the world were not always viewed as a threat to the establishment, namely the Church and the State. The participants of this great Scottish enterprise had a genuine desire to move forward on a range of academic and intellectual fronts. However, religious leaders flexed their muscles on occasions to protect their position. For example, they blocked David Hume's candidacy for the Professorship of Moral Philosophy at the University of Edinburgh in 1745 and later for the Chair of Logic and Rhetoric in Glasgow on the grounds of his alleged atheism. Such actions demonstrated that the Church still had a powerful bite. Hume appeared early in the Scottish Enlightenment story and his eloquently phrased and loudly proclaimed religious scepticism was a considerable challenge to the Church's authority. However, as the period of intellectual ferment unfolded, more ordained ministers were swept up in this process of intellectual development, so the Church's stance in relation to new ideas softened considerably. By the second half of the eighteenth century, Scotland was becoming, by and large, a society that tolerated a range of different views on the arts, science, economics and religion.

Forty-one year-old James Hutton was an entrant to this world, but he was not entirely unknown in Edinburgh's intellectual and polite circles. His long-time friendship with the well-connected John Clerk of Eldin and his brother George Clerk Maxwell oiled the wheels for introductions to a more extensive social circle, and his work on the Forth and Clyde Canal project would have also widened his social and professional horizons.

David Hume (1711–76)

David Hume was an intellectual colossus of the Scottish Enlightenment. He was a philosopher, historian and economist of note. He published great works throughout his life including *An Enquiry Concerning the Principles of Morals and The History of England*. When Hutton became acquainted with Hume, he found Hume's philosophical ideas of interest and value in developing his own thinking. The statue of the man in Romanesque garb, which was the style of the time, is located on Lawnmarket, on Edinburgh's Royal Mile, just in front of the High Court of Justiciary.

Alan McKirdy

The Philosophical Society

In 1739 Colin Maclaurin, Hutton's maths tutor, started a learned discussion group called the Philosophical Society. As a man of many interests and accomplishments, it was a natural step for Hutton to join during his first months back in Edinburgh. He read a number of papers at the meetings of this society, but only one was published.

Hutton's first publication in 1777 was titled *Considerations on the Nature, Quantity, and Distinctions of Coal and Culm*. 'Culm', not a widely used geological term today, refers to poor quality coals partially comprised of sandstones and shales in addition to a component of combustible coal. This 37-page pamphlet discussed the question of whether or not this lower grade material should attract the same level of taxation as higher quality coal. Indeed Hutton probably had experience of both culm and coal as he helped to drive the Forth and Clyde Canal through rocks of Carboniferous (coal-bearing) age of central Scotland.

Although not a bestseller, it was a small step on the road to more significant publications and achieved modest success in its aims. Playfair (1805) reported that 'an exemption from duty was obtained for the small coal of Scotland [culm], and this regulation was owing to a great degree to the satisfactory information contained in Dr Hutton's pamphlet'. In undertaking the background research on coal and culm, and coming up with a workable solution, Hutton demonstrated a pragmatic approach to solving everyday problems that had an immediate practical application.

Hutton's circle of friends grew substantially as a result of his membership of the Philosophical Society. Most beneficial was his introduction to Dr Joseph Black who was already a chemist of distinction and had

previously presented papers to the society that were of interest to Hutton. Black was born in Bordeaux, where his Scots father was in the wine trade. Black himself trained in chemistry and medicine in Belfast and Glasgow and subsequently worked as a physician for a short period. (It is said that he attended the birth of Walter Scott in 1771 in his role as a medical doctor.) He then went on to make a substantial name for himself in the world of chemistry with two main discoveries. First, he observed that a proportion of the air we breathe was comprised of a gas hitherto unknown to science, i.e. carbon dioxide: he called it 'fixed air'. Second, in 1762 he discovered and defined the concept of 'latent heat', a subject familiar to school science students today. This is the energy required to convert a solid into liquid, or a liquid into vapour without a change in temperature.

Joseph Black

It is perhaps fitting that the Raeburn portraits of Joseph Black and James Hutton hang close to each other in the Scottish National Portrait Gallery in Edinburgh. They became close friends and were both members of the Oyster Club.

Stipple engraving by J. Posselwhite. Wellcome Collection, Public Domain Mark 1.0

James Hutton and Joseph Black

Hutton and Black deep in conversation – 'their sonsie faces full of science'. Playfair (1805) said of them 'Dr. Black dreaded nothing more than an error, and that Dr Hutton dreaded nothing more than ignorance; that the one was always afraid of going beyond the truth, and the other of not reaching it. Dr Black respected at all times the prejudices and fashions of the world; that of Dr Hutton was more careless, and was often found in direct collision with both'. They sound a perfect foil for each other, perhaps explaining their close friendship.

John Kay

The Oyster Club

In the late eighteenth century, there was assembled in Edinburgh men of prodigious talent covering every imaginable discipline of the age. William Smellie, likewise a man with an enormous range of interests and accomplishments, said:

> Mr Amyat, the King's Chymist, surprised me with a curious remark. He said that I can stand at what is called the Cross of Edinburgh and can, in a few minutes, take fifty men of genius and learning by the hand. In Edinburgh, the access of men o' pairts is not only easy, but their conversation and the communication of their knowledge are at once imparted to intelligent strangers with the utmost liberality.

Caves Tavern

The Caves Tavern in the Cowgate in Edinburgh was the place where the Oyster Club members met on a weekly basis. Recent excavations around the site turned up quantities of oyster shells – an indication of what may have been on the menu for these meetings. Oysters are considered to be an exotic delicacy now, however in eighteenth-century Edinburgh, they were standard fare for all classes as they were readily available from the Firth of Forth.

Alan McKirdy

Some of the main characters in this drama of ideas, philosophies and radical thinking have already been identified. What they required were regular places to meet to exchange their thoughts and ideas. Edinburgh's taverns and coffee houses provided the venues for many of these new clubs and societies that rapidly became the engine of the Enlightenment. Each had their own rules and norms that members had to observe. Such gatherings were male-only, well-lubricated affairs with prodigious quantities of claret consumed, at least by some of the participants. It was an excuse to leave the everyday cares and concerns behind and, in some instances, to behave badly. And so it appears that, almost by accident, a serious purpose to these occasionally debauched gatherings emerged.

For a contemporary account of these regular events, we turn to John Playfair (1805) once more as he describes Hutton's weekly meetings thus:

> Hutton was, perhaps in the most enviable situation in which a man of science can be placed. He was in the midst of a literary society of men of the first abilities, to all of whom he was peculiarly acceptable .... He used also to regularly unbend himself with a few friends, in the little society known by the name of the Oyster Club.
>
> The original members of it were Adam Smith, Joseph Black, and Dr Hutton, and round them was soon formed a knot of those who knew how to value the familiar and social converse of these illustrious men. As all three possessed great talents, enlarged views and extensive information, without any stateliness and formality which men of letters think it is sometimes necessary to effect; as they were all three easily amused; were equally prepared to speak and to listen; and as the sincerity of their friendship had never been darkened

Above: John Kay, self portrait, 1786

James Hutton, by John Kay

James Hutton with hammer in hand, chipping bits off a rock face that showed many of his contemporaries in profile. Those visages would have been well known to Kay's Edinburgh audience back in the day.

John Kay

John Kay (1742–1826)

In an age without cameras, there was the same desire as there is today to record the extraordinary, the humdrum and the fashionable aspects of daily life. The painters and cartoonists who operated during the Scottish Enlightenment were vital in capturing the personalities and the sights of the age.

There were many who plied that artistic trade during the second half of the eighteenth century, but John Kay and Sir Henry Raeburn (1756–1823) were arguably the most note-worthy and eclectic in their wide-ranging work. They produced accomplished portraits of the great and the good and, in Kay's case, the humble and the extraordinary. There were also many writers producing word pictures in prose and poetry, including Robert Burns and Sir Walter Scott. Kay and Raeburn caught the spirit of the age with their sweeping canvasses (Raeburn) and intricate pen and ink cartoons (Kay). Both Kay and Raeburn produced notable images of James Hutton and his coterie of friends, colleagues and acquaintances. Theirs is the most remarkable social history recorded in paint and ink that adds colour and substance to the biography left to us by John Playfair's account of Hutton's life and times.

John Kay was born in Dalkeith, just to the south of Edinburgh. He moved to Leith, aged six, where he was boarded with family connections who treated the young boy badly, almost to the point of his death. From an early age he found that he was a talented artist and produced excellent work with the most rudimentary of materials.

With his new wife, Kay pitched up in Edinburgh around 1762, after serving his apprenticeship as a barber and wigmaker. He made a living for a short time cutting hair before moving to premises in Parliament Close where he opened a print shop. The prominent members of Edinburgh society were never far from his front door and many likenesses were 'captured' as they walked past his shop. He also drew chimney-sweeps and sedan chairmen (the taxi drivers of the age), as well as judges, members of the clergy, lords, ladies and academics, indeed anyone whom he considered worthy of a portrait. James Hutton was featured in many of Kay's cartoons, as were his friends Joseph Black and Adam Smith.

In later life, Sir Henry Raeburn, who was Portrait Painter to King George IV, had access to Edinburgh's high society. His subjects included the usual 'high-end' suspects of lawyers, landed gentry, writers and local politicians, but also many of the prominent Enlightenment figures such as James Hutton, Joseph Black, John Playfair and Robert Adam. Many of Raeburn's portraits hang in the Scottish National Portrait Gallery in Queen Street, Edinburgh. Others are exhibited in the Raeburn Room in the Old College of the University of Edinburgh.

> by the least shade of envy; it would be hard to find an example, where everything favourable to good society was more perfectly united, and everything adverse more entirely excluded. The conversation was always free, often scientific, but never didactic or disputatious; and as the club was much the resort of the strangers who visited Edinburgh, from any object connected with art or with science, it derived from thence an extraordinary decree of variety and interest.

Playfair paints a delightful picture of the Oyster Club as a sociable and sober club with a very serious purpose. It was formed around this tightly knit group of men who clearly helped each other to develop their particular subjects and areas of expertise.

The Royal Society of Edinburgh

As the Philosophical Society lost momentum and members, so a new body was proposed to fill the intellectual void. The Royal Society of Edinburgh was that new and energised focus for scholarship and it received its charter from King George III in 1783. As an existing member of the Philosophical Society, Hutton automatically qualified as a founding member of the Royal Society of Edinburgh.

Hutton, Black, Smith and Playfair were among the members of its first Council and Hutton later joined Black as joint-President of the Society's Physical Class. The other wing of the new society was the Literary Class. From 1786 until he became too unwell to attend, Hutton chaired many meetings. When not presiding, he was often a speaker.

The first meetings were held in the library wing of the principal buildings of the University of Edinburgh. After Hutton's time, the Society moved to Physicians Hall on George Street and eventually, via The Mound, to its current location at 22–24 George Street in 1909. The papers presented and the discussions they prompted were published in the *Transactions of the Royal Society of Edinburgh*. Hutton used the pages of this august and learned journal to disseminate his groundbreaking ideas on geology.

The series of volumes that comprised the *Transactions* appeared irregularly in Hutton's day. Volume 1 was published in 1788, Volume 2 in 1790, Volume 3 in 1794 and Volume 4 in 1798. The frequency of publication was probably just a function of the availability of suitable papers required to fill each issue. Inevitably, there was a considerable lag time between papers being presented to the Fellows of the Society and the published version appearing in print. Nonetheless, they are a treasure trove of the many and varied subjects that were placed in front of the *literati* of Edinburgh.

Hutton the polymath and environmentalist

The pages of the *Transactions of the Royal Society of Edinburgh* reveal the prodigious scope of Hutton's interests. In *Transactions* and published books, his extraordinarily wide-ranging contributions covered geology, medicine, agriculture, chemistry, climate, philosophy, religion, the nature of knowledge and 'written language as a sign of speech'. Such a range marks Hutton out as a man of extraordinary talent, surely qualifying him for the epithet of 'polymath'; an individual whose in-depth knowledge and experience spans many different disciplines and subjects.

Some topics on which Hutton addressed the Society are unexpected, with no hint of a prior interest. His paper on written language and speech is perhaps the most striking. It was delivered in three sessions to RSE Fellows, from 1 June 1786 to 20 November later that year. Hutton sets out his subject thus: 'It is the purpose of the paper to show, in what manner we arrive at the knowledge of simple sounds, by the analytical examination of our speech, or the resolution of it into its principles.' Over ten published pages, he describes his rationale and findings. He concluded that 'there is no fixed relation between writing and pronunciation of our language.' Hutton also comments on the orthography of the Chinese language, which concerns the conventional spelling system for that language. In none of the many biographies written on Hutton does his interest in language figure prominently, so it would be difficult to make the case that his influence on this subject was either profound or long-lasting. However, his commentary on language and speech was considered to be of sufficient importance that it was granted three separate presentation slots to the Fellows and a prominent place in the most learned journal of the day.

Perhaps more consistent with his agriculture roots Hutton, with Dr Black and a Mr Russell, produced a short report on a Dr Hunter and Mr Hornby's 'process of producing an ardent spirit from carrots'. Published in the same volume as Hutton's paper on language, their report reads:

> We have examined the sample of spirit which was sent by Dr Hunter of York to The Royal Society and we have read the account of the experiment on the fermentation and distillation of carrots by which the said spirit was produced.

The report concludes that the 'manufacturing of spirit from carrots may be attended with more expense than manufacturing it from malt ... and the saving of corn for other purposes is an object worthy of attention and encouragement'. Although a spirit made from carrots did not become a commercial success, Hutton considered it worthy of exploration and evaluation at the time.

Another contribution made by Hutton to this volume of *Transactions* concerned *The natural appearance of the ground on the hill of Arthur's Seat.* This eight-page paper is illuminating, not just for the subject matter, but as an illustration of the way in which gentlemen scientists of the Enlightenment collaborated on interesting natural phenomena that were not necessarily of the utmost importance, but fell into the 'unexplained' category. Here Hutton, Professor Adam Ferguson (1723–1816) and Dr Joseph Black, three of the most eminent scientists of their day, inspected a linear strip of grass near the summit of Arthur's Seat that had withered and died. The intrepid observers considered that the damage to the turf had not been caused by sheep or the passage of shoe leather attached to human feet. Hutton listed his observations on the nature of the damage to the vegetation from 1–7 and speculated on the possible causes. 'Thunder or the operation of insects' seemed to be the most likely culprits. But Hutton 'had not observed the actual connection of these different events' so this conclusion remained 'merely conjecture.'

Although this paper has not echoed down the ages as some of Hutton's later work has, it tells us something important about the man – that he was endlessly curious about all aspects of the natural world, from rocks and fossils, language, the yield from crops grown for food, to every conceivable aspects of the weather. He had no students to teach or wife and family to support, so he was entirely free to follow his curiosity. James Hutton was undoubtedly a polymath of the highest distinction. He could perhaps even be credited as the first environmentalist as he displayed such an informed and analytical interest in so many aspects of the natural world.

Hutton the natural philosopher

There are echoes of Aristotle (384–322 BC), the ancient Greek philosopher's approach to science, in Hutton's exploration of the world around him. Aristotle, student of Plato, based his scientific writings on observation and evidence. He commented upon the slow rate of geological change and that a human lifetime was insufficient to appreciate natural modifications to the Earth's surface. Aristotle also connected science and philosophy in a manner reminiscent of the ideas later expressed in Hutton's third book *Principles of Knowledge*. Aristotle was a true empiricist and around a third of his vast output was about biology and the natural world. This is one of his most memorable quotes: 'Those whom indulgence in long discussions has rendered unobservant of facts are too ready to dogmatise from few observations.' Hutton followed this advice to the letter, as all his observations were based on what he saw with his own eyes. He drew conclusions only when the evidence was compelling; very much in Aristotle's philosophical tradition.

Aristotle

Although Hutton referred to the philosophical works of John Locke (1632–1704) and his friend David Hume in his writings, it is highly likely that he was exposed to the works of Aristotle during his undergraduate years at the University of Edinburgh.

Wikimedia Commons

The University of Edinburgh Library was established in 1583 and was well-stocked with books on logic, astronomy, ethics and mathematics during Hutton's time. It would have held texts by Aristotle and other Greek philosophers who could well have influenced Hutton. As an alumnus of the university, Hutton would have had access to this rich storehouse of knowledge and ideas. Was it just Hutton's brilliant mind independently aligning with his classical forebears? Or had Hutton absorbed some of these works and was now standing on the shoulders of giants, having developed his own take on these established concepts?

Celebrating the one hundred and fiftieth anniversary of the death of James Hutton in 1947, Professor Sergei Ivanovich Tomkeieff gave an address to the Royal Society of Edinburgh. His talk was entitled 'James Hutton and the Philosophy of Geology'. Tomkeieff observed: 'It was Hutton who provided geology with a theory; and here we must take theory, not as something remote and opposed to fact, but in its original meaning in Greek, namely comprehension.'

Donald McIntyre attended Professor Tomkeieff's talk and penned his own tribute to Hutton some 16 years later. McIntyre entitled his contribution *James Hutton and the Philosophy of Geology*, intentionally to mirror that of the earlier paper. He argued that

> … it was Hutton, and Hutton alone, who provided geology with a dynamic scheme – a theory, in the original sense of 'something of the mind'. Thus Hutton played the same role in geology as Newton in astronomy, or Darwin in biology. Comprehension is the power of the mind to understand, and these intellectual giants have given us comprehension of the great processes that go on around us.

It is interesting to note that in his signature work, *Theory of the Earth*, Hutton only very occasionally used the word 'geology' or 'geological' and never described himself as a 'geologist'. He describes those who investigate aspects of the natural world, such as the 'subterraneous fires', a significant element of his new theory, as 'philosophers'. *Theory* is peppered with references to 'philosophy', 'philosophers' and occasionally 'mineral philosophers' – so that is clearly how he saw himself.

McIntyre said that 'Prior to Hutton, geology did not exist, and I think it is generally agreed that the science was created in the 50 years between 1775 and 1825'. Hutton clearly felt that his geological work was largely that of a natural philosopher trying to make sense of the world he saw around him and attempting to explain how it functioned. In writing the 1795 version of his *Theory*, some 20 years after the subject of geology was founded, the g-word had yet to enter Hutton's lexicon. Although 'geology' rarely appears in the text, the word 'science' (meaning 'knowledge') frequently does. Science has a much older root that can be traced back to ancient Egypt and Mesopotamia around five or six thousand years ago.

Perhaps it is now justified to describe James Hutton as a polymath, natural philosopher and one of the world's first environmentalists.

The Theory of Rain

Hutton read a paper to the Royal Society of Edinburgh on 2 February 1784 on *The Theory of Rain*. He presented Part II on *The Theory of Rain Applied to Natural Appearances* on 12 April of the same year. These were published together in the *Transactions*, Volume 1, in 1788. He had started to take measurements of the weather, particularly rainfall, while living in Slighhouses and this practice continued when he moved to St John's Hill. In a 45-page paper he outlines his arguments, with the aid of one small graph and a few headings.

His thesis was that warmer air holds more water vapour than cold air and, when the air is cooled, rainfall is likely to result. He concluded that the solubility of water vapour must increase with temperature at an accelerating, rather than at a constant rate. Hutton studied climate data from other parts of the world and concluded that rainfall is largely regulated by the humidity of the air and mixing of air masses in the atmosphere. He wrote, 'According to the theory, nothing is required for the production of rain besides the mixture of portions of the atmosphere, sufficiently saturated with humidity, and in different degrees of heat'. This theory was applied by him to the monsoon rains in India and the weather patterns experienced in Africa and Peru.

Below left: ***Theory of Rain***

Hutton's caption relating to this graph, as figured in his paper on *The Theory of Rain*, reads, 'These three rates of evaporation, or solution of water in air, may be represented geometrically thus'. The remainder of the 46 pages of the paper comprises a tightly argued text with no further illustrations.

From *Transactions of the Royal Society Edinburgh* 1788, Volume 1

Below: Monsoon season

Street business carries on amid heavy rain and floods in Jaipur, Rajasthan, India., August 2020.

Shutterstock

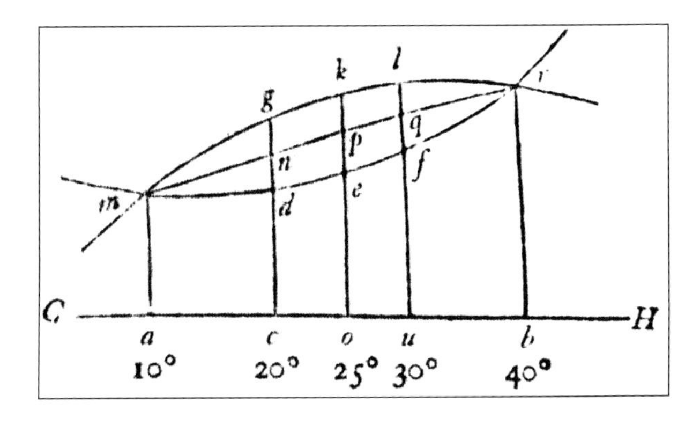

Arts and science collide

Edinburgh was an extraordinary melting-pot of the arts and science. In this clubbable world, eminent men from across the spectrum of accomplishments met at a variety of venues. Professor Adam Ferguson was a regular host to men of achievements in his affluent residence at Sciennes House in Edinburgh. It was on one such occasion where we can say with certainty (almost!) that Hutton met up with Robert Burns and Walter Scott. The latter was just a lad of 15 at the time Charles Martin Hardie (1858–1916) created his painting *The Meeting of Robert Burns and Sir Walter Scott at Sciennes Hill House* (see opposite), but the 28-year-old Burns was at the height of his powers. In 1787, publisher William Creech threw a party to celebrate the publication of the Edinburgh edition of Burns' poems and Hardie captures the assembled company of 'men o' pairts'. Just to add a dash of international glamour, the Italian aeronaut Vincenzo Lunardi was also present, although not immediately identifiable in the painting. The picture now hangs in the library of Abbotsford House, near Melrose, the home of Sir Walter Scott for many years.

No correspondence has been discovered between Robert Burns and James Hutton. However, in the modern era, Scotland's first national poet or Scots Makar, Edwin Morgan (1920–2010), was certain there was a link. He cites the Burn's poem 'My Luve is like a red, red rose' as the evidence. The third verse bears close reading:

> Till a' the seas gang dry, my dear
> And the rocks melt wi the sun;
> And I will luve thee still, my dear,
> While the sands o' life shall run.

During the Scottish Enlightenment there was a strong interaction and intermixing of people and ideas. Hutton's geological conjectures were communicated by his presentations to the Fellows of the Royal Society of Edinburgh and by his written communications in the *Transactions* of the Society. So his new ideas were given a considerable airing. Hardie's picture suggests that Hutton and Burns met, so it's not so far fetched to imagine that the geologist influenced the writings of our national bard.

Edwin Morgan's own tribute to Hutton was made in one of his key poetic works, *Sonnets from Scotland* in 1984 (reprinted here by kind permission of Carcanet Press, Manchester, UK).

James Hutton that true son of fire who said
to Burns 'Aye, man, the rocks melt wi the sun'
was sure the age of reason's time was done:
what but imagination could have read
granite boulders back to their molten roots?
...
They died almost
together, poet and geologist,
and lie in wait for hilltop buoys to ring,
or aw the seas gang dry and Scotland's coast
dissolve in crinkled sand and pungent mist.

Sir Walter Scott's meeting with Robert Burns

This oil painting by Charles Martin Hardie is as much an invaluable social historical record as it is a work of art. From left to right, it features the host Adam Ferguson, Robert Burns, Sir Walter Scott (standing), Ferguson Jnr (seated), Dugald Stewart, Joseph Black, Adam Smith, John Home, and finally James Hutton.

Perhaps destroying, or at the very least questioning, the cosy reality the picture depicts, although the actual meeting took place in 1787, the picture was not completed until six years later. Thus there may well have been additions to or deletions from the 'actuality' of its composition.

The Abbotsfort Trust

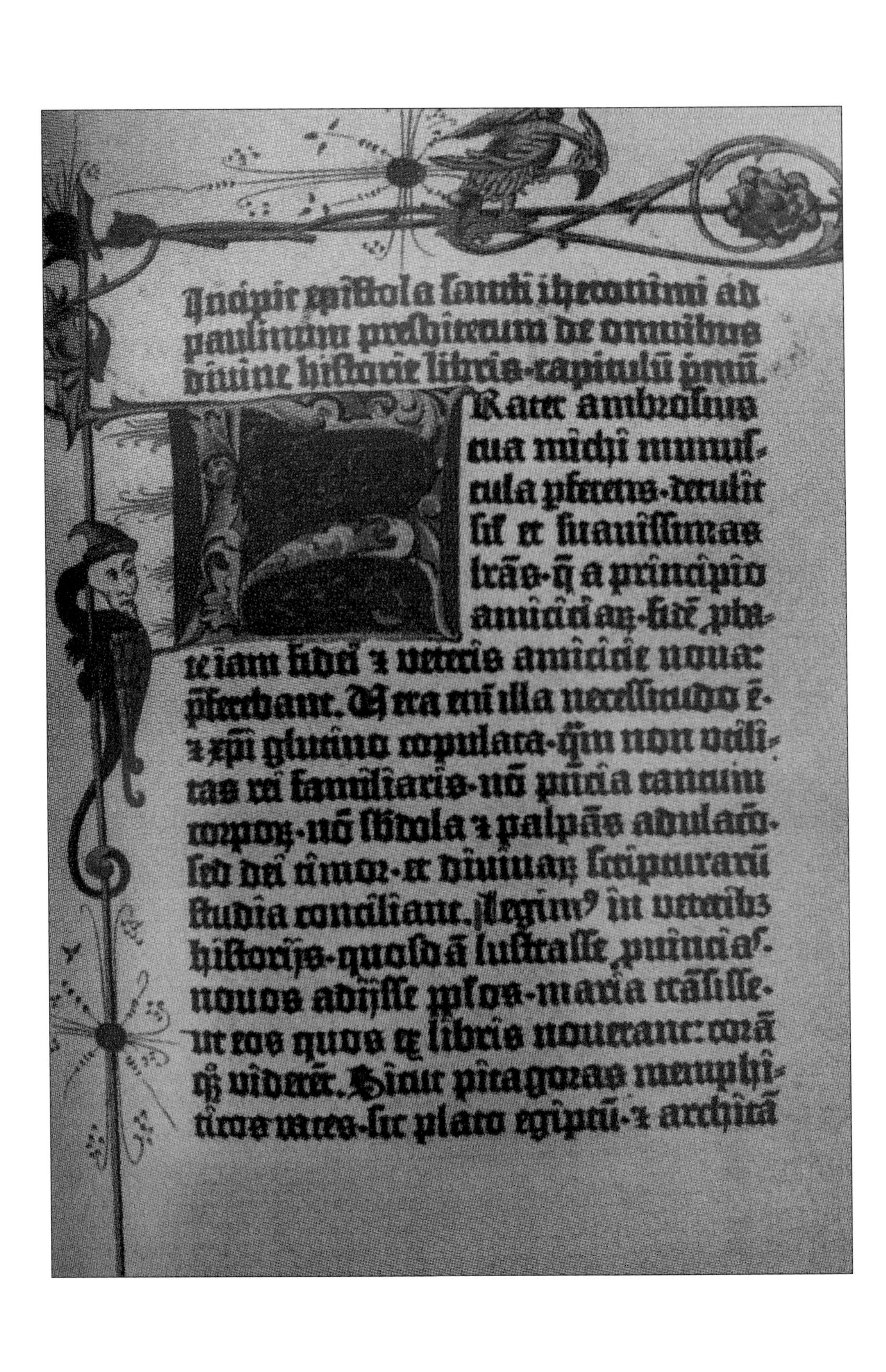

Incipit epistola sancti iheronimi ad
paulinum presbiterum de omnibus
divine historie libris-capitulū primū.

FRater ambrosius
tua michi munus-
cula pferens-detulit
sil et suavissimas
lrās-q̄ a principio
amicitiaꝝ-fide p̄ba-
te iam fidei ⁊ veteris amicitie nova:
pferebant. Vera enī illa necessitudo ē-
⁊ xp̄i glutino copulata-q̄m non utili-
tas rei familiaris-nō p̄ntia tantum
corpoꝝ-nō subdola ⁊ palpās adulacō-
sed dei timor-et divinaꝝ scripturarū
studia conciliant. Legimꝰ in veteribꝫ
historijs-quosdā lustrasse p̄uincias-
novos adiisse pplos-maria transisse-
ut eos quos ex libris noverant: corā
q̄ꝫ viderēt. Sicut pitagoras memphi-
ticos vates-sic plato egiptū-⁊ architā

Chapter 6
Theory of the Earth

Age of the Earth

John Playfair (1805) estimates that James Hutton did not start thinking seriously about geology until 1755. He said, 'It was not, I imagine, till after the year 1760 that they came to take the form of a theory'. Hutton further ruminated on the subject and wrestled to get it into shape for a further 25 years. Only then was it presented for public consumption.

Playfair (1805) further commented that 'Hutton was in no haste to publish his theory; for he is one of those who are much more delighted with the contemplation of truth, than with the praise for having discovered it'. It was effectively a life's work, so we can only presume that Hutton wanted to get as close to the truth of the matter as he possibly could. During that almost 30-year period, he had collected a great deal of information that now had to be processed and crystallised into a rational theory. Playfair wrote that 'Dr Hutton's papers do not afford so much information as might be wished for …'. So he kept to himself and his immediate associates many of the thoughts that were starting to inform the development of his theory. That is, at this point, he did not commit them to paper.

Since Roman times, scholars have speculated about the age of the Earth. Genesis, the first book of the Bible, provided the comforting reassurance that the work of creating the Heavens and the Earth was accomplished in six days followed by a day of rest. However, it was an open question as to when this deed was done.

It was an Irish cleric, Archbishop Ussher, who provided what was then thought to be the definitive answer from the same unassailable source, the Bible. Writing in 1658 in *The Annuals of the World*, he calculated that the world was created at 'nightfall on twenty second day of Octob [*sic*], in the year 4004 BC'. He even produced an elaborately illuminated manuscript that demonstrated the authenticity of his calculation.

Ussher laboured on his task for decades, looking for clues in the most ancient versions of the Bible he could find, thinking that the more ancient

Opposite: Ussher's manuscript

In Archbishop James Ussher's (1581–1656) illuminated manuscript, he outlined the evidence for his calculation of the age of the Earth. He relied on biblical and observed astronomical events to support his timescale.

James Ussher, *Annalium pars posterior* (1654)

the manuscript, the closer he would be to the truth. Astronomical events, the motion of the stars, and the number of generations he could identify in Genesis, all informed his giddy calculation. He also predicted that the world would end after 6000 years, in October 2004. Although such pronouncements seem fanciful to us now, based on no substantive scientific evidence whatsoever, it was regarded as the best estimate of the age of the Earth for the centuries that followed. The eminent scientists Sir Isaac Newton and later Lord Kelvin both had a crack at solving the puzzle. It was left to an adopted Scot, Professor Arthur Holmes, who did his best work when Regius Professor at the University of Edinburgh in the 1950s and '60s. Holmes developed the science of geochronology that allowed rocks to be accurately dated. We now know that the date the Earth was formed is around 4,540,000,000 years ago.

Hutton had the good sense not to try to put a figure on the age of the Earth. He knew the timescale had to be unimaginably long to accommodate the various processes of erosion and renewal he had seen at work on his travels across the length and breadth of the country. One of his most famous and oft quoted sayings is that, in terms of geological time, he could 'see no vestige of a beginning and no prospect of an end.' He left it there as he had no means or evidence to be more precise. That precision would only come two centuries later.

Hutton's *Theory of the Earth* takes shape

Hutton's ideas were beginning to take shape. It is said that the best geologist is the one who has seen more rocks than anyone else and it is doubtful if any contemporary scientist, in Britain or abroad, knew the subject better than he did. More than 30 years of field observations had convinced him that most rocks are recycled deposits of older rocks. Stratified rocks are the most common on the Earth's surface and he interpreted them as sediments derived from the weathering and erosion of pre-existing rocks.

Subsequently, consolidated by heat and compaction, these sedimentary layers were raised from the bottom of the sea to form dry land. As the geological processes of erosion, sedimentation and uplift are very slow, the Earth must be vastly older than the age derived by a literal interpretation of the Bible. He also thought of the planet as a heat engine, where heat from a deep source in the Earth could convert loose material into hard rock. We take these processes as a given now but, in the late eighteenth century, this was new thinking of the most radical kind.

There was an alternative school of geological thought that was already very well established. Hutton's ideas were a direct challenge to the doyen of European geology, one Abraham Gottlob Werner (1749–1817). He had an influential position as professor at a mining academy in Saxony and attracted students from many countries with his powerful presence and uncompromising but charismatic manner of expressing his views. Werner's basic geological thesis was that every rock and feature of the Earth's surface was deposited from a primordial Noah's flood seemed to feature large, so it all fitted in nicely with the conventional church teachings. Anyone who opposed this view was automatically branded as a sceptic. He considered the earliest rocks to be granite and also altered rocks, such as gneiss and schist. According to Werner, the age of these rock types trumped any other, regardless of the way in which the rock layers were arranged.

Reading the rocks

Sedimentary strata that have been deposited by an ancient river, but made from sand grains that were eroded from even older rocks.

Shutterstock

Hutton also challenged Werner's idea that granite was the oldest rock of all, supposedly precipitated from a primeval ocean. He thought it was more likely that granite had formed from a molten state, backing up his ideas with observations from his extensive travels across Britain and parts of Europe. He insisted that the basis for any claims must be a detailed study of the rocks as they occur in the landscape. 'Let us, therefore, open the book of Nature, and read her records' he was later to write in *Theory of the Earth*.

Werner and his followers were described as Neptunists, after the Roman god of the sea, whilst Hutton was described as a Plutonist, as he invoked fire and heat as playing a part in the formation of some rocks. It was a battle that would be played out for the rest of Hutton's life and, in fact, well beyond.

Hutton knew that his ideas ran contrary to the accepted norms and it would be difficult to gain wider acceptance. The way to command greater support was to gather irrefutable evidence that his ideas were correct. As a result of his extensive travels and field observations, he felt that he had done enough to establish a viable theory that could be presented to his peers for

Goat Fell

Some of Scotland's most stunning scenery is carved in granite bedrock. Hutton visited Arran in 1787 and observed the granite peak of Goat Fell, part of the ice-scoured Northern Mountains.

consideration and discussion. As it turned out, however, there was much more fieldwork to be done to bolster his ideas further.

Publication and presentation of *Theory of the Earth* (1785)

In the interim, Hutton presented his ideas orally to an audience of the Fellows of the Physical Class of the Royal Society of Edinburgh. Or, at least, that was the plan. But come the day, 7 March 1785, Hutton called in sick and was unable to present his paper in person. Perhaps he was overcome by anxiety as he knew how controversial his new ideas would be to those who had not heard them before.

Joseph Black, as his substitute, presented at least part of the new theory to the *literati* of Edinburgh, and an additional date of 4 April was hastily arranged to present the second part of the paper. By that time, Hutton had recovered sufficiently to face his critics and supporters. This was the first outing of his theory and he must have felt worried about the reception it would receive. He knew that many of the ideas were new and challenged the accepted norms.

The world would need to wait three years until the full text of Hutton's paper became available but, in the interim, an Abstract was published in 1785, the year the paper was read at the Royal Society of Edinburgh. This short publication, 'a small book 7½ in. by 5 in.', provided a brief outline of what was to follow. He wrote the Abstract in fulfilment of the Royal Society of Edinburgh's requirement to capture the essence of his presentation.

The first full version of *Theory of the Earth – an INVESTIGATION of the Laws observable in the Composition, Dissolution, and Restoration of Land upon the Globe* was published in 1788 in the *Transactions of the Royal Society of Edinburgh*, Volume 1, pages 209–305. Hardly the snappiest title for a paper that would ultimately become the basis for the new science of modern geology.

It was a modest paper, by Hutton's standards, of just under 100 pages. The language used in the 1788 version of *Theory of the Earth* is convoluted, almost laboured, but careful reading unearths many gems that Hutton had been brooding over for the previous 30 years. These five gems are described below – the Rock Cycle, the Earth as a heat engine, 'the present is the key to the past', deep time and soils.

Between them, Hutton and Black presented the paper to their peers and Fellows in the meeting room of the RSE. It was without illustrations and headings, or indeed many punctuation marks to break up the text, and must have been a marathon for those in the audience. The text meanders somewhat and appears to the observer over 200 years later as an outpouring of ideas in search of a final format and a clearer organisational framework.

For a better appreciation and comprehension of this important work, the product of almost 30 years of Hutton's life, the key points have been grouped under some major headings: his 'big ideas' for want of a better phrase. To a large extent, this paper and associated presentation was just a draft of the final work. This would be published some seven years later in 1795.

At this stage, Hutton was testing the water and did not have all the evidence that he required to make a telling case. That was the purpose of his travels and field visits undertaken between 1785 and 1788. We will hear of those later.

Main points of *Theory of the Earth* as presented in 1785

The Rock Cycle

One of James Hutton's most radical ideas was his first draft of what we now call the Rock Cycle. Every geology student today knows that as soon as mountains are formed they are energetically attacked and eroded by natural processes involving ice, wind and water.

The products of erosion – boulders, cobbles, sands, gravel and mud – are then transported by streams, or indeed gravity, to lower ground or into lakes, seas and oceans, where they build up and create new strata. These layers of rock are made solid and then later raised up to form new lands.

Hutton wrote:

> If, for example, in a mass of marble taken from a quarry upon the top of the Alps or the Andes, there shall be found once cockle-shell, or piece of coral, it must be concluded, that this bed of stone had been originally formed at the bottom of the sea. If one bed of limestone is thus found to have been of a marine origin, every concomitant bed of the same kind must be also concluded to have been formed in the same manner.

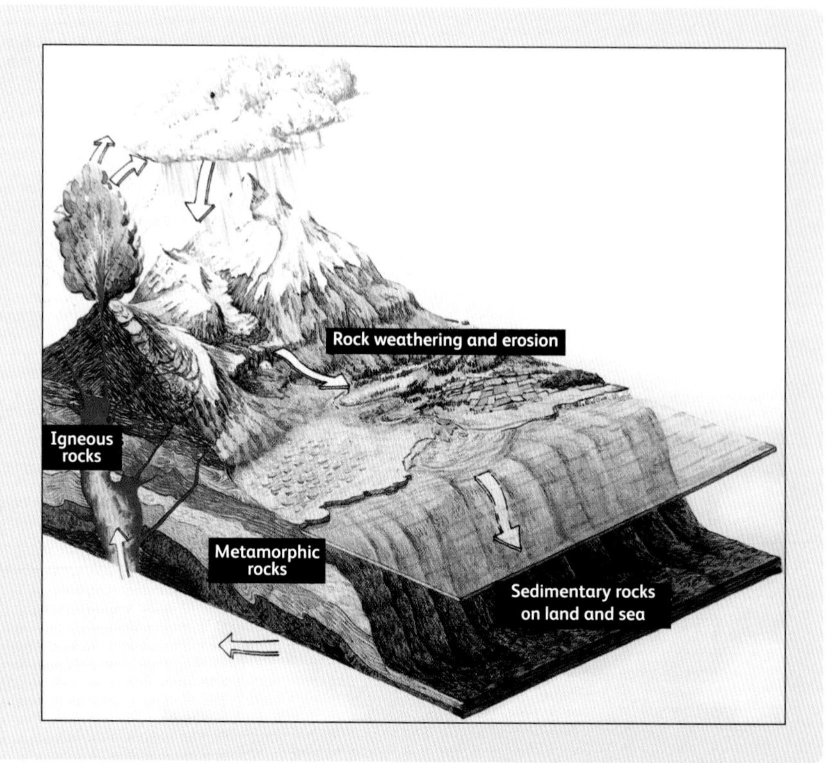

The Rock Cycle

Hutton saw this circularity of the processes of erosion and the creation of new lands. It was an echo of his observations whilst clearing the drainage ditches of soil at Slighhouses. Weathered rock and soil is swept from the high ground to the sea. It builds up in layers on the sea floor. The mechanism by which new lands were raised from the seabed was yet to be discovered. We now know that mechanism to be plate tectonics. When new mountains form, the processes described above are repeated – that is, the Rock Cycle.

Robert Nelmes

Further, he wrote:

> We are thus led to see a circulation in the matter of the globe, and a system of beautiful economy in the works of nature. This earth, like the body of an animal, is wasted at the same time as it is repaired. It has a state of growth and augmentation; it has another state which is that of diminution and decay. This world is thus destroyed in one part, but it is renewed in another.

Rock weathering

Hutton witnessed the evidence of destruction and renewal of the Earth's surface at locations such as this one on Cairngorm. Here blocks of granite are weathered and fall to lower levels, where in time, they may form new sedimentary deposits.

Lorne Gill/NatureScot

Hutton did not have a convincing explanation as to how this 'raising up' from the sea floor might take place. We had to wait two centuries for the concept of plate tectonics to provide the mechanism that allowed us to understand how new mountains are formed. We must, however, 'doff our caps' to Hutton for seeing the process of erosion, transportation, deposition and consolidation, without ever knowing how the uplift from the ocean floor element of the Rock Cycle might be achieved.

The Earth as a heat engine

Hutton's second big idea was that the Earth acted as a heat engine and that the planet's internal heat played a role in consolidating loose sediments into

Hutton's Section in Holyrood Park

John Clerk of Eldin's drawing bears a remarkable resemblance to what can be viewed today. The molten dolerite rock must have been in a liquid state to displace the lump of sandstone into which the dolerite was intruded. This disruption of the underlying layers indicates that a degree of force was involved in this injection of hot rock. This was not the only place that Hutton observed the behaviour of igneous rocks as a once viscous liquid, but it is perhaps the best known. This is known as Hutton's Section, located just off the Radical Road on Salisbury Crags. Why the figures are shown as smaller than life size remains a mystery. Perhaps Clerk was demonstrating his playful side.

Sir John Clerk of Penicuik

solid rock. He also observed evidence that some rocks, at some time in the past, existed in liquid form. We now recognise that these rocks are igneous, from the Latin word *ignis* which means 'fire'. All rocks so described have a volcanic origin. For rocks to exist in a liquid or molten state, Hutton reasoned that a sustained subterranean heat source was an obvious requirement. A vital clue for this idea presented itself on Edinburgh's Salisbury Crags, a stone's throw from the house where he lived.

Hutton exercised caution and refused to proceed beyond the point that he could validate through field observations. He wrote:

> But how describe an operation which man cannot have the opportunity of perceiving? We only know that the land is raised by a power which has for principle subterraneous heat; but how that land is preserved in its elevated station, is a subject in which we have not even the means to form conjecture.

Hutton knew that the increased temperatures with depth in the Earth played a role, but he wasn't prepared to and, in all conscience he could not, speculate further.

Many familiar landscape features he had encountered also carried the hallmark of the Earth's heat engine. Hutton also knew the land between Edinburgh and Glasgow and northwards to Crieff very well. Today we know this area is littered with ancient volcanoes, their associated lava fields and offshoots of once molten rock, known as sills and dykes, that were forced into (or 'intruded' to use the geologist's term) adjacent rock layers.

For Hutton, all these prominent landscape features, and many others he would encounter in his later travels, were evidence of the Earth's internal heat engine. 'Masses such as whinstone (basalt), porphyry and granite, which are interspersed amongst strata, or raised up in pyramids, as they often appear to be, through the midst of them' (Hutton 1795). When he visited Glen Tilt in Perthshire immediately after his oral presentation and

Galloway the next year, he would be able to confirm that granite was, at the time of its intrusion, in molten form. He had already seen the upstanding solid slab of dolerite rock that cuts cross-country between Crieff and Auchterarder and eastwards towards Perth where it intersects the current course of the River Tay at Campsie Linn.

Two centuries later, Hutton's gut feeling on the role of heat was vindicated. We now know that heat leaking from the core of the Earth, through the next layer up, known as the mantle, drives a slow convection in the upper layers. This movement causes the continents to grind across the surface of the Earth and has the potential to raise up new mountain chains.

Hutton's dyke near Crieff

This prominent landscape feature was observed by Hutton in 1764. It stands as a wall because this once molten rock is more resistant to weathering than the rock that surrounds it.

Alan McKirdy

Campsie Linn

This feature at Campsie Linn near Perth breaks the surface of the River Tay. Hutton thought that it might be an extension of the dyke he had already observed at Crieff.

Donald B. McIntyre

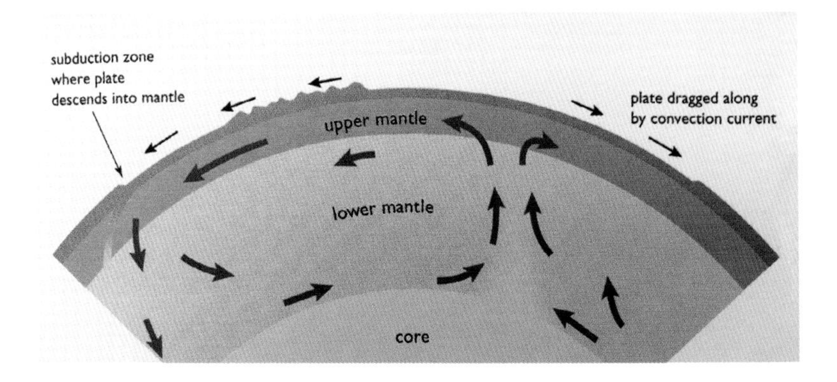

Moving continents

Hutton's concept of 'the Earth as a heat engine' is still relevant today. The Earth's core is around 6,000°C and it loses heat to the mantle and onwards to the crust at a fairly constant rate. It is this upwelling of heat that drives the Earth's tectonic plates across the globe, creates earthquakes and tsunamis and energises volcanic activity.

Jim Lewis

This was perhaps the most important discovery of the twentieth century in the geological world. We know this concept today as 'plate tectonics'. See pages 136–37 for a fuller description.

'The present is the key to the past'

His third 'big idea' was that the 'present is the key to the past'. The French naturalist Comte de Buffon (1707–88), in his treatise on *Histoire Naturelle*, had already outlined this concept, but Hutton developed it further. This idea was later promoted using the unnecessarily baffling name 'uniformitarianism' by Sir Charles Lyell, an eminent Scottish geologist born in 1797, the same year Hutton died. It is really quite a simple concept. If we look at processes acting on the surface of the Earth today, such as erosion of a cliff by the sea or the eruption of a lava flow, we can then identify signs of exactly the same operations having taken place in the geological record. If we can understand how erosion, deposition of sands and gravels or eruption of volcanic lavas take place today, the signs we are then looking for in the geological record are much easier to identify and interpret correctly. Hence understanding the way in which the Earth works today is the key to figuring out what happened in the geological past. To this day, it remains one of the most important guiding principles for the field geologist to observe.

Deep time

The most significant idea that Hutton described in his lifetime was about geological time, or 'deep time' as it was later called. It found little reference in the 1785 presentation, except for a tantalising mention in the last line of the paper. This arguably became his most famous quotable quote: 'The result, therefore, of our present enquiry is, that we find no vestige of a beginning, – no prospect of an end.' He was yet to have exposure to the places, particularly Siccar Point on the Berwickshire coast, that would deliver his eureka moment, further unlocking his ideas on 'deep time'.

'The present is the key to the past'

This pair of images illustrate the concept that 'the present is the key to the past' perfectly. This image shows the mighty Colorado River that has sliced through bedrock to form the Grand Canyon. The flowing water has transported a series of huge boulders to their present location. The boulders have all been rounded as they were carried along by the river, colliding and tumbling over each other, as they cascaded downstream. Now look at the lower photograph.

Here we see very large rounded boulders stacked up in a pile. They form part of a cliff face at Stonehaven. This deposit of conglomerate or 'puddingstone' is comprised of a series of boulders very similar in size and scale to that on the bed of the Colorado River. So, we can legitimately conclude that a river just as big and powerful as the Colorado River must have dumped them here in the geological past at a date we now know was 400 million years ago. By studying the way in which natural systems operate today, we can peer back into the depths of time when we identify deposits that would have been formed in a similar fashion.

Images: Donald B. McIntyre

Soils

Hutton took a keen interest in agriculture and he realised the fundamental role played by soils. Here are a few of the guiding principles on soils that he enunciated:

- Soils are the key substrate that support plants and animals.
- Crop rotation is necessary to maintain soil fertility.
- Study of living things is completely integrated with the physical world.

He wrote:

> The most solid rocks moulder and decay upon the surface of the earth, and thus procure a soil, either immediately upon the place which, thus, had given it birth, or remotely upon some other place where it may be transported by the water or the wind. For this greater purpose of the world, the solid structure of the earth must be sacrificed; for the fertility of the soil depends upon the loose and incoherent state of its materials; and this state of the fertile soil necessarily exposes it to the ravages of the rain upon the inclined surface of the earth.

Hutton returned to the subject of soils in his unpublished work *Elements of Agriculture*, where he considerably developed his ideas on the crucial importance of soil management.

Hutton the observer

All these ideas were a product of Hutton's special skills as an observer. As Playfair (1802) put it:

> Long and continued practice had increased his powers of observation to a high degree of perfection .... With an accurate eye for perceiving the character of natural objects, he had in equal perfection the power of interpreting their significance, and of deciphering those ancient hieroglyphics that record the revolution of the globe .... None was more skilled in marking the gradations of nature, as she passes from one extreme to another.

Playfair (1805) added: 'Dr Hutton possessed, in an eminent degree, the talents, the acquirements, and the temper, which entitle a man to the name of a philosopher.'

These five big ideas (Rock Cycle, heat engine, 'the present is the key to the past', deep time and soils) – and the many others besides outlined in 1788 and 1795 versions of *Theory of the Earth* – were decades ahead of their time, but it was John Playfair who made them much more accessible through a rewriting of Hutton's rather tortured use of the English language. Playfair published this account in *Illustrations of the Huttonian Theory of the Earth* in 1802, some five years after Hutton's death.

Charles Lyell (1797–1875) undertook a further development of some of Hutton's ideas, producing a series of editions of his *Principles of Geology*, the most authoritative book on the subject of its age that relied on some of the concepts Hutton had previously enunciated. Lyell said of Hutton: 'He laboured to give fixed principles to geology, as Newton had succeeded in doing for astronomy.' Higher praise would be difficult to come by. Lyell quoted the essence of Huttonian theory thus:

> The ruins of an older world are visible in the present structures of our planet, and the strata which now compose our continents have been once beneath the sea, and were formed out of the waste of pre-existing continents.

When the first edition of Lyell's *Principles* came out in 1830, the Neptunists, with their stuff and nonsense about primordial oceans and Noah's flood, had already folded up their tents and left the stage, leaving the study of geology to more serious scientists. As we will see later, Hutton sadly never saw the day when his ill-informed and noisy critics fell silent.

Chapter 7

Trial of Hutton's *Theory of the Earth* by fieldwork

Conjectures and refutations

In Hutton's day, it was the fashion in science and other intellectual pursuits to propose a conjecture or, put more simply, a new idea or concept. This conjecture was then tested by experiment and further observation to see if it was correct. If it was found to be wanting, it would then be refuted and a new idea put in its place, or the existing idea modified, to explain the accumulating evidence. Hutton saw his presentation to the Royal Society of Edinburgh in March and April 1785, and subsequent publication of the paper, as his initial conjecture. Now came the serious business of testing whether or not his *Theory of the Earth* would stand up to his own rigorous scrutiny.

Geology was different to the chemical experiments pursued by his great friend Joseph Black. If one of Black's conjectures turned out to be incorrect, he would just return to his laboratory and look for answers by adapting his experimental technique or considering a new approach. With Hutton and his newfangled ideas on geology, he realised that the unalloyed truth lay 'out there' in the 'record of the rocks' of his native land. Hutton instinctively knew what was required to confirm or refute his conjectures. He had to saddle up and hit the road once again.

Visit to Glen Tilt in 1785

One of the issues that weighed most heavily on Hutton's mind was the role of granite. The Neptunists were convinced it was the basement, the lowest and the oldest strata of all, on which all else was built. No evidence was produced for this claim. It just seemed likely, as granite landscapes look timeless and immovable.

Hutton already had in his possession a lump of rock where it looked as though a vein of granite had been introduced ('intruded') in a molten state

Left: Granite veins at Glen Tilt

At Glen Tilt, Hutton found granite veins that invade the older schistus rocks, proving that the granite was at one time in liquid form and also that it is younger than the schistus.

Donald B. McIntyre

Below: Boulder at Glen Tilt

This drawing of a boulder found at Glen Tilt was made by John Clerk of Eldin, Hutton's field companion. It shows the granite cutting across the layering of the schistus, which was itself cut by a later vein of 'red porphory' (a variety of igneous rock related to granite). By observing these relationships, geologists can build up a sequence of events of 'what happened in which order'. Hutton and Clerk established the order with great clarity and precision.

Sir John Clerk of Penicuik

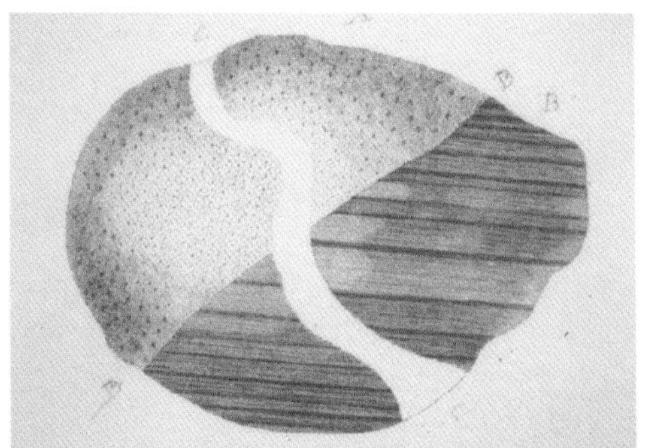

into the host rock. That means the host rock must, of course, be of an even greater age than the granite. The granite must also have been in a liquid state when it was intruded. Hutton deduced that the Earth's heat engine provided the required energy to heat up the granite to beyond its melting point. If he established these matters with field observations, these would provide two indisputable facts to support his *Theory*.

He scoured his memory of past travels to identify a place where a mass of granite might share a boundary with an even older rock. Hutton quickly identified a likely location as the land that lay between the Rivers Dee and Tay in the southern hills of the Scottish Highlands. Glen Tilt lay within that geographic range and Hutton thought this location was most likely to provide the evidence required to confirm his conjecture. His reasoning was that the River Dee carried boulders of granite and the Tay was choked with Highland rocks that we now call Dalradian schists, or 'schistus' to use Hutton's vocabulary.

Hutton was accompanied on this trip by Clerk of Eldin, who brought along a sketch pad to record some of the key evidence. He and Clerk quickly found what they were looking for. The granite veins were shot through the Dalradian rocks, establishing a geological chronology (a demonstrable sequence of geological events) that had created the rocks which lay in front of the two keen observers. First, the granite must have been in liquid form to be injected into the surrounding rocks; and second, the granite must be younger than the rocks into which it has been intruded. Double whammy!

Hutton was anxious to observe an *instantia crucis* or 'crucial instance', which decides between two competing conjectures of Plutonism and Neptunism. The mixed exposures of granite and Dalradian schists high up on a desolate and probably windswept and rain-sodden Scottish glen were his *instantia crucis*. *Theory of the Earth* immediately received two ticks of confirmation. Playfair observed:

> The sight of objects that verified at once so many important conclusions in Dr Hutton's system, filled him with delight: and as his feelings, on such occasions, were always strongly expressed, the guides who accompanied him were convinced that it must be nothing less than the discovery of a vein of silver or gold, that could call forth such strong marks of joy and exultation.

See page 10, where Donald McIntyre recreated that moment of discovery around two centuries later.

Visit to Ayrshire and Galloway in 1786

The following year, Hutton and Clerk set off to look for 'something decisive with regard to granite' in the Southern Uplands of Scotland. They travelled by way of the Clyde coast and correctly identified a number of features of geological interest on the way. These included raised beaches, demonstrating that the sea level once stood at a higher level than today, and geological dykes at Skelmorlie near Wemyss Bay on the Firth of Clyde coast.

The granites of Galloway and the south-west of Scotland are obvious landscape features, so our two intrepid travellers would have been able to identify the best places to look quite easily. In addition, they scoured the local burns and streams for signs of granite boulders. Where they found them, Hutton and Clerk walked upstream to find the bedrock source of the boulders. This is Hutton's account their quest for granite among the Galloway hills:

> We saw schistus (the local rock surrounding the granite) pretty erect ....
> Upon the left we had granite appearing through the sandy shore: and above,

the granite hill seemed to impend upon the erect strata. We saw the place nearly where the granite and the schistus must be united; but this place was bushy; and thus our fears and expectations remained for a moment in suspense. But breaking through the bushes and briars, and climbing up the rocks bank, if we did not see the apposition of the granite to the side of the erect strata so much as we would have wished, we saw something that was much more satisfactory, and to the purpose of our expedition. For here we found the granite interjected among the strata, in descending among them like a mineral vein, and terminating in a thread when it could penetrate no farther. Mr. Clerk's drawings, and a specimen which I took of the schistus thus penetrated, will convince the most sceptical with regard to this doctrine of the transfusion of granite.

We may now conclude that, without seeing granite actually in a fluid state, we have every demonstration possible of this fact; that is to say, of granite having been forced to flow in a state of fusion, amongst strata broken by subterraneous force, and distort in every manner and degree.

Granite vein

In Hutton's words: 'we found the granite ... injected amongst the strata ... terminating in a thread where it could penetrate no further'. They found this rock exposure at Colvend in Galloway.

Donald B McIntyre

Field sketch of granite vein

This is an adjacent exposure at the same location as above, drawn by John Clerk of Eldin.

Sir John Clerk of Penicuik; photograph by Gerhard Ott

Hutton felt his conjecture was now proven: granite was not the oldest rock as his opponents had alleged, and that the granite had been mobilised to be injected into older host rocks by the application of heat. At this second location, key elements of his *Theory of the Earth* had been once again vindicated.

Visit to the Isle of Arran in 1787

Hutton again had granite on his mind when he set out for the Isle of Arran off Scotland's west coast. As he had never visited before, it is unclear how he was aware that the northern mountains of Arran, rocky and untamed, were made of granite. He travelled with John Clerk's son, later Lord Eldin. He 'had but one objective in view; this was the nature of the granite, and the connection of it with contiguous strata' (Playfair 1805). As in Glen Tilt and Galloway, he was hoping to establish that granite veins invaded the surrounding strata, proving that granite was younger than the rocks that enclosed them. However, he and Clerk did much more than that: between them they created the most extraordinary, and geologically correct, cross-section through the northern part of the island. It shows the granite rising from deep within the bowels of the planet and displacing the older rocks in its path as it ascended through the Earth's crust. This demonstrated an awareness of geological processes that was decades ahead of its time. They

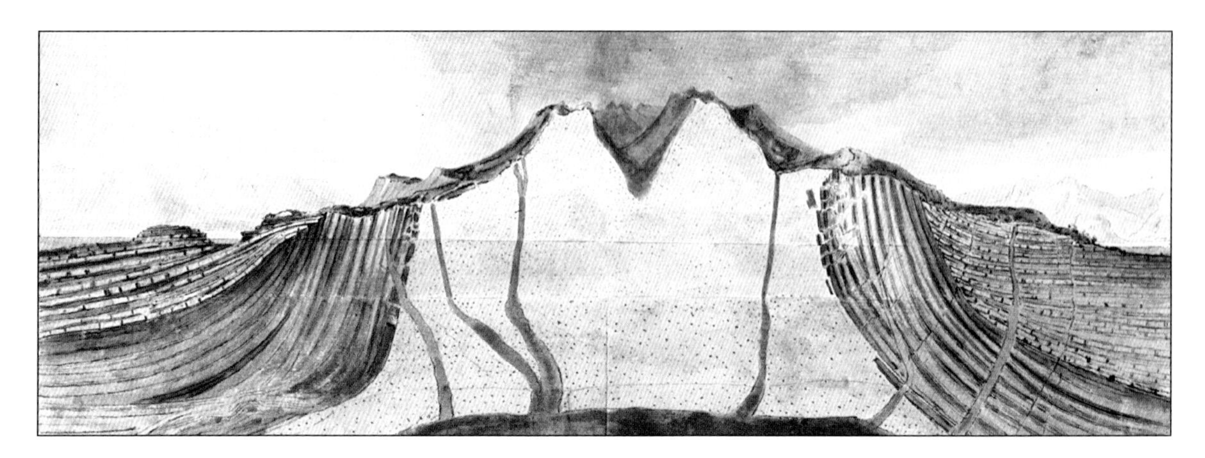

Arran

This is one of the most extraordinary diagrams Hutton and Clerk constructed together. It indicates that they were developing a firm grasp of how igneous rocks behave. They clearly understood that the granite was originally in a molten state and rose from deep in the crust to displace the existing strata in its path. At a time when others were still working to a biblical timescale and the central role thought to have been played by Noah's flood, this interpretation of the geology of Arran was decades ahead of its time.

Sir John Clerk of Penicuik

clearly understood that the granite mass had been molten and upwardly mobile. As no one else had come even close to that level of appreciation and understanding, we must pay tribute to Hutton, the accomplished field geologist and to Clerk, his companion. We can only wonder at how many hours of discussion between the pair led to their groundbreaking conclusions.

They also found a series of dykes, pulses of thin ribbons of once-molten rock, that cross-cut older sandstones. Some of these slivers were of unusual composition, comprising dark green glass, known as pitchstone. Hutton correctly identified these dykes as igneous intrusions, comparing them with samples of bottle-green glass. To him, the existence of these dykes was more overwhelming evidence that they had once been molten, created by the Earth's heat engine.

He also identified the junction between older alpine schistus – rocks we now call Dalradian schist – and younger sedimentary layers of sandstone. This was at the northern extremity of the island at a place known as Cock of Arran. We now call this juxtaposition an 'unconformity'. Playfair chronicled Hutton's satisfaction with his Arran adventure thus:

> [He] had returned from this tour highly gratified and used often to say that he had no where found his expectations so much exceeded, as in the grand and instructive appearances with which nature had adorned this little island.

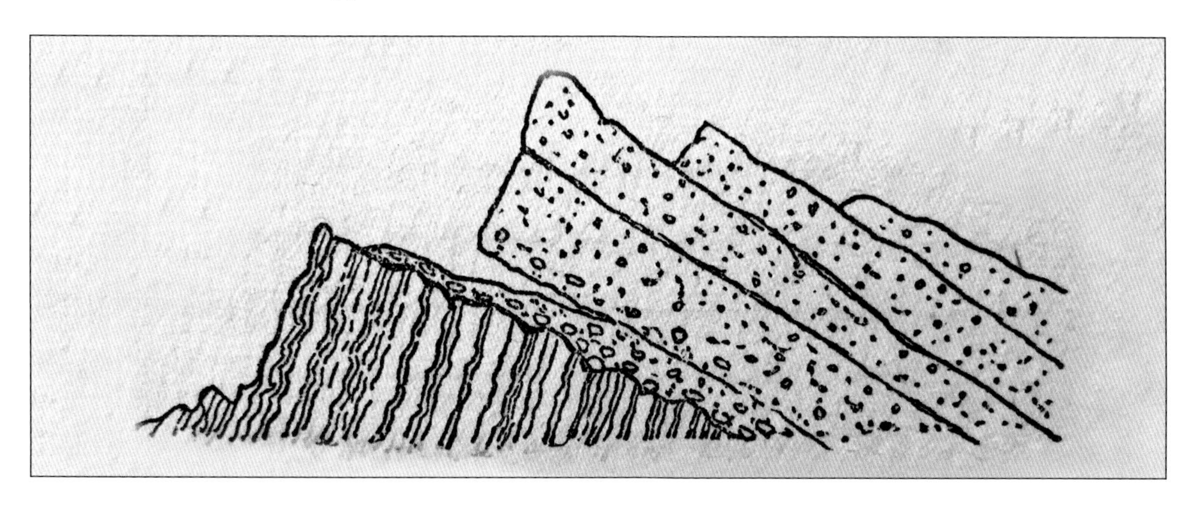

Cock of Arran

Although not the primary purpose of their expedition, Hutton visited the Cock of Arran at the north end of the island. There he described the first unconformity observed anywhere in Scotland. He sketched the feature that he saw, but it was reported that this drawing was later lost. This crude sketch was made by the Scottish geologist Professor Archibald Geikie, who visited this location a century after Hutton. It lacks the artistic flair Clerk would have brought to the task, but it shows the key elements of the red sandstones lying above the upended schistus.

James Hutton, *Theory of the Earth*, Vol. III, p.235

An unconformity and how it reveals Planet Earth's antiquity

Hutton visited three places that we know about where he identified a phenomenon completely new to the emerging science of geology. Today we call these features 'unconformities'. Cock of Arran, Allar's Mill near Jedburgh, and Siccar Point on the Berwickshire coast (see below) have become classics of Scottish, and indeed, world geology.

But what is all the fuss about? And why are these features so fundamentally important in understanding how the Earth works? The biblical timescale could not have even come close to accommodating the time required for natural processes to accomplish the various stages that Hutton had identified. Together, Cock of Arran, Allar's Mill and Siccar Point convinced Hutton (1795) that there was 'no vestige of a beginning – no prospect of an end' to the time required to create the natural world around us.

a. Graptolite c. Orthocone
b. Trilobite d. Crinoid

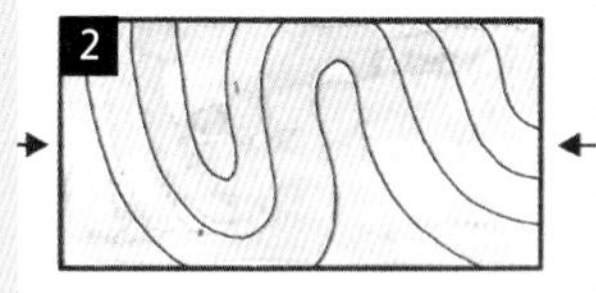

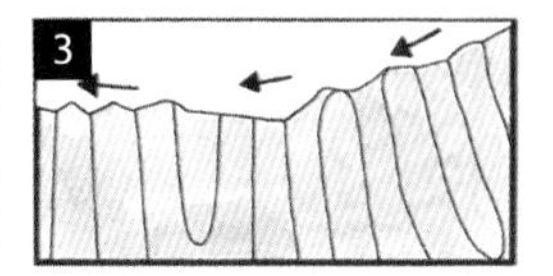

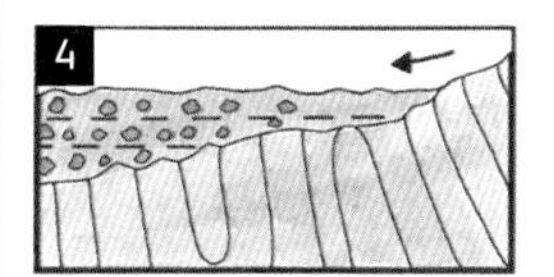

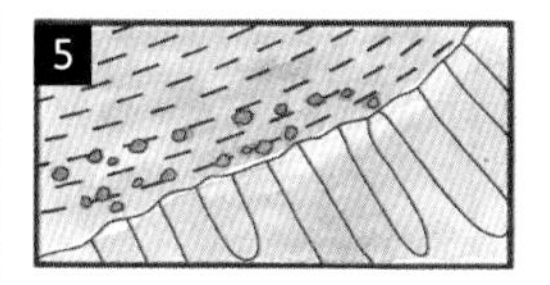

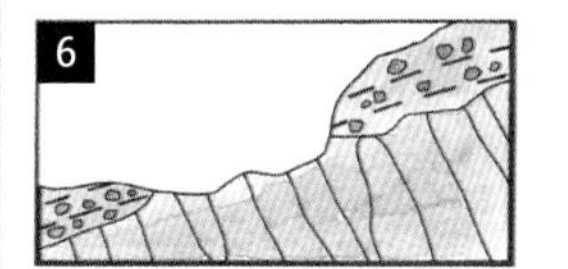

Left: Forming an unconformity

These six diagrams show the successive phases in the formation of an unconformity [**1**]. The oldest rocks were laid down as sands and muds at the bottom of deep seas, in some cases, inhabited by floating organisms known as graptolites and animals with hard parts such as trilobites, orthocones and crinoids [**2**]. These sedimentary layers were later folded as movements took place in the Earth's crust. As a result, some of these layers were buckled from a flat-lying orientation through 90° to form vertical sheets of rock. These earth movements also had the effect of raising these layers of rock from the bottom of the ocean to become dry land [**3**]. The new land was immediately subjected to erosion by wind and water, planing down the surface and creating rock debris, such as boulders, pebbles, sand and mud [**4**]. The rock debris built up across the surface of the eroding landscape to form new layers of sedimentary rock [**5**]. The new rock layers were tilted as earth movements continued [**6**]. Erosion continued and cut into the new layers of rock that have just been formed. The material eroded from the layers of sandstone would have been transported to the sea to build new sedimentary layers on the ocean floor. So the whole process is an oft-repeated cycle of creating new land and then destroying it through a process of erosion.

NatureScot

Below: Siccar Point

The surface that separates the old and the younger rocks is known as an unconformity (pink line). It represents a break in the geological record where no events are recorded. Hutton could not have even guessed at the gap in geological time that the unconformities at these three sites represent. We now know that at Siccar Point, this gap in time between the age of lower vertical rocks and the later sandstones is around 50 million years. What Hutton demonstrated was that slow moving natural earth cycles of destruction and repair were at work.

Stuart Monro

Visit to Allar's Mill, Jedburgh in 1787

Later in the year of his visit to Arran, Hutton and Clerk chanced upon another unconformity near Jedburgh 40 miles to the south-east of Edinburgh. It was indeed a serendipitous encounter as he recorded in *The Theory of the Earth*: 'I rejoiced at my good fortune in stumbling upon an object so interesting to the natural history of the earth, and which I had long looked for in vain.'

The topsoil of the surrounding land at Jedburgh is coloured brick red, mirroring the hue of the underlying rocks – the Old Red Sandstones. The Jed Water had excavated a deep gorge along its course and cut through the sandstone into the grey Silurian-aged rocks below. The colour contrast between the two sets of strata would have been striking to the two travellers. There were other contrasts too. The sandstones at the top of the cliff are almost horizontal, whereas the rocks on which they are perched are almost vertical. Separating the two layers is a thin band described by Hutton (1795) as 'puddingstone composed of the wreck of the schistus'. Clerk caught that relationship beautifully in his drawing. It would be a full year later, during his visit to Siccar Point, that the penny would drop, and Hutton would be able to explain this extraordinary juxtaposition.

Visiting this place today is perhaps disappointing, as so much of the rock exposure available to the collective gaze of Hutton and Clerk is now covered by a dense canopy of trees and shrubs. Little can be seen of the classic unconformity. However, it is still there; just not currently visible.

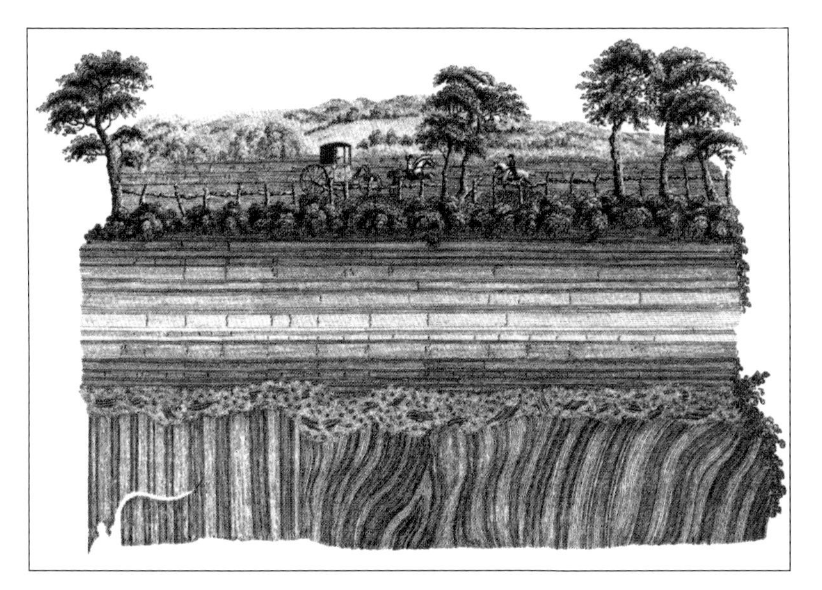

Allar's Mill

This is perhaps the best known image that John Clerk sketched. It has been widely reproduced and is the inspiration behind the logo of The James Hutton Institute.

Sir John Clerk of Penicuik

Visit to Siccar Point in 1788

Playfair's account of this field visit is one of the most celebrated in geological literature of this or any other age and is reproduced in full below. This turned out to be one of Hutton's final trips into the great outdoors that had been his laboratory and the inspiration for his *Theory of the Earth*. It was also to be one of his most significant and productive forays. He was trying to better understand the nature of the unconformities he had already observed in Arran and at Jedburgh, and was now focusing on the contact between the sedimentary layers of the Old Red Sandstone and the underlying, and older, schistus that we now know built much of the Southern Uplands of Scotland.

Hutton asked his friend and local landowner Sir James Hall to search for the point at which the two rock units came into contact, a location duly identified in the Tower Burn that flowed across Hall's land. Hutton thought that this same relationship between the sandstone and the underlying rocks might also be seen at some point along the adjacent coastline. A boat trip was arranged to see if they could find any likely locations. Hutton himself provides us with a detailed account of the trip:

Siccar Point by boat

This is a reconstruction, prepared by the Edinburgh Geological Society, of the visit by boat of the three intrepid scientists, Hutton, Playfair and Hall, as they travelled towards Siccar Point.

Siccar Point

The flat-lying sheets of red sandstones partially cover the underlying upended Silurian strata.

Alan McKirdy

> Having taken boat at Dunglass Burn, we set out to explore the coast. At Siccar Point, we found a beautiful picture of this junction washed bare by the sea. The sandstone strata are partially washed away by the sea, and partly remaining upon the ends of the vertical schistus; in many places, points of the schistus are seen standing up through amongst the sandstone, the greatest part of which is worn away. Behind this again we have a natural section of those sandstone strata, containing fragments of the schistus. Most of the fragments of the schistus have their angles sharp; consequently they have not travelled far, or been worn away by attrition.

John Playfair's account is equally dramatic, evocative of great science in the making. As the three pioneers – Hutton, Playfair and Hall – stood on the wave-washed shore, they pieced together the evidence they saw in front of them. It truly was a journey back into the 'abyss of time'. Playfair (1805) wrote:

> On us who saw these phenomena for the first time, the impression will not be easily forgotten. The palpable evidence presented to us, one of the most extraordinary and important facts in the natural history of the earth, gave a reality and substance to those theoretical speculations, which, however probable, had never till now been directly authenticated by the testimony of the senses. We often said to ourselves, what clearer evidence could we have had of the different formations of these rocks, and of the long interval

Unconformity at Siccar Point

This is Sir James Hall's sketch of the unconformity at Siccar Point. Although it lacks the artistic merit of one of Clerk's compositions, it clearly shows the break between the strata that have been folded into the vertical plane and the overlying sandstones.

Sir John Clerk of Penicuik

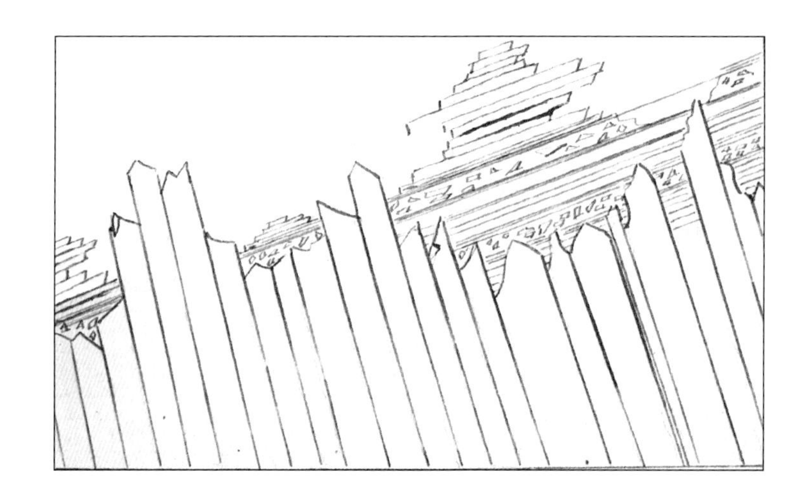

> which separated their formation, had we actually seen them emerging from the bosom of the deep? We felt ourselves necessarily carried back to the time when the schistus on which we stood was yet at the bottom of the sea, and when the sandstone before us was only beginning to be deposited, in the shape of sand or mud, from the waters of a super-incumbent ocean. An epoch still more remote presented itself, when even the most ancient of these rocks, instead of standing upright in vertical beds, lay in horizontal planes at the bottom of the sea, and was not yet disturbed by that immeasurable force which had burst asunder the solid pavement of the globe. Revolutions still more remote appeared in the distance of this extraordinary perspective. The mind seemed to grow giddy by looking so far into the abyss of time; and while we listened with earnestness and admiration to the philosopher who was unfolding to us the order and series of these wonderful events, we became sensible how much further reason may sometimes go than imagination may venture to follow.

With this thunderbolt of brilliant deductive reasoning, James Hutton had changed the science of geology forever. He had confirmed his conjecture that wrecks of previous worlds were everywhere to be found. The dominant process that shaped the landscape were cycles of erosion of existing lands by wind and water, deposition of new sedimentary layers on the sea floor and then uplift to form new lands. Of course, this all took place on a timescale where 'we find no vestige of a beginning and no prospect of an end': the 'abyss of time', using Playfair's evocative words.

Geology remains founded on these two pillars today. Professor Stephen Jay Gould, the prominent American evolutionary biologist, said that Hutton had 'burst through the boundaries of time, thereby establishing geology's most distinctive and transforming contribution to human thought – Deep Time'. (Gould 1988)

Sir James Hall (1761–1832)

James Hall, who accompanied Hutton on his visit to Siccar Point that day, was an early pioneer of experimental petrology and owned a foundry in East Lothian. In his furnace, he placed charges of powered rock and fired them to high temperatures sealed in a gun barrel. Remarkable transformations were achieved in these samples, which included starting mixes of ground-up limestone, chalk, marble and 'shells of fish'. Such changes were similar to those that occur in nature when rocks are metamorphosed by the application of heat and pressure.

Hall undertook over five hundred experiments using this technique with the gun barrels placed either vertically or horizontally in the furnace, demonstrating that these starting materials were converted into crystalline marble by the application of heat. He also established that lavas, such as basalt, 'must have cooled from a very hot liquid' publishing a paper on the subject in the *Transactions of the Royal Society of Edinburgh* in 1799.

Hall accompanied Hutton to Siccar Point in 1788 when they made their biggest discovery of all.

Sir Joshua Reynolds

Visit to the Isle of Man in 1788

It may have seemed like an anticlimax after the intellectual heights climbed at Siccar Point, but James Hutton continued on his travels later that year; this time to the Isle of Man. We are informed by Playfair that Hutton was, on this occasion, accompanied by John Clerk of Eldin and also by the Duke of Atholl, who had inherited the island in 1736; Atholl also took the title of governor-in-chief of the Isle of Man. The purpose of the trip was to undertake a mineral survey of the island but, according to Playfair (1805), 'what he saw there was not much calculated to illustrate any of the great facts of geology'. We can conclude that Hutton was slightly underwhelmed by what he observed on the island. He did, however, correctly connect these rocks with those of the South of Scotland, noting that 'they correspond well with that in Galloway'.

Observations on Granite

Hutton read a paper to the Royal Society of Edinburgh on 4 January 1790 about his findings on granite, published in *Transactions* four years later. This short paper, complete with the discussion from Fellows that his presentation prompted, was a first draft of his ideas on granite that would later

Above: Pettico Wick near St Abbs Head

Another contribution made by Hall was in the field of structural geology, the study of how rocks respond when subjected to intense pressure and heat. Previously horizontal strata are usually folded or faulted as a result. As Hall observed from a vantage point near St Abbs Head, the rocks of the Southern Uplands are buckled as a result of earth movements. He described folded rocks in a paper *On the Vertical Position and Convolutions of Certain Strata ….* Hall continued to carry out geological research long after Hutton's death.

Lorne Gill/NatureScot

Below: Ardwell Bay

Hutton correlated the folded strata exposed along the coast of Ardwell Bay, just to the south of Stranraer, with the rocks of the Isle of Man.

Lorne Gill/NatureScot

appear in *Theory of the Earth*. He wrote, 'I have been employed in examining many parts of the country in order to enquire into the natural history of granite. In this undertaking, I have succeeded beyond my most flattering expectations ...'. He described his trips to Glen Tilt, Arran, and the coast of Galloway in *Theory of the Earth*, citing evidence from the rocks that he and 'Mr Clerk' saw at these locations. In Galloway, Hutton

> ... was much satisfied that the granite had invaded the schistus having not only broken and floated the schistus in every possible way. We found the granite intruded for some length in small veins between the stratified bodies, giving every mark of the most fluid injection among the broken and distorted strata.

Triumphantly, Hutton concluded that 'Granite, which has been hitherto considered by naturalists as being "the original or primitive part of the earth", is now found to be posterior to the Alpine schistus ...'. This massive 'raspberry' was blown in the direction of his persistent critics – the Neptunists. The definitive evidence that Hutton and his field companion Clerk had collected, effectively kicked over one of the fundamental pillars of their world view.

Of the Flexibility of the Brazilian Stone

In the same issue of *Transactions* as his paper on granite, published in 1794, he wrote a nine-page article on *Of the Flexibility of the Brazilian Stone* – another of Hutton's rather unexpected contributions to the scientific literature. The opening paragraph reads: 'No quality is more inconsistent with the character of stone than flexibility. A flexible stone, therefore, presents an idea which naturally strikes us with surprise.'

Presented to the RSE Fellows on 7 February 1791, Hutton describes in considerable detail a small specimen of rock that was '12 inches in length, breadth of 5 inches across and half an inch in thickness'. What caught his attention was the fact that this small baton of rock 'bent a quarter of an inch from the straight line'. The origin of this enigmatic rock was not fully revealed by Hutton in the paper, or indeed why he described it as the 'Brazilian Stone'. Instead he describes the detailed nature of his examination, which involved the use of a hand lens and microscope, and finally heating the rock with a 'blow-pipe' to see if its characteristics changed after it was torched. He then split the stone with his knife and found that the specimen had 'a fully foliated structure ... which admits some flexure'. This investigation was not the most significant scientific inquiry undertaken by Hutton, but it provides further evidence of his almost obsessive interest in understanding the unexplained.

HUTTON'S THEORY OF THE EARTH
VOL. I
HUTTON'S THEORY OF THE EARTH
VOL. II
HUTTON'S THEORY OF THE EARTH
VOL. III

Chapter 8
Hutton's final years

A prodigious output of books and papers (1792–97)

Hutton's wide-ranging field visits across Scotland had provided him with the information and observations needed to complete *Theory of the Earth* in what he planned to be four volumes. However, his later years were dogged by declining health, preventing further field visits and curtailing his social interactions. From 1789 onwards until the end of his life, his main objective was to commit as much material to paper as he possibly could. During his periods of illness, progress was understandably slow, but he was as determined in this enterprise as he had been in pursuing his twin passions of geology and agriculture during his earlier years.

Despite these problems, Hutton's output during these years was prodigious. Without the aid of modern paraphernalia of word processors and the internet, he churned out lengthy manuscripts on a wide variety of subjects – quite an achievement for a life that would be lived, particularly during the winter months, illuminated only by a flickering candle in a cold and draughty dwelling atop of St John's Hill in Edinburgh.

Hutton had previously written everything in manuscript but, as his health failed, he dictated the content of some of his scientific papers to his eldest sister, Isabella, who had outlived her two female siblings, Jean and Sarah. In later years, whilst suffering from ill health, Hutton's sister Isabella became his nurse and would have offered vital support during the period of his post-operative care and enabled him to continue writing until the very last days of his life. Her handwriting was flowing and legible, which was fortunate, as his manuscripts were voluminous. Isabella was described as his '*amanuensis*', or scribe. Her beautiful copperplate hand decorates the pages of her brother's final manuscript, *Elements of Agriculture*. Recent detailed study of the manuscript reveals variations in the copperplate hand, implying that there may have been several scribes who helped to produce the final copy. However, we shall never know the truth of it, and Isabella is credited with the majority of the manuscript pages.

Opppsite: Hutton's *Theory of the Earth*, volumes I–III

Logic might have dictated that he would concentrate on the completion of *Theory of the Earth* after securing the evidence he sought to confirm his 1785 conjecture. Instead he immediately launched into another, and slightly tangential, project. His first book, published in 1792, was entitled *Dissertation on Different Subjects in Natural Philosophy*. This publication, which ran to 696 pages, contained a reprise of his thesis on rain, as earlier presented to the Royal Society of Edinburgh, and also a discussion about aspects of fire.

It had long been held that all combustible material contained a mystery substance called 'phlogiston' that was released when flammable materials, such as wood or paper, caught fire. This idea was first advanced in 1667 by Johann Becher, a German alchemist and physician. Despite having distinguished adherents like Hutton, it was later shown to have no basis in fact. This was perhaps the first occasion when Hutton committed himself in print to an idea that later turned out to be completely wrong.

In 1794, Hutton published his second book, entitled *A Dissertation Upon the Philosophy of Light, Heat, and Fire* in 326 pages. He made a presentation on its contents to the Royal Society of Edinburgh on 7 April 1794 and also at subsequent meetings later that year where he developed his ideas on these three topics of light, heat and fire. He was still, however, flogging the 'phlogiston' idea and was convinced that

> … though heat be necessary in general to the burning of bodies or kindling of fire, it is not heat which is immediately produced in fire but … the solar substance lodged in those phlogistic bodies, which is then made to emerge in light and to excite that heat which appears on those occasions as the effects of fire.

In this book, Hutton attempted to bolster the arguments to support the existence of phlogiston, but with limited success. Subsequent inquiries have determined where the truth lay.

Publication of *Principles of Knowledge*

Hutton's third book was the longest of all his published works. *An Investigation of the Principles of Knowledge, and of the Progress of Reason, from Sense to Science and Philosophy*, published in 1794, ran to three volumes consisting of 2138 pages. Professor Dennis Dean, who wrote an academic account of Hutton's life and achievements in 1992, described Hutton's third book thus:

> It began with a wide-ranging discussion of human knowledge and its sources in sensation, perception, conception, passion and action; we also learn the

> nature of ideas and reason. Man alone is granted science, by which Hutton meant conscious principles leading to wisdom and truth. These principles include time and space, unity and number, and cause and effect. Next Hutton considered various kinds of proof, balancing evidence with doubt, truth with probability, analogy with testimony, the real with the imaginary, and the physical principles with mathematical truths.... Finally, Hutton concluded that man is drawn by his mindfulness of both God and immortality to accept morality, piety, and religion, but must not allow religion to be corrupted by those ignorant of science and philosophy.

These dense volumes are a revealing description of the intellectual and moral compass which guided the direction of Hutton's investigations and signposted the way in which his ideas and theories were formulated and validated. However, the great length and erudition of such works came at a high price. Playfair (1805) noted, with characteristic candour, that 'the great size of the book, and the obscurity which may justly be objected to many parts of it, have probably prevented it from being received as it deserves'.

Hutton on evolution

Hutton's volumes on *Principles of Knowledge* also contained a nugget of intellectual brilliance that has almost been lost in the wordiness of his prose. Although better known for his work on geology and agriculture, he provided the first draft of the theory of evolution and natural selection. Although Dr Charles Darwin (1809–82) would become the most celebrated scientist of the nineteenth century after his publication of *On the Origin of Species* in 1859. it was James Hutton who published a version of this groundbreaking idea some fifteen years before Darwin was even born.

The issue of whether or not species are fixed and immutable was widely debated during Hutton's time. It is known that he was in touch with Darwin's grandfather, Erasmus Darwin (1731–1802), who had sketched out some ideas on 'survival of the fittest', a concept his grandson subsequently developed much more fully using evidence collected during his voyage on HMS *Beagle*. The following paragraph is Hutton's take on this subject, which he first published in *Principles of Knowledge*. He subsequently wrote a passage in *Elements of Agriculture* that covered similar ground.

> If an organised body is not in the situation and circumstances best adapted to its sustenance and propagation, then, in conceiving an indefinite variety among the individuals of that species, we must be assured, that, on the one hand, those which depart most from the best adapted constitution, will be most liable to perish, while, on the other hand, those organised bodies, which

> most approach to the best constitution for the present circumstances, will be best adapted to continue, in preserving themselves and multiplying the individuals of their race.

He gave instances using dogs as an example. Where an individual possessed innate 'swiftness of foot and quickness of sight', they were most likely to survive. Individuals who are 'the most defective in those necessary qualities, would be most subject to perish.' He also speculated that the same principle of variation would also affect 'every species of plant, whether growing in a forest or meadow'.

Hutton never used the terms 'evolution' or 'natural selection.' He did, however, foresee the mechanisms by which these processes operated in the world with which he was most familiar.

There is no suggestion that the nineteenth century's most distinguished scientist Charles Darwin plagiarised the ideas on natural selection that Hutton had published some 65 years earlier. Darwin's extensive collection of notebooks, illustrated by detailed drawings and commentary, are testimony to a fiercely original, independent and analytical mind at work. However, both were Edinburgh-educated medical scientists, so the possibility exists that Hutton's ideas on this subject, published in a half-forgotten turgid tome during the previous century, may have wafted under Darwin's gaze. We shall never know the truth of it.

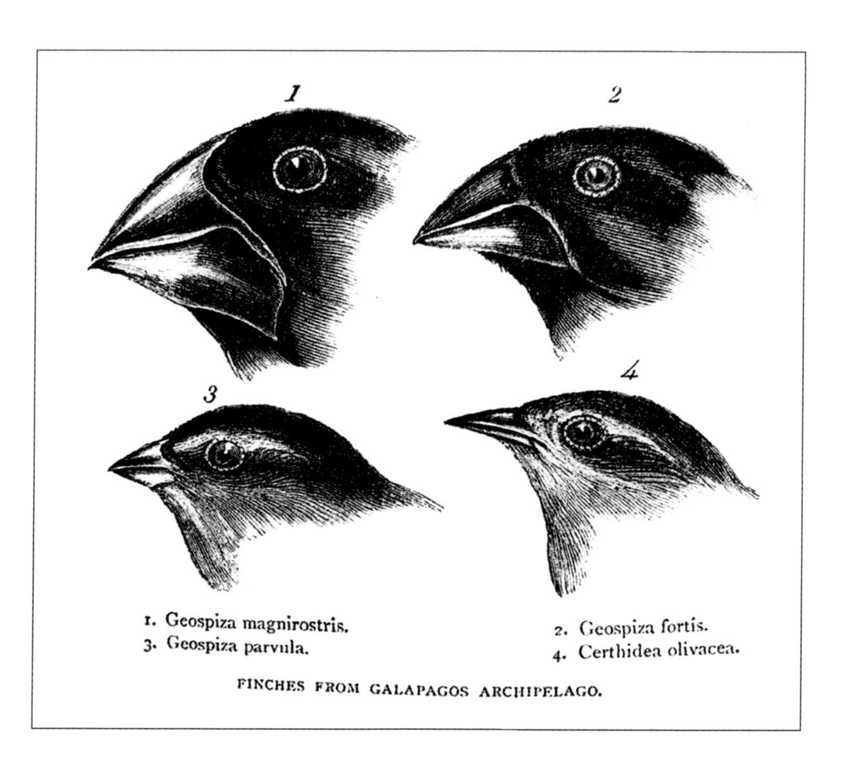

Darwin's finches

Charles Darwin's drawings of finches from the Galapagos Archipelago demonstrated his idea that the form of the head and beak of these different species evolved according to the function they were required to perform.

Charles Darwin, *Charles Darwin and the Origin of Species*, illustrated edition, page 414

The Reverend David Ure – a fellow geologist

In his declining years, Hutton had the reassurance of a fellow Scot and kindred spirit who published on geological matters. The Reverend David Ure (1750–98) was ordained in 1783 and appointed to preach at East Kilbride. Ten years later he published a classic work, *The History of Rutherglen and East Kilbride*, which contained descriptions of fossils he had found in the local rocks, including those of ostracods (a variety of crustacean that commonly exists throughout geological time and to the present day), and the now-extinct rhizodont (or lobe-finned) fish. Ure's book was financed by subscription from 700 patrons, a 'crowd funding' of its time. The list of supporters includes some of the eminent scientists of the day including James Hutton and John Playfair. Ure appreciated the significance of his fossil finds, writing:

> It is evident that these bodies possessed organisation and life, in the same manner that shell-fish and other marine productions do at present. It is almost certain that most of them lived and died in the places where now found; and that these places were once covered by the sea.

As Hutton had financially supported the publication of Ure's book, we can assume he would have received and read his copy. Perhaps this publication strengthened his resolve to write *Theory of the Earth*, his final published work, as Ure's ideas largely coincided with his own.

David Ure's collection of fossils was passed to the Royal Society of Edinburgh, and then to the Hunterian Museum in 1910. For this contribution to the study of fossils, he has been described as the 'Father of Scottish Palaeontology.'

Reaction to *Theory of the Earth* – the 1788 version

Communication across Europe in the eighteenth century was slow and laboured. Reaction to the radical ideas contained in the 1788 edition of *Theory of the Earth* was understandably somewhat delayed. But when it came, it was fierce, contesting Hutton's views with vigour and vitriol. Abraham Gottlob Werner, the doyen of the Neptunists, published a paper in 1791, saying that Hutton was wrong about the molten origins of rocks of any kind. He particularly contested that basalt had been erupted from a volcano. Werner clearly had not travelled very far – intellectually or geographically. In the same year, Swiss-born Jean Andre Deluc also weighed in with a withering assessment of Hutton's ideas. As an unrepentant believer in the literal truth of Genesis, in his view James Hutton had transgressed against the word of God.

Most ferocious of all was the Irish cleric, lawyer and scientist, Richard Kirwan (1733–1812). He was to become Hutton's loudest and most wounding critic, both during Hutton's lifetime and, unforgivably, after his death. His first paper on the subject, read to the Royal Irish Academy in Dublin and published in 1793, on 'Examination of the Supposed Igneous Origin of Stony Substances', contained detailed rebuttals of all Hutton's key arguments, with a ruthless dissection of Hutton's *Theory*. Kirwan also reaffirmed the prevailing view that granite was the oldest rock of all, or 'primary' as he described it, existing 'from the Creation'. It must have been galling for Hutton to read such wildly unsubstantiated claims, particularly as he had spent so much time and energy establishing the true facts of the matter. Hutton's ideas of the Earth as a heat engine, driven by subterranean fires, also drew scorn from Kirwan, who went on to state that Hutton's ideas of an infinite timescale was anti-Christian, the lowest blow of all to a committed believer such as Hutton.

Playfair (1805) caught Hutton's mood after he had read and digested Kirwan's blistering assault, noting that the 'attack … was rendered formidable, not by the strength of argument it employed, but by the heavy charges it brought forward, and the gross misconceptions in which it abounded'.

Hutton fought back in the only way that he knew, by returning to the unfinished *Theory* and bolstering its fundamental ideas with his painstakingly acquired field evidence. Playfair wrote:

> The very day, however, after Mr Kirwan's paper was put into his hands, he began the revival of his manuscript and resolved immediately to send it to the press. The reason he gave was that Mr Kirwan had in so many instances completely mistaken both the facts and the reasoning in his *Theory*, that he saw the necessity of laying before the world a more ample explanation of them.

Hutton on religion

The *literati* of Edinburgh were largely believers in a Christian god. Hutton's *Theory of the Earth* and other published tomes do not specifically address his beliefs, but they embrace an implicit acceptance that a benevolent creator designed the system of decay and renewal he described. The opening lines of *Theory of the Earth*, Volume 1, read: 'We perceive a fabric, erected in wisdom, to obtain a purpose worthy of the power that is apparent in the production of it'. A page later, Hutton continues:

> We shall thus also be led to acknowledge an order, not unworthy of Divine wisdom, in a subject which, in another view, has appeared as the work of chance, or as absolute disorder and confusion.

Here are two indications that Hutton accepted the involvement of a divine hand in the creation of his world and is, therefore, perhaps best described as a 'deist', one who believes in the existence of a supreme being through reason and observation of the natural world.

After Hutton had delivered his first public presentation of *Theory of the Earth* in 1785, he clearly became concerned that he would be accused of 'impiety', so he penned this defence shortly afterwards in the same year. This perhaps gets closest to his religious beliefs and convictions:

> It belongs to religion to teach that God made all things with creative power, that perfect wisdom had then presided in the election of ends and means, and that nothing is done without the most benevolent of intentions. But it belongs not to religion to give a history of nature or to inform mankind of those things that actually are; it belongs not to religion to teach the natural order of events which man, in his science, may be able to unfold and, in the wise system of intellect, find means to ascertain.

There is much more besides, but this is the essence of the defence he lodged before the inevitable assaults rained down from his critics.

It seems almost certain that Hutton would, therefore, have rejected the literal interpretation of the formation of life and the rocks that supported them as described in Genesis, the first book of the Bible. He would also have found the 'six days of labour and one of rest' timetable for the formation of the heavens and the Earth less than credible. Much of the above was inconsistent with the evidence witnessed with his own eyes.

The charges laid against him by Kirwan and others, that he was an atheist and ungodly were, therefore, groundless and deeply hurtful. But they persisted during Hutton's lifetime and for many years after his death. Kirwan resumed his assaults in 1799, two years after Hutton passed, in what are known as his 'Geological Essays', in one paper in 1800 and four more in 1802. What Kirwan hoped to achieve by these ill-judged, scientifically illiterate, pseudo-analytical and demonstrably incorrect ramblings against a man who was already cold in his grave is difficult to imagine.

As a final comment on Hutton's tormentor-in-chief, in 1780 Kirwan became a Fellow of the oldest and most prestigious scientific society in the world when he was invited to join The Royal Society. Two years later he won their highest award, the Copley Medal, 'for his labours in the science of chemistry'. But he was also the last adherent of the ill-starred phlogiston theory of heat and combustion, so Kirwan already had form in backing the wrong horse.

The writers who criticised Hutton on religious grounds were all from overseas. In contrast, the Church of Scotland, which was initially in conflict with Enlightenment figures such as David Hume, apparently became more accommodating of the ideas emerging from more homegrown intellectual ferment. A recent trawl through the Records of the General Assembly of the Church of Scotland, covering the last 20 years of the eighteenth century, are entirely silent on Hutton's work and the new science of geology. The General Assembly discussed all the key issues of the day, but perhaps Hutton and his new-fangled ideas were not considered to be of sufficient importance to be discussed. We can either assume that he flew below the Church's radar and no one had noticed his rather dull new volumes on geology, or alternatively that there was a degree of tacit support from the Church for this new subject. It is interesting to note that John Playfair and David Ure were both Church of Scotland ministers who had already entirely bought into the new science as active practitioners.

These scientific, philosophical and theological debates also helped to focus the battlelines between the 'Plutonists' and 'Neptunists' in Edinburgh's wider polite society. It is said that no one could enter a well-appointed Edinburgh drawing room during the latter period of the Enlightenment without declaring for one side or the other. It is difficult to imagine today that such an obscure scientific debating point could form an important part of everyday discourse.

As a tailpiece to this discussion on religion, it is interesting to note that James Hutton was not a member of the Freemasons. This brotherhood was strongly represented amongst Edinburgh's *literati* in the late eighteenth century, but his name does not appear on any membership records, either at the Grand Lodge of Scotland or the nearest Masonic lodge to Slighhouses in Duns. Many of his closest collaborators – such as James Watt – were active members; as were more distant associates – including Robert Burns. Some benefited materially and spiritually from membership of this fellowship, but Hutton clearly felt no desire to join them.

Publication of *Theory of the Earth* – Volumes I and II in 1795

Playfair's biographical account of Hutton is silent on the enormous effort that must have gone into turning the 1788 published account into the more polished and greatly extended version of *Theory* published in two volumes in 1795. Taken together, this was a colossal undertaking by a man who was clearly unwell and close to the end of his life. However, he had shown pluck and determination throughout his life and it is not really surprising that he got the work done.

The two volumes are a difficult read for contemporary scientists and almost a closed book for those without a background in geology. Hutton's style and use of English is famously 'prolix' (Hutton & Geikie (ed.) 1899) and some sentences require to be read several times before their meaning becomes clear. The text is heroic in scope; a majestic sweep of the current state of knowledge and understanding of the emerging science of geology as it existed in the late eighteenth century. Not that the words 'geology' or 'geological' made many appearances in the text; instead, he preferred to use the terms 'philosopher' or 'naturalist' to describe practitioners of the subject. These two volumes combined are more than ten times the length of the original *Theory* as it was presented to the RSE Fellows in 1785 and appeared in *Transactions* in 1788. Hutton had clearly developed his thinking and comprehension of the natural world considerably in that ten-year period, informed by his extensive field experiences and travels in the latter half of the 1780s. This time he focused much more precisely on the key questions that required to be posed and answered in order to develop these more coherent ideas. Hutton was mindful of the views of his detractors, particularly Mr Kirwan, and dedicated a whole chapter to the Irishman's criticisms of the 1788 version of his *Theory*.

It would require a separate publication to do full justice to the content and conclusions of the two published volumes, and a third that would remain in manuscript for another 100 years. What follows is very much a summary for the general reader.

Although the text is repetitive, it is structured in a logical fashion. Some of the chapter headings are as follows:

Volume I:

- An Investigation of the Laws observable in the Composition, Dissolution, and Restoration of Land upon the Globe;
- An Investigation of the Natural Operations employed in consolidating the Strata of the Globe;
- An Examination of Mr KIRWAN's Objections to the Igneous Origin of Stony Substances; and
- The Nature of Mineral Coal, and the formation of Bituminous Strata, investigated.

Volume II:

- Facts in confirmation of the *Theory* of elevating land above the surface of the sea;
- The *Theory* illustrated, with a view of the summits of The Alps;
- The *Theory* illustrated by adducing examples from the different quarters of the globe; and
- Summary of the doctrine.

In both volumes, there are substantial passages quoted in French. These contributions are from other eminent scientists of the day and are not Hutton's prose. Hutton spent two years of his life in Paris and presumably became fluent in French during that time. He clearly thought that his audience would be able to cope with these linguistic shifts. No attempt is made to translate or summarise arguments offered in French. It also demonstrates Hutton's awareness of scientific advances made internationally, and perhaps he also wanted to encourage a new audience for his work from abroad. He referenced many sources, but Messieurs Pallas, le Comte de Buffon and Deluc, all French geologists, are quoted more than most.

His writings have an international flavour in terms of the places described. The geology of parts of Russia is briefly described in Volume I:

> The Ural Mountains form a very long chain, which makes the natural division betwixt Europe and Asia, to the north of the Caspian. If in this ridge, as a centre of elevation, and of mineral operations, we shall find the greatest manifestations of the violent extension of subterranean fire.

Hutton had already envisaged molten granite on the Isle of Arran rising up from the depths, so perhaps he saw a parallel with the Ural Mountains.

He also makes observations about rocks in Africa and Germany. We have no evidence that he visited many of these far-off places described in his work. Hutton must, therefore, have relied on scientific literature from abroad, accessed from the University of Edinburgh library. His observation, 'How valuable for science to have naturalists who can distinguish properly what they see, and describe intelligently what they distinguish', is a very modern view of how science should proceed.

Hutton's scientific vocabulary is very similar to that used by 21-century geologists. He peppers his prose with the names of rocks and minerals, as in a modern scientific book or paper. 'Porphory', 'feldspar', 'basalt', 'granite', 'quartz', 'marble', 'limestone', 'black slate' and 'coal', are terms he used that are recognised today. The only slight departure is his use of the term 'schistus'. Today, we would describe such rocks as 'schists'.

A theme to which Hutton constantly returns is the role of the sea:

> I have endeavoured to prove, that every thing which we now behold, of the solid parts of the earth, had been formerly at the bottom of the sea, and that there is, in the constitution of this globe, a power for interchanging sea and land.

He used the presence of marine fossils in rocks that are now many metres about sea level, as one piece of evidence to prove this idea. We have known for many years that this overstates the role of the sea, but Hutton clearly appreciates that the geography of the world has significantly changed over geological time. Plate tectonics would only emerge as a unifying theme some 200 years later, but this is a valiant first stab at understanding the nature of our dynamic and ever-changing planet.

Hutton also recognised how coal formed – by the compression of vegetation as younger rocks are piled on top. He returns to the subject in a number of chapters, but this is how he describes succinctly the formation of coal in chapter VIII of Volume I: 'We may investigate through all the stages of their change, from vegetable bodies produced on the habitable earth, they are now become a mineral body, and the most perfect coal ….'

Hutton closes the two-volume account of his *Theory of the Earth* with a chapter titled 'Summary of the doctrine which has now been illustrated', bringing together all the key arguments made in the previous chapters, like an advocate delivering a closing statement to a court of law. He attempts high-flown prose, but is again afflicted by his wordy style. Nonetheless, this closing quote sums up his *Theory* most effectively:

> We have now given a theory founded upon the actual state of this earth, and the appearance of things, so far as they are changing, and we have, in support of that theory, adduced the observations of scientific men, who have carefully examined nature and described things in a manner that is clear and intelligible.

Playfair tells us …

> The work was published, in two volumes octavo, in 1795; and contained, besides what was formerly given in the *Edinburgh Transactions*, the proofs and reasoning much more in detail, and a much fuller appreciation of the principles to the explanation of appearances. The two volumes, however, then published, do not complete the theory: a third necessary for that purpose, remained behind and is still in manuscript.

The bigger and more complete version of *Theory of the Earth* was subsequently planned as a four-volume work but, mainly due to his illness, this complete vision did not fully materialise.

In fact the two completed volumes were published by a London-based company, Cadell and Davies, for the princely sum of fourteen shillings 'in boards' (i.e. hardback). Around 200 copies were retained in London and slightly more were supplied to William Creech, Hutton's Edinburgh publisher, making a total print run of around 500 copies. This groundbreaking text was therefore in very short supply until the work was reprinted in more recent times.

Preparation and publication of *Theory of the Earth* – Volume III

The first two volumes of *Theory of the Earth* were published during Hutton's lifetime. The text for the third volume was completed, but languished as an unpublished manuscript for over a century after his death. The world had to wait until 1899 for its publication.

The manuscript was initially in the safekeeping of John Playfair. However as the drawings, which were required to illustrate the text, were not forthcoming, the publication stalled. It was only in 1978 that John Clerk's accompanying illustrations, which have become known as the *Lost Drawings*, were published.

After John Playfair's death, the manuscript of the third volume passed through various hands and eventually to the Geological Society of London, which saw it through to publication. By that stage, it was noted that 'the volume had evidently been lying some time unbound, for the first page has been soiled and torn, and has been repaired by the pasting of another leaf at the back' (Hutton & Geikie (ed.) 1899).

Editorial work on the battered manuscript was undertaken by Sir Archibald Geikie (1835–1924), a former professor of geology at the University of Edinburgh and later Director General of the Geological Survey of Great Britain. Geikie wrote that 'the Council of the Geological Society has, at my request, undertaken the publication of the Hutton manuscript in the Society's possession and has placed the editing in my hands'. In the book he wrote a glowing foreword to his fellow Scot:

> And I would fain hope that the present long-delayed publication of a portion of his third volume may be the means of directing renewed attention to his immortal work, which must ever remain one of the great landmarks in the onward march of science.

The third volume of *Theory of the Earth* provided even more detail on Hutton's travels across Scotland from 1785 and the following two years, particularly to Glen Tilt, the Clyde coast, Dumfriesshire and to Arran. Throughout the book, Geikie gives a running commentary on Hutton's detailed site descriptions, concluding that its author 'was a diligent and enthusiastic worker in the field'. These extensive notes also further illuminate the meaning of Hutton's narrative that Geikie concluded 'suffers from obscurity and prolixity' (Hutton & Geikie (ed.) 1899). Clearly Hutton's clarity of expression had not improved much with age and experience.

In the first account to appear in this volume, Hutton peppers his geological descriptions of his excursion to Glen Tilt in 1785 with reports of deer shot by members of his party, particularly John Murray, 4th Duke of Atholl, who took an active role in the expedition. The narrative lurches between informal accounts of routes taken across the hill, followed by detailed geological descriptions of the land Hutton surveyed. Hutton and Clerk were 'nobly supported by the most kind and hospitable assistance' of the Duke and stayed at a hunting lodge in Glen Tilt (Hutton & Geikie (ed.) 1899).

The second excursion, undertaken in 1786, was, according to Hutton, 'a circuit of the coast, from Glasgow around the shires of Ayr and Galloway", and he describes the dykes at Skelmorlie on the Clyde coast. The account was decorated, in the published volume, by a geological map produced later by the Geological Survey.

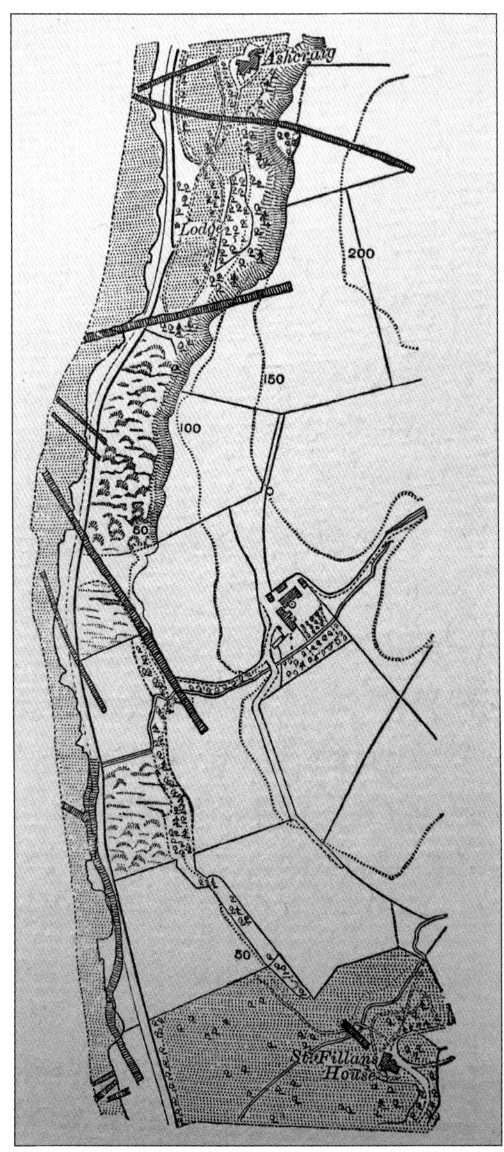

Left: Skelmorlie

Geological map of Skelmorlie, Ayrshire prepared by the Geological Survey.

James Hutton, *Theory of the Earth*, Vol. III, p.32

Above: Basalt dyke at Skelmorlie

These exposures were seen and correctly interpreted by Hutton as pulses of hot magma injected into the surrounding Old Red Sandstone conglomerates and sandstones.

Donald B. McIntyre

Cairnsmore Fleet

John Clerk's drawing shows the granite hill of Cairnsmore of Fleet towering over Creetown. Hutton did not have far to look to find the rocks he sought.

Sir John Clerk of Penicuik

Onwards they travelled to Maybole and Girvan, and thence towards the Rhins of Galloway. Cairnsmore of Fleet was their next destination as Hutton already knew that the area was underlain by granite. With three large granite masses in this vicinity, there was ample opportunity to study them in more detail. Hutton found what he was looking for and again ascended into poetic raptures on seeing the granite invading the surrounding rock. This demonstrated that the granite must have flowed in a molten state into the older rocks – another clear confirmation of a key element of his theory.

Chapter VI of the third volume begins with a massive understatement on Hutton's part: 'I have been particularly anxious about this subject of granite'. In this chapter, he compares the geological account of the Alps given by Horace Benedict de Saussure, a Swiss geologist and mountaineer, with the granite mountains of Scotland. M. de Saussure's *Voyages dans les Alpes*, particularly pleased Hutton as, according to Playfair, 'it became the last study of one eminent geologist, as they were the last work of another'. Hutton wrote, 'the purpose of this chapter is to endeavour to show that M. de Saussure has described something of the same kind with that which I have now several times observed in this country'. He then quoted his Swiss source at extraordinary length in the author's native French tongue to complete this chapter.

Chapter VII is headed 'Theory confirmed by observations made upon the Pyrenean Mountains'; while Chapter VIII draws on examples from Calabria. In his final months of productive work, Hutton would have found it comforting to seek confirmation of his ideas from similar geological terrains across Europe.

In the final chapter, Hutton focused on 'the mineral history of the Island of Arran'. He was accompanied by 'Mr. Clerk, junior', as it was not convenient for Clerk, senior to make this particular excursion. In his com-

mentary, Archibald Geikie reminds the reader that, 'had this chapter been published in Hutton's lifetime, it would have been the first general account of the geology of the island'. The travellers were indeed breaking new ground.

Many detailed accounts have followed on the geology of this island, often referred to as 'Scotland in miniature'. It contains many of the geological elements of the country as a whole. Hutton writes:

> In setting out upon this expedition, I had but one object in view: this was the nature of the granite, and the connection of it with the contiguous strata. But upon examining the island, I have found it sufficiently interesting and comprehensive to make it the subject of a natural history, in describing the particular constitution of that small portion of the earth.

What follows in this final fascinating chapter of the third volume of *Theory of the Earth* is a detailed account of rocks and landforms that he observed on the island. This was to be his final written contribution on the subject of geology.

Arran

Arran is known as 'Scotland in miniature'. Its geological complexity and variety attracts students and amateurs alike.

Alan McKirdy

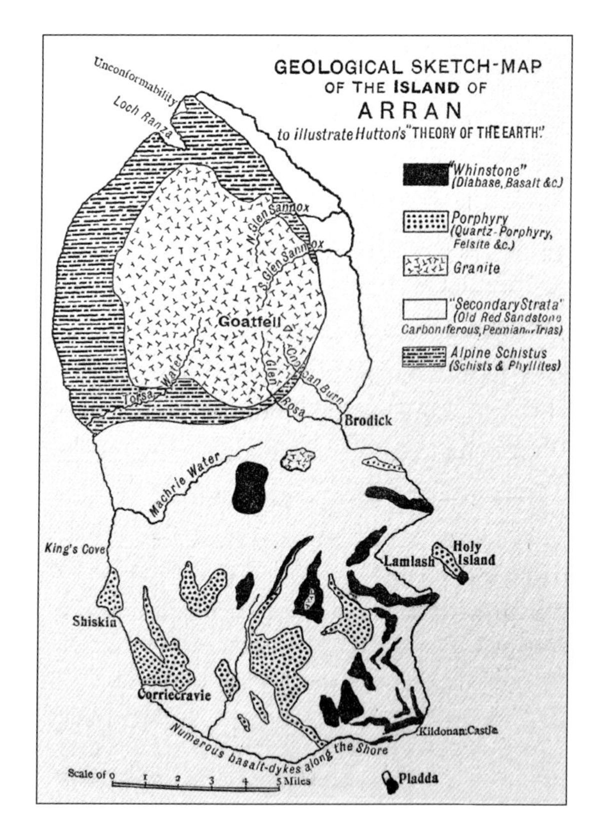

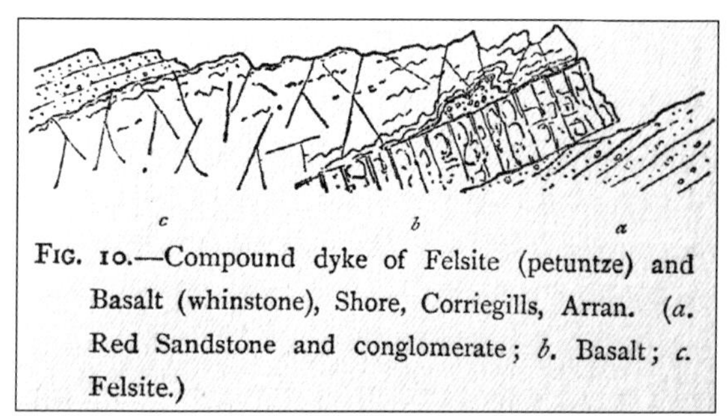

FIG. 10.—Compound dyke of Felsite (petuntze) and Basalt (whinstone), Shore, Corriegills, Arran. (*a.* Red Sandstone and conglomerate; *b.* Basalt; *c.* Felsite.)

Left: Geological sketch map of Arran

This map was added later by Geikie, drawing on survey work undertaken by the Geological Survey. It is captioned 'Geological sketch map of the island of Arran to illustrate Hutton's THEORY OF THE EARTH'.

James Hutton, *Theory of the Earth*, Vol. III, p. 32

Above: Corriegills

This diagram was prepared by the Geological Survey and published in the third volume of *Theory of the Earth* to illustrate Hutton's description of complex igneous intrusion found at Corriegills. The original caption is included.

James Hutton, *Theory of the Earth*, Vol. III, p. 241

Today, on every Easter holiday, the island of Arran is thronged with student geologists in helmets and garish high visibility jackets learning their craft. How many of them realise that they are looking at the very rocks Hutton and Clerk first examined some 240 years earlier, which helped to lay the foundations of their subject? Indeed they will see today exactly what our intrepid pioneers would have noted in the late 1780s, minus a few corners knocked off by nature – and pounding geological hammers.

Eighteenth-century agricultural practices in Scotland

Hutton's comments on the practice of agriculture should be seen in the context of the work of others who were similarly gripped by an 'impetus to improve'. In the second half of the eighteenth century, Scotland's universities ran courses on the promotion of 'improved agriculture'. Papers were written with elegant, albeit meandering, titles such as *The Gentleman Farmer being an attempt to improve Agriculture by subjecting it to a test of Rational Principles* and *The Principles of Agriculture and Vegetation* that raised the profile of these 'landscapes of improvement'. All had common cause: to improve and enrich the rural economy of Scotland. It was greatly in need of it.

Innovation was in the air. Consideration was given to crop rotation and the introduction of different breeds of cattle and crops. Many of these improved practices were first noted in the northeast of Scotland and in the lowlands, with changes happening slightly later elsewhere. Advances in understanding the sciences, specifically geology and chemistry, aided this process.

In a very practical sense, James Hutton was the embodiment of these changes. From his earlier life as a practical farmer, he understood the need for improvement and to manage the land intelligently to gain the best return. His view of agricultural practice was an echo of his geological thesis: that successful land management must be a dynamic process and he focused on the 'repair' of the soil through the use of fertilisers and manure. In *Elements of Agriculture*, his final *magnum opus*, Hutton discussed in detail the connection between soils, climate and vegetation in a manner that had not been done before. Attention to the soil lay at the heart of maintaining fertility and productivity. In addition, Hutton took the view that 'the art of agriculture promotes the social state of human society and sows the seeds of order, empire and government'. The education of those involved with agriculture was another objective. A bold ambition, and one that was never realised as the manuscript was not published during his lifetime, or indeed for many lifetimes thereafter.

Preparation of the *Elements of Agriculture* manuscript

Buoyed up by the successful publication of the first two volumes of *Theory*, and preparation in manuscript of the third, Hutton was unburdened of a lifetime's work on geology. He was now ready to tackle his final project – *Elements of Agriculture*.

His expertise in all things agricultural had already been recognised by The Royal Academy of Agriculture in Paris. Hutton had already established a reputation in France as an agricultural expert when he was invited to become a Fellow of the Academy. He was clearly very proud of this recognition as, for every paper published in *Transactions*, he is described thus: 'James Hutton, M.D. FRS Edin. and member of the ROYAL ACADEMY OF AGRICULTURE at Paris'. The Academy's archives were destroyed in the 1910 Great Flood of Paris and, as Stephen Baxter established during his researches for his biography of Hutton (2003), all records of Hutton's involvement with the Academy were lost.

In this, Hutton's final 'download' of a lifetime's knowledge and practical experience, he covered the span of agricultural topics most comprehensively. Jean Jones, his biographer, estimated that the number of pages devoted to each topic in *Elements of Agriculture* was as follows:

- crop rotation – 190 pages
- the effect of climate, particularly heat on plant growth – 150 pages
- types of crop and methods of cultivating them – 150 pages
- the origin and fertility of soils – 150 pages
- agricultural implements – 150 pages
- plant physiology – 110 pages
- farm management – 110 pages
- politics and economics – 70 pages
- animal husbandry – 60 pages.

As with some of the other works Hutton completed during this sunset period of his life, the text of *Elements of Agriculture* has been described as 'rambling, poorly arranged and repetitive' (Jones 1985) However, a recent reappraisal of the manuscript, suggests this is unfair. Individual sections are well ordered and structured. Although in places, the prolix style

Preface

The Board of Agriculture appears to have
proceeded with great judgment in procuring prope[r]
statements of the husbandry from the different parts o[f]
the kingdom; by this means people concerned in this
valuable art, may (are) be enabled to consider (discover), how far that
which is successfully practised in one place should (may) be
attempted (to advantage) in another place where it may be as yet (has been hitherto)
unknown.

The present undertaking has another
object in view: this is to examine agriculture in
general, by treating (and to treat of it) scientifically of the subject, in order
to enable those concerned in that art (husbandmen) to judge of every (how far)
any particular practice, how far this may be found (is) con-
-form[ably] to the general principles. It is this that may be
[illegible] the science of the art, or that generalization

Extracts from *Elements of Agriculture*

The Preface was written by Hutton's own hand and the other pages were scribed in part in copperplate form by Hutton's sister, Isabella. Later editorial marks on the page were likely to have been made by Hutton himself.

James Hutton, *Elements of Agriculture*

noted by most Hutton scholars persists, generally the manuscript is clearly written, often following the methodology of 'conjecture and refutation', as described earlier.

Hutton was no doubt aware that his life was drawing to a close, so he probably pushed himself beyond comfortable limits to try to complete the manuscript, but, on the positive side of the ledger, the pages are full of wisdom and are encyclopaedic in their scope. Bizarrely, this massive outpouring of accumulated knowledge, information and data had no title. We only know of his intentions from his biographer, Playfair. Faint and unsteady pencil marks on the manuscript, particularly in the preface, are probably those of Hutton's making. They have been interpreted as an indication of his worsening health.

He starts his tome with a description of soils and climate, demonstrating that he understood how farmers should select the most appropriate crops to grow, given their particular local physical and climatic circumstances. It is perhaps the first time that edaphic factors (an understanding of the soil in terms of its inherent characteristics, such as fertility, ability to hold water, nutrients, drainage, structure and texture) had been systematically considered in the context of the optimal management of a farming enterprise. Hutton stresses that soil fertility is key in that regard, and crop and livestock rotation critical in ensuring it is maintained. He then described farm implements and, unsurprisingly, focused particularly on the Suffolk plough.

Hutton was also aware of a key overarching political dimension related to agriculture. He understood that the primary function of agriculture was, and remains, the need to feed and clothe the nation's population. Hutton included a discussion of food security in his treatise and argued that agriculture was too important to a nation's wellbeing to be left to the vagaries of the market. Government intervention would be required to ensure the nation was properly fed. In *Elements of Agriculture* Hutton wrote that, 'while the husbandry of a country is promoting the prosperity of the state, there is a reciprocal duty which the country owes to the husbandry of the country'. He also felt that high rents and short leases obliged tenants to adopt practices that were to the long-term detriment of soil fertility; and that 'the industrious husbandman [farm labourer] should reap the fruits of his skill and labour'. Thus he set out a radical agenda for progressive and sustainable agricultural improvements.

In eighteenth-century Scotland, there was a much greater requirement for each part of the country to be self-sufficient in its food and raw material supply chain. This was an age before meat and vegetable products could be flown in, trucked and shipped across the country, or indeed the world. One of the great revelations of the last decade is that shopping local is to be encouraged. In Hutton's day, there was no choice in the matter.

The *Elements of Agriculture* manuscript is a compilation of ideas and writings that was partly based on essays that Hutton had earlier composed, some written while he lived and worked in Slighhouses. All of these essays are now lost, so the source material is no longer available to biographers and historians. This was the manuscript that occupied Hutton's attentions until the last breath in his body finally ebbed away. In fact, it is not a completed work as Hutton's life reached its conclusion before the final planned chapters were written. He was part way through a discussion on the growing of potatoes when the narrative came to a grinding halt. We can only hazard a guess at how much more he had to say on the topics he had already introduced, or subjects that were still to be addressed.

The manuscript of *Elements of Agriculture* was mysteriously lost for over half a century until it fell into the safe hands of the Edinburgh Geological Society. It was then in the care of the Royal Society of Edinburgh from the late 1940s onwards. Now held in the National Library of Scotland, it remains unpublished. Selected pages from the manuscript have been placed on show to the public as part of a wider display of works from the Scottish Enlightenment period.

Hutton's ill health and passing

James Hutton died on Saturday 26 March 1797 in his house on St John's Hill after a long illness, a problem with his kidneys that had required painful and ineffectual surgery a few years before his eventual passing. It was his friend Joseph Black who had performed the operation in 1791, most likely to remove kidney stones. His recuperation was slow from what would have been a fairly brutal and, by today's standards, hugely risky procedure, and a recurrence of kidney problems in 1794 required a further operation. He was never again to leave his house on St John's Hill.

Such health issues frustrated Hutton's efforts to undertake any further fieldwork to ground-truth his geological conjectures, should that have been required. Conversely, it had the effect of 'confining him to barracks' so that he could commit to paper all his ideas on the wide variety of subjects that had interested him during his long and varied career.

In a letter to James Watt, the manner of Hutton's passing was described thus:

> He left us without a struggle in half a minute – after speaking with the utmost clearness. He was busy with another large volume and had engaged the engraver to come and get his order after that in which he died.

It is probable that this discussion would have been about the production of engravings for Volume III of *Theory of the Earth*. He was clearly fully engaged in his work right up until his last breath.

At 70 years old, Hutton had made it to a few months beyond the traditional 'three score years and ten' life expectancy, but the last years of his life were uncomfortable and his social contacts significantly diminished.

Hutton had not made a will before he died, but Joseph Black acted as his executor. Hutton's sister Isabella, who had nursed him through his final years, also ensured his affairs were in good order and she became guardian of all his worldly goods, properties and papers.

Isabella died on 1 March 1818 at 94. John Bell, Writer to the Signet, prepared an inventory of her possessions two years later. Her will and this inventory of her assets are lengthy and complex documents, but they have been pain-stakingly transcribed. These documents became the focus of interest because she inherited Hutton's estate in its entirety.

The widespread trade in enslaved people was active throughout Hutton's lifetime. Many commercial and social enterprises, such as the funding of the Forth and Clyde Canal project, were made possible by this enhanced cash flow to Scotland. So the question arises; was Hutton a participant or beneficiary in any way? There is no reference to the ownership of any overseas properties or assets that can be construed as relating to trading in enslaved people. Isabella could have disposed of these tainted assets, but again we find no evidence that she did. From these, the most relevant documents, we can reasonably conclude that – although the Scottish economy benefited greatly from the additional revenue this trade brought to the country – Hutton had no direct involvement with, or investments in, the trade in enslaved people.

James Hutton's was a life well-lived and his wide-ranging scientific contributions are remembered to this day. He was buried in Greyfriars Kirkyard in Edinburgh in what has become known as the Covenanters' prison. His grave was unmarked for 150 years after his death but, on that anniversary in 1947, a memorial stone was placed above his unmarked grave. It lies in the yard of the Balfour family.

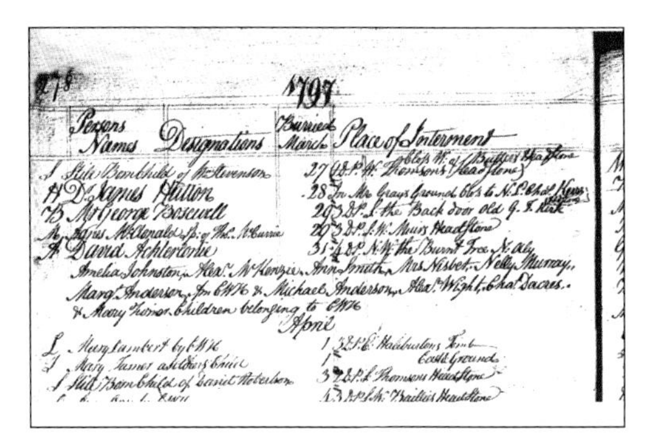

1797

Persons Names	Designations	Buried March	Place of Interment
Dr James Hutton		28	

Record of Hutton's death

This is an extract from the Old Parish Registry that records Hutton's passing in 1797.

Hutton's memorial stone

Memorial stone placed to mark Hutton's burial site.

Alan McKirdy

ILLUSTRATIONS

OF THE

HUTTONIAN THEORY

OF THE EARTH.

By JOHN PLAYFAIR,

F. R. S. EDIN. AND PROFESSOR OF MATHEMATICS
IN THE UNIVERSITY OF EDINBURGH.

Nunc naturalem causam quærimus et assiduam, non raram et fortuitam.

SENECA.

EDINBURGH:

PRINTED FOR CADELL AND DAVIES, LONDON, AND
WILLIAM CREECH, EDINBURGH.

1802.

Chapter 9
Hutton's legacy

John Playfair to the rescue

If it had not been for John Playfair's paper published in 1802, the possibility exists that James Hutton's insights and brilliant deductions about the way the Earth works may have sunk without a trace. He was, by Playfair's accounts, an extremely sociable and engaging character who could light up a room with his mere presence and sparkling conversation. However, his ability to getting his groundbreaking ideas and concepts down on paper in a manner that would inform and inspire his readers was sadly limited. His use of the English language was scratchy and dense, and the structure of his manuscripts sometimes poorly organised and repetitive. Readers, other than his fiercest critics who were looking for matters to find fault with, were put off from finishing his *Theory of the Earth*. Its immediate impact across the wider scientific community was, therefore, more limited than it could and, indeed, should have been. That is often the fate of people possessed of towering talents or intellects who make their contribution but die in relative obscurity, only for their ideas or art to be 'discovered' later after their own life has drawn to a close.

In an enterprise that demonstrated the greatest act of friendship and admiration for his now deceased friend and colleague, Playfair undertook a re-presentation, or repackaging in today's parlance, of Hutton's ideas in a manner that would reach a wider and more sympathetic audience.

With admirable tact and diplomacy, the foreword to his paper on *Illustrations of the Huttonian Theory of the Earth* reads:

> The Treatise here offered to the Public was drawn up with a view of explaining Dr Hutton's *Theory of the Earth* in a manner more popular and perspicuous than is done in his own writings .... Throughout the whole, I have aimed at little more than a clear exposition of the facts, and a plain deduction of the conclusions grounded on them; nor shall I claim any merit to myself if in the order which I have found it necessary to adapt some

Opposite: ***Illustrations of the Huttonian Theory of the Earth***

The fronticepiece and cover of John Playfair's *Illustrations of the Huttonian Theory of the Earth* published in 1802.

> arguments may have taken a new form and some additions may have been made to a system naturally rich in number and variety of its illustrations .... Having been instructed by Dr Hutton himself in his theory of the earth; having lived in intimate friendship with that excellent man for several years, and almost in the daily habit of discussing the questions here treated of; I have the best opportunity of understanding his views, and becoming acquainted with his peculiarities, whether of expression or thought.

This is a marvellously self-effacing description of the service Playfair offered to the scientific world. In fact he salvaged Hutton's ideas so that they might live on into the next century and beyond. A brilliant mathematician in his own right, Playfair is commemorated with a memorial on Calton Hill, Edinburgh. This act of brotherly affection towards his old friend and coadjutor is perhaps the greatest contribution that he made to the Scottish Enlightenment.

Charles Lyell picks up the baton

Charles Lyell was born in Kinnordy, near Kirriemuir, Forfarshire, in 1797, the same year that Hutton died. He was from a well-to-do family of lairds and landowners. When still a child, the Lyell family moved to Hampshire in the south of England, although connections were maintained with the Scottish estate.

Charles studied Classics at Exeter College, Oxford, and later qualified as a lawyer, practising for many years in the law courts as a barrister. He also

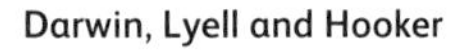

Darwin, Lyell and Hooker

Charles Lyell was socially well-connected with the great scientists of the day. Amongst these influential connections was the greatest of them all – Charles Darwin. Here are Darwin and Lyell with another celebrated naturalist, Joseph Hooker (right) at Down House.

Vesuvius

The section of Lyell's seminal book *Principles of Geology* on volcanoes was largely focused on Vesuvius and Mount Etna, two of the largest active volcanic structures in Italy.

In Volume 1 of *Principles of Geology*, he dedicates twenty pages to the subject of 'Causes of earthquakes and volcanoes' – two natural phenomena that we now know are closely related. This is a contemporary view of the crater of Vesuvius, largely unchanged from Lyell's day.

Alan McKirdy

developed an interest in geology, firstly by studying a course on mineralogy taught by the famous palaeontologist William Buckland. His interest in the subject blossomed and he was elected as a Fellow of the Geological Society of London. Soon geology became his primary concern and he worked collaboratively with scientists in this country and on the continent. Latterly, he visited Glen Tilt, scene of one of Hutton's greatest field excursions, with William Buckland and saw the place that Hutton had described over twenty-five years earlier.

Lyell was familiar with Hutton's work through his reading of Playfair's 1802 paper and became an enthusiastic convert to many of the ideas it contained. He travelled far and wide in Britain and abroad, taking in the south of France, Vesuvius on the Amalfi coast, the buried city of Pompeii and Europe's most active volcano Mount Etna.

His experience and knowledge grew, Charles Lyell was appointed Professor of Geology at King's College London. His main contribution to geology was to articulate his ideas in a book that became the first authoritative text on the subject, *Principles of Geology*. First published in 1830, it ran to many editions. In this book, he plunged a dagger into the heart of Neptunism, the deeply-flawed idea that had haunted Hutton for the latter part of his life, although some writers, particularly William Buckland, continued to maintain doggedly the veracity of the deluge and strongly defended its biblical connection. But now the balance of scientific opinion had irrevocably shifted away from this error-strewn interpretation and Lyell further developed the concept of 'uniformitarianism', where 'the present is the key to the past', also confirming Hutton's idea about the immensity of geological time.

In homage to Hutton, Lyell's *Elements of Geology* – as distinct from the more popular *Principles of Geology* – featured a woodcut panorama of Siccar Point on the front cover of the book.

Charles Darwin and *On the Origin of Species*

Charles Lyell was well-connected socially amongst the educated elite of southern England. He counted Charles Darwin, later to become one of the most famous scientists in the land, as a close friend, visiting him at Down House in Kent on many occasions where they exchanged ideas on a wide range of scientific issues.

When Darwin undertook his epic voyage on HMS *Beagle* in 1831 as naturalist to that expedition, he took with him a copy of Lyell's *Principles of Geology*. He already had a keen interest in the subject and was said to have exclaimed at one point, 'I am a geologist'! Just before he set sail in HMS *Beagle*, he spent the summer improving his knowledge, taking part in an expedition with University of Cambridge Professor Adam Sedgwick, to North Wales where the pair honed Darwin's practical and observational skills.

By way of Playfair's 1802 paper, Hutton's ideas had already heavily influenced Lyell's presentation of the emerging science. Darwin wrote:

> I have brought with me the first volume of Lyell's *Principles of Geology* which I have studied attentively; and this book was the highest service to me in many ways .... There are few authors who could write profound science and make a book readable.

Charles Darwin

Darwin in later life.

Howarth-Loomes Collection at the National Museum of Scotland

It was of greater value than just a good bedtime read. Lyell's confirmation of the immensity of geological time allowed for the possibility of what was arguably the most important idea of the nineteenth century, namely Darwin's theory of evolution. Such a conjecture required many generations of a particular species to develop and evolve. Without the necessary requirement for 'deep time', the concept of the origin of species by natural selection would have been dead in the water.

Hutton's geological collection

James Hutton had been an avid collector of geological specimens and curiosities throughout his life. Sir Henry Raeburn's portrait (see pages 2–3 and 132) shows many of them artistically arranged in front of one of Hutton's unpublished manuscripts in the foreground. Hutton studied these specimens intently and they were an important part of his development of new ideas and perspectives on the geological world. He displayed some of them when he gave a paper on granite to the Royal Society of Edinburgh in January 1790 as key exhibits in making a compelling argument to his peers. Although he collected most of the specimens himself, others were sent from friends and colleagues who had visited places Hutton had not.

The question arises: what became of the rocks he collected from every corner of the kingdom? Jean Jones tells a sorry tale of malice and incompetence in the manner in which this national treasure was treated. Fast forward to the outcome: the collection was broken up, lost and generally treated with contempt. It was as though it had no scientific or heritage value.

Who were the culprits? As one of Hutton's oldest friends, Joseph Black was asked to take charge of curating the collection after Hutton's death. However, Black was ill when required to act, so he offered the collection to the Royal Society of Edinburgh. In the days before the National Museum of Scotland existed, it was then passed on to the University of Edinburgh's museum as the RSE did not have the facility to look after Hutton's sizeable collection of rocks.

The Reverend John Walker, the museum curator, and his successor in that role, Robert Jameson (1774–1854), had little time for Hutton's fanciful ideas. Jameson, a committed Neptunist, made no attempt to maintain or to display the collection, so its value was rapidly diminished. Instead he squirreled some of it away in boxes 'in a garret or spare room where it can never be seen'. A few of the specimens were enormous: Hutton had collected a boulder of 'granite traversing schistus' from Glen Tilt that weighed in excess of 600 lb. Another specimen from Arran was even bigger. Clearly, they must have been transported back to Edinburgh from these relatively far-flung places. The logistics must have been challenging to say the least.

Although the inventory of specimens was also lost, we know the collection consisted of a wide range of rocks and minerals, including ores, septarian nodules, agates, jasper, concretions, geodes, basalt, pitchstone, marble from Portsoy, gneiss, granites, puddingstones, breccia, sandstone and some fossils (wood, scallop shells, belemnites).

Both hiding and then breaking up this priceless collection of scientific artefacts, just because they did not support curators' ideas, was nothing less than a grievous act of scientific vandalism. However, Robert Jameson redeemed himself ever so slightly by the 1830s when notes recovered from one of his students' notebooks suggested he had renounced his early Wernian ways and accepted the truth of Hutton's ideas concerning the volcanic origins of some rocks.

As a tailpiece to this ongoing debate, the Edinburgh Geological Society had its inaugural meeting on 4 December 1834 at Robertson's Tavern in Edinburgh. The subject under discussion was the origin of Salisbury Crags.

Septarian nodule

This septarian nodule is possibly the only one of Hutton's specimens to survive. It has been in the geological collection of the National Museum of Scotland for a long time, but is of unconfirmed provenance. Whilst an identification cannot be made with absolute certainty, a similarity to the specimen lying on the table beside Hutton in the Henry Raeburn portrait was recently noted by Museum curator Dr Rachel Walcott (see also page 3). A paper making the case for these specimens being one and the same is currently in preparation.

Above: *Sir Henry Raeburn: Portrait of James Hutton 1726–79. Geologist.* PG 2686: National Galleries of Scotland. Purchased with the aid of the Art Fund and the National Heritage Memorial Fund 1986.

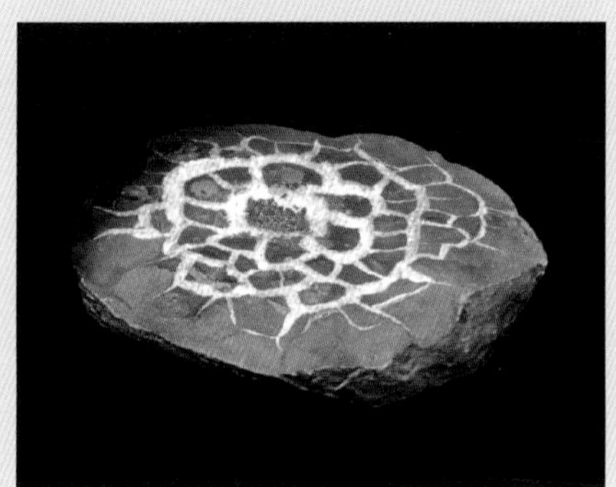

Right: Septarian nodule: Image © National Museums Scotland

Was it a precipitate from a primordial ocean or did it have a volcanic origin? The majority view was that it was the latter.

The Lost Drawings

Hutton was accompanied on his forays into the field, mainly by John Clerk of Eldin, but also, on occasion, by others, including Clerk's son. Both father and son were accomplished artists who had the uncanny knack of capturing the key elements of the geological relations between rock structures that Hutton struggled to describe in words. Many of Clerk's field sketches and drawings, the equivalent of a comprehensive photographic record that geologists today would take to illustrate their visits, were lost for the best part of 200 years.

It was the efforts of a descendent of Hutton's companion, Sir John Clerk who brought them to light. His desire to share them with the wider world, and a grant from the University of Edinburgh, ensured that the drawings at last saw the light of day. They were published, in a limited edition, entitled *James Hutton's Theory of the Earth – The Lost Drawings* jointly by Scottish Academic Press in association with the Royal Society of Edinburgh and the Geological Society of London in 1978. Professors Gordon Craig and Donald McIntyre and Dr Charles Waterston wrote the accompanying commentary.

The *Lost Drawings* are significant in that they demonstrate a much greater understanding of the structure and evolution of the Earth than had been hitherto assumed. Forty-one drawings were reproduced in this publication and most at their original size. Three are reproduced below.

In these three drawings and the others recently discovered, we can see the modern science of geology taking shape before our eyes. The level of understanding of the geological processes at work in shaping the landscapes in this country and around the world – erosion, development of new sedimentary layers, folding of those rock layers and the relationship with volcanic and more deep-seated igneous rocks – takes geology from a dark place where myths, legends and superstitions dominated, into the light where logic, careful observation and deduction hold the key to understanding the world around us. If these drawings and his copious outpouring of books and papers are our evidential basis, there can be no doubt that James Hutton, assisted by John Clerk and others, must be crowned as the 'Founder of Modern Geology'. All of this was achieved by recording and correctly interpreting what he saw within a couple of hundred miles of his Edinburgh home.

In the text that accompanies the publication of the *Lost Drawings*, Craig, McIntyre and Waterston write:

> The drawings and manuscripts, whilst increasing our respect for Hutton's genius, highlight especially John Clerk of Eldin as a major contributor to the Huttonian Theory. His keen eye, artistic pen, scientific precision and geological acumen are clearly revealed in his drawings and papers. We will probably never know the precise roles that the two friends played in the creation of the drawings, and it is perhaps more profitable to recognise the philosopher and the artist as a remarkable partnership.

With many of our other homegrown scientific and engineering heroes, there are frequent reminders of their achievement – James Watt and the steam engine, John Logie Baird and the television, Alexander Graham Bell and the telephone, Thomas Telford and his bridges, and Alexander Fleming with his discovery of penicillin. With Hutton and his fellow travellers, their achievements are perhaps more difficult for the general public to identify with because those daily reminders and connections just do not exist.

Three of *The Lost Drawings*

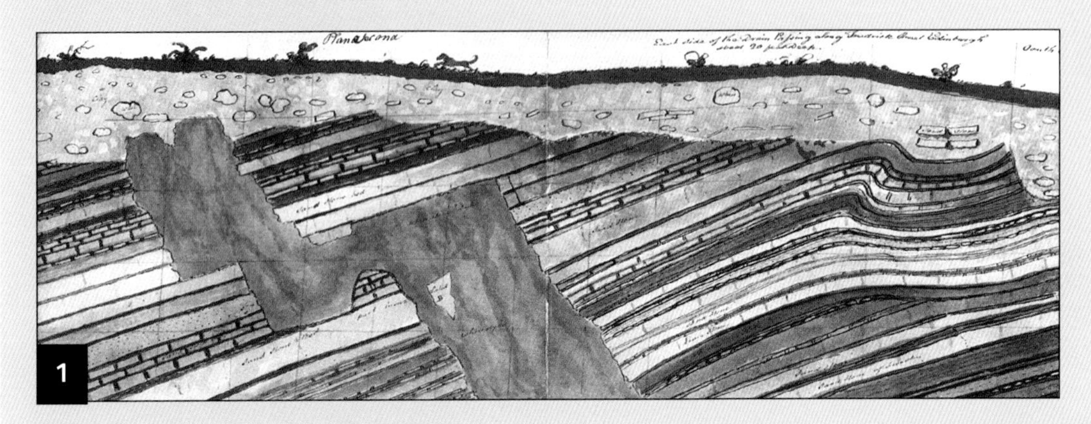

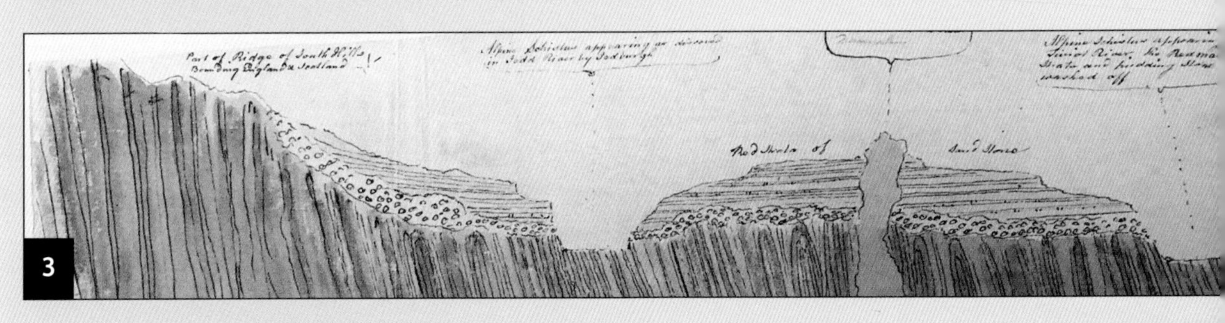

1 Frederick Street, Edinburgh

This drawing illustrates the 'east side of the drain passing along Frederick Street in Edinburgh about twenty feet deep – south end' as labelled by John Clerk of Eldin the artist. A northerly dipping sequence of 'sandstone, freestone, schistus or slate, limestone and whin (basalt)' are identified in the drawing. Hutton makes no mention of these excavations that were undertaken to facilitate the construction of the New Town in Edinburgh, but we can almost take it as read that he would have seen and studied them and been informed by what he saw. The drawing is dated as 1785.

2 Arthur's Seat and Salisbury Crags

This remarkable geological section of Arthur's Seat and Salisbury Crags was drawn by John Clerk of Eldin around 1785. The drawing links the present-day topography with the underlying geological strata. It stands comparison in terms of its accuracy with more recent studies done of the Arthur's Seat volcano by Dr George Black in 1966, and also by later investigators. This is a magnificent achievement by our two intrepid geological pioneers, as it indicates they had a firm grasp of the geological mapping and logging techniques that are commonly used today.

3 Cross-section from the Scotland–England border to the outskirts of Edinburgh

The *Lost Drawings* give clear insights into Hutton and Clerk's geological appreciation of landscapes they viewed. This section is no less extraordinary than Clerk's other productions. It is a cross-section running forty miles approximately on a north-south line from the Scotland–England border to the outskirts of Edinburgh. It shows the steeply dipping and tightly folded schistus that we now identify as the sandstones and shales of Ordovician and Silurian age, overlain by conglomerates and layered sandstones of the Old Red Sandstone and cut through by a volcanic vent. The whinstone (basalt) volcanic pipe is shown, slicing through the older sedimentary layers and coming from a deep source. Having this level of understanding and appreciation of large-scale geological structures and the relationships between rocks of various ages and origins is truly remarkable. The drawing is dated at '1787 or later'.

Sir John Clerk of Penicuik

A modern view of how the Earth works

It is extraordinary that the most complex pieces of 'equipment' that James Hutton had at his disposal were an acute sense of observation and an open mind that embraced new ideas and possibilities. Despite the rather primitive nature of his circumstance, his legacy lives on today. Isaac Newton famously said that 'we stand on the shoulders of giants', meaning that each new scientific development builds on the last. We can indeed trace the development of plate tectonics, the unifying paradigm in the geological sciences, back through the ages to James Hutton and his 'heat engine'.

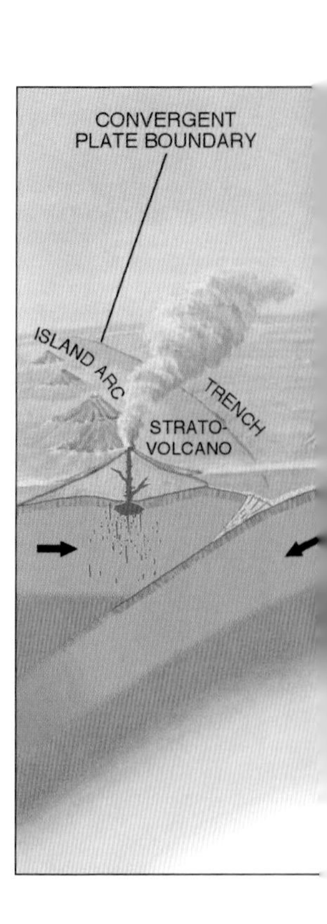

Plate tectonic model

Our current understanding of how the Earth works is informed by the plate tectonic model. The Earth's surface is divided into seven large plates and many smaller ones. Heat escaping from the Earth's core has set up a series of convection cells in the layer above the core, known as the mantle. This slow convection motion drags the overlying continents across the surface of the planet, eventually causing continents to collide. When this happens, new mountains form as the accumulated sediment on the floor of the formerly intervening oceans are squeezed and compressed. This forms new lands, which are immediately subjected to rapid erosion by ice, wind and water. Hutton could not have foreseen such a unifying theory that explains the workings of the surface of the Earth so neatly, but he did propose that the Earth operated as a heat engine and understood the cyclical nature of the processes involved.

Robert Nelmes

The Earth's tectonic plates are driven by heat emanating from the core of our planet. Hutton talked a great deal about the role of heat in changing sedimentary layers into solid rock. He also foresaw the cyclical nature of the way the world works: eroded rocks forming new layers at the bottom of the sea and being raised from the depths to form new lands. Hutton's ideas of the immensity of geological time dragged the subject from the clutches of religious dogma that constrained the timescales over which natural processes could operate. He also foresaw the possibilities of evolution and natural selection.

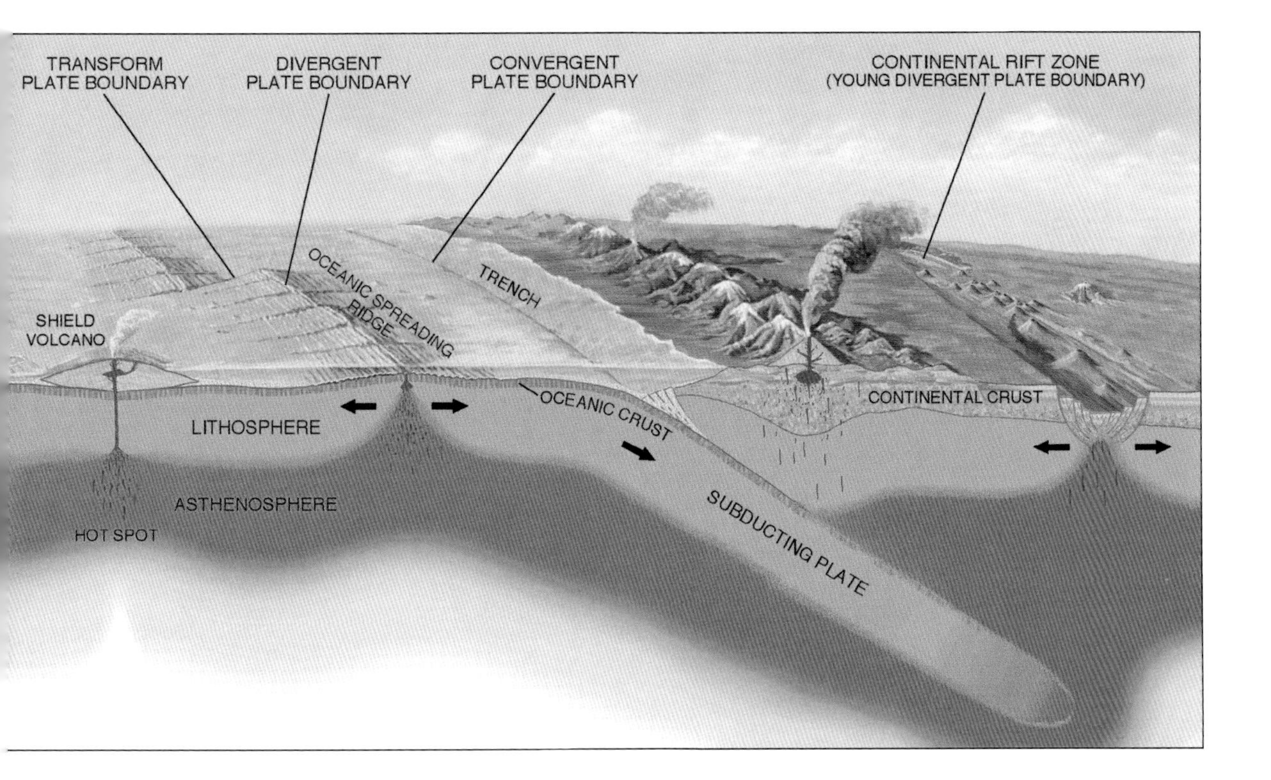

Plate tectonics in operation

New slabs of crust are created along the mid-ocean ridges. These active volcanoes are the largest, yet mostly invisible structures, on the face of the Earth. They add new material to the ocean floor and, in so doing, force the continents apart. To balance things, the ocean floor is consumed in subduction zones, or ocean trenches, where slabs of crust are forced back into the mantle. It was well over 150 years after Hutton's death that the technology existed to build this picture of how the world works. At the very least, Hutton knew that the Earth's internal heat engine played an essential role.

US Geological Survey, José F. Vigil

The James Hutton Institute and James Hutton Foundation

The James Hutton Institute, Scotland's premier environmental and agricultural research organisation, was created on 1 April 2011 from an amalgamation of the Macaulay Land Use Research Institute and the Scottish Crop Research Institute. Its vision is 'to be at the forefront of innovative and transformative science for sustainable management of land, crop and natural resources that supports thriving communities'. The Hutton Institute employs around 550 staff and covers all the areas of science undertaken by James Hutton and today conducts science in his image. The Institute has also created a James Hutton Foundation to help celebrate his legacy.

Their three scientific challenges are:

- Develop new crops and production methods that help deliver food security while better protecting the environment;
- Protect and enhance the resilience of ecosystems for multiple benefits; and
- Deliver technical and social innovations that support sustainable and resilient communities.

Hutton Institute scientists follow the inspiration of James Hutton, after whom they are named, and deliver global impact through excellent science, collaboration and innovation. James Hutton's work on agricultural and climate research that he started in a rather primitive manner at Slighhouses and before, lives on and is now championed by a truly world class twenty-first century research establishment.

Drought resistent crops

Vertical crop production technology developed to maximise food production of high value crops under tightly controlled conditions.

The James Hutton Institute

Royal Society of Edinburgh

A view of the Royal Society of Edinburgh building in George Street, Edinburgh.

Shutterstock

The Royal Society of Edinburgh

Another element of James Hutton's legacy is the Royal Society of Edinburgh, of which he was a founder member. Today, it goes from strength to strength, with the aim of playing a leading role in the development of a modern enlightenment that will enable Scotland to contribute significantly to addressing the global challenges facing humanity in the twenty-first century. RSE Fellows include people drawn from a wide range of disciplines: science and technology, arts, humanities, social science, business and public service. This breadth of expertise makes this institution unique in the United Kingdom.

Writers on James Hutton

James Hutton has attracted considerable attention from biographers and science writers. John Playfair was his only contemporary biographer, but many who have come after Playfair have described the life and works of this pioneer. As already described, Hutton's ideas, via Playfair, were taken on board and refined by Charles Lyell. In his classic text on *Principles of Geology*, published in 1830, Lyell paid generous tribute to his fellow Scot:

> Hutton communicated the results of his observations unreservedly, and with the fearless spirit of one who was conscious that love of truth was the sole stimulus for all of his exertions.

The Geological Society of London published the third volume of James Hutton's *Theory of the Earth* in 1899. Sir Archibald Geikie wrote a glowing tribute to Hutton in an eight-page foreword to this publication. It was he who first coined the phrase of Hutton as the 'Founder of Modern Geology.' In 1905, Geikie wrote a book, *Founders of Geology*, that placed Hutton in an authoritative historical context. Lucidly and entertainingly written, the opening remark on the first page reads:

> In science, as in all other departments of inquiry, no thorough grasp of the subject can be gained, unless the history of its development is clearly appreciated.

Geikie's text charts the course of geological thought from its earliest beginnings, through Aristotle to Herodotus (484–25 BC) who realised that Nile sediments record past events, and concluded that Egypt had formed from slowly accumulating river deposits. Geikie then recounted the contribution made by other observers such as Leonardo da Vinci and the English cosmologist Robert Hooke. Two chapters are devoted to the work of Hutton and his associates Playfair and Hall, with the former's contribution described thus:

> ... with singular sagacity, he recognised early in life the essential processes of geological change, devoting himself with unwearied application to the task of watching their effects and collecting proofs of their operation, and who combined the results of his observation and reflection in a work which will ever remain one of the great classics of science.

In terms of the new ideas developed by Hutton, Geikie wrote that, 'nobody before Hutton's time had been bold enough to imagine a series of subterranean intrusions of molten matter'. Right on Hutton's doorstep and across central Scotland lie the results of ancient volcanic episodes of various ages; Castle Rock, Arthur's Seat, the Ochil and Fintry Hills to name but a few. Geikie reminded his readers that Hutton was the first to recognise their true origin. He also acknowledged the struggles that Hutton had in getting his new ideas accepted by his peers, noting:

> We shall better appreciate the sagacity and prescience of Hutton and Playfair, if we remember that their views on this subject were in their lifetime, and for many years afterwards, ignored or explicitly rejected.

Rather out of keeping with the rest of his serious academic tome, Geikie also commented on Hutton's personality:

> His character was distinguished by its transparent simplicity, its frank openness, its absence of all that was little or selfish, and its overflowing enthusiasm and vivacity. In a company, he was always one of the most animated speakers, his conversation full of ingenious and original observation, showing wide information, from which an excellent memory enabled him to draw endless illustrations of any subject that might be discussed.

Geikie was not moved to makes similar comments about any of the other geological pioneers discussed in his book, so we take this as a considerable compliment to Hutton's personal qualities.

It took until 1947 and Sir Edward Battersby Bailey's commemoration of the 150th anniversary of Hutton's death before the third significant retrospective assessment (after Playfair and Geikie) of his work appeared. Bailey was an eminent geologist in his own right, leading the Geological Survey of Great Britain at the time, and undertaking geological surveys across the Highlands and Islands of Scotland. Bailey's homage to Hutton's work was delivered as an address to the Royal Society of Edinburgh in 1947 and a 14-page written account published in *Transactions* two years later. Professor Sergei Ivanovich Tomkeieff, a Lithuanian geologist, who published extensive geological accounts of volcanic rocks in the Scottish Borders, also wrote a glowing tribute to Hutton and the 'philosophy of geology' in 1949. Then in 1969, Gordon L. Davies from Trinity College Dublin published *The Earth in Decay*, which included an influential chapter on Hutton.

The focus of attention then switched across the Atlantic Ocean. Dennis Dean, Professor of English and Humanities at the University of Wisconsin, Parkside, published a short account of Hutton's work in *Annals of Science* in 1973. After a great deal more research, he published the first full-length biography of Hutton and his work in 1992. Later W. H. Galbraith from the University of Pittsburgh completed a PhD on *James Hutton: an analytic and historical study*.

The most prominent Hutton biographer of the 1980s was prolific in her output of carefully researched and beautifully written papers and book chapters. The late Jean Jones, who was brought up on a farm near Kelso in the Scottish Borders and graduated from the University of Oxford with an English degree, took up the Hutton story with great gusto. She described his farming activities, canal building exploits, and the fate of his geological collection.

The 1990s saw the 200th anniversary of the death of James Hutton. Many publications came out during that decade – and either side of it – to celebrate his legacy. Donald B. McIntyre, Martin Rudwick, Gordon Craig, Stuart Monro, Sandy Crosbie, Ian Dalziel, Iain Stewart, Norman Butcher, Charles Waterston, Robert Dott, Denise Walton and Stephen J. Gould, to name but a few eminent scientists, all produced worthy books, articles, papers, book chapters, conference proceedings, a Hutton trail and a television programme that described Hutton's contribution to geology and agriculture.

Stephen Baxter and Jack Repcheck wrote very entertaining books on Hutton, both published in 2003. They are heartily commended for writing texts that tell his story in an accessible manner. Their works continue to be readily available. For the first time, Hutton's achievements were not presented as a paper in a difficult to get hold of scientific journal or out of print academic book that only a tiny fraction of the interested public is able to access.

Helen Gordon's book *Notes from Deep Time* is a recent, and very welcome, addition to the literature on popular geology. She assesses Hutton's legacy of books and papers with flair and an understanding of the profound contribution he made to the subject. She writes: 'If geologists had a Mecca, it would surely be a place called Siccar Point.'

Jeanne Donovan created a family tree for Hutton on the Ancestry website which identifies relatives who preceded and followed him. It is a rich source of genealogical research.

'The Great Tapestry of Scotland' was unveiled in 2013. It tells the story of this land, capturing the lives, hopes, triumphs and disappointments of a nation in 160 linen panels. The Scottish Enlightenment is generously featured in this tableau, with James Watt, Adam Smith, David Hume and James Hutton each commanding their own place in the story. Panel 74 entitled 'James Hutton's Theory of the Earth', describes his twin passions of farming and geology. His most famous contribution to science – 'No vestige of a beginning, no prospect of an end' – is stitched into the cloth for posterity.

Despite these copious outpourings of print and embroidery on Hutton's achievements, he remains a man in the shadows. We rightly celebrate our bards, artists, scientists, engineers, inventors and sports men and women, but James Hutton finds only a minor place in that pantheon of creative and intellectual stars of Scotland. Even in the school history curriculum in Scotland the Scottish Enlightenment in general, and Hutton in particular, are almost invisible. Perhaps this explains why few people have heard of him today. Surely, we must do better with more prominence given to Scotland's unparalleled and unrepeated golden age of intellectual curiosity, leadership and achievement.

I hope that this book will go some way towards shining a bright light on this remarkable man and his insights that still inform and guide our current understanding of how the Earth works.

'The Great Tapestry of Scotland' [detail]

The panel on James Hutton's *Theory of the Earth* from 'The Great Tapestry of Scotland'.

With kind permission of Alistair Moffat and Birlinn. Photograph © Alex Hewitt. Panel design © Andrew Crummy

Chapter 10

Places to visit

The story of James Hutton and the Scottish Enlightenment unfolded over 220 years ago. However, here are many places in Scotland that you can visit to get closer to Dr Hutton, his Enlightenment contemporaries, and the locations which shaped his understanding of farming practice and the workings of the Earth.

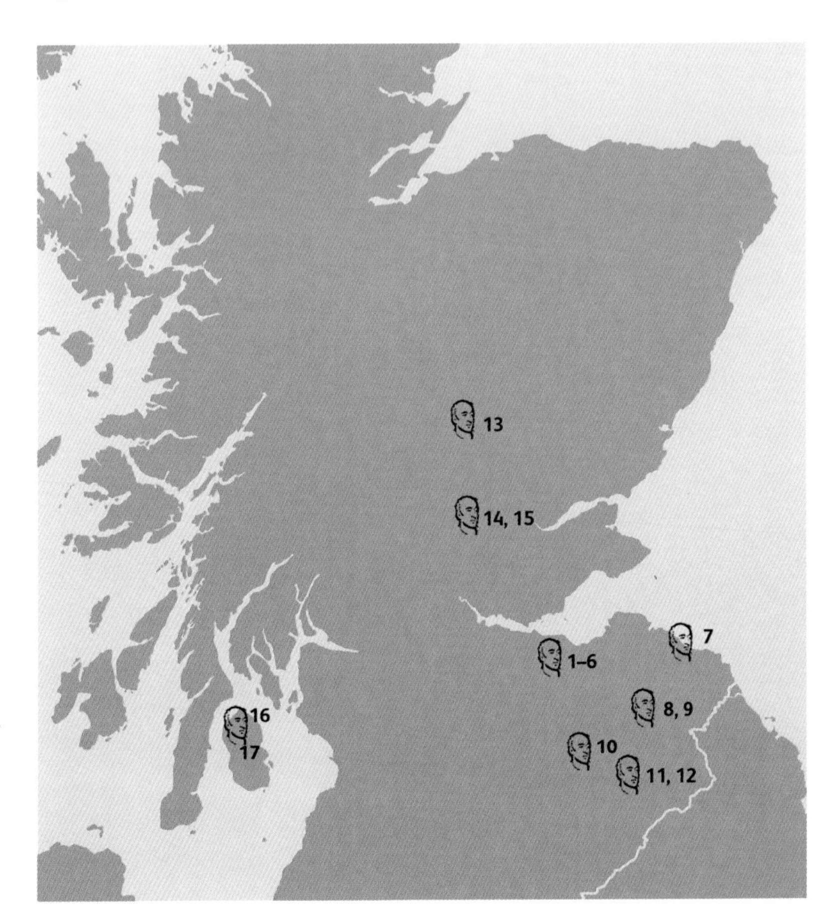

Map showing distribution of Hutton localities across Scotland.

The numbers relate to the localities listed opposite.

Adapted from a graphic supplied by The James Hutton Institute

Edinburgh

1 Hutton's Section in Holyrood Park still demonstrates the evidence that Hutton used to show that some rocks were once in a molten state. What is now called Hutton's Section was once an active quarry, so it cannot be guaranteed that the exposures seen today are those observed by Hutton two hundred and fifty years ago.

2 James Hutton Memorial Garden, St John's Hill, marks the site of Hutton's house. The garden was commissioned in 2001 by the Edinburgh Geological Society and the Royal Society of Edinburgh on land owned by the University of Edinburgh as a place of quiet contemplation. The boulders placed in the garden were chosen to represent Hutton's 'big ideas' as described in his *Theory of the Earth*.

3 Scottish National Portrait Gallery, Queen Street, Edinburgh, has portraits of many important figures from the Scottish Enlightenment, including Hutton and Joseph Black. A statue of the former is perched high above North St Andrews Street on the exterior wall of the building. There is also a frieze showing Hutton in the company of the inventors, engineers, poets, scientists and lawyers of the day in the entrance hall.

4 Greyfriars Kirkyard is where James Hutton was laid to rest. His grave is in a locked part of the graveyard, known as the Covenanters' Prison. If you want to view the grave, you will need to arrange access with Greyfriars Kirk.

Below left: Hutton's Section, Holyrood Park

Moira McKirdy

Below: Donald McIntyre

Donald in full flow as he shows visitors around Greyfriars Kirkyard.

Ian MacDonald

Hutton at the National Museum of Scotland

Exhibition boards that form a glowing tribute to Hutton's pioneering work at the National Museum of Scotland.

5 The National Museum of Scotland, Chambers Street has a geology gallery that pays tribute to James Hutton. It largely focuses on his interpretation of the rocks at Siccar Point. The 'Beginnings' gallery on Level 1, which explores the first three billion years of Scotland's history and uncovers the origins and evolution of its landscape, flora and fauna, is also worth visiting.

6 Dynamic Earth has a gallery where the three Scots – James Hutton, Charles Lyell and Arthur Holmes – who have done most to unravel the extent of geological time are celebrated. A hologram of Hutton and representations of the other two scientists bring their stories to life as they discuss their respective contributions to the debate. It is definitely worth a visit.

Scottish Borders

7 Siccar Point, Berwickshire, is a place of pilgrimage for geologists from around the world. This is where modern geology began and its importance to scientists and historians cannot be overstated. Siccar Point is on the Berwickshire coast. Although wild when lashed by winter storms from the North Sea, on a summer's day it is a place of peace and serenity where Hutton and friends peered into 'the abyss of time'. Access to the top of the cliff is readily available and affords a good view of the unconformity below. However, for those who want to venture to the foot of the cliffs to get a closer look, the journey is precarious. There is no path, so it is a scramble down a steep and slippery grassy bank. Please take the utmost care.

Siccar Point

This is a view of the world famous Siccar Point from the cliff top. The upended Silurian strata are clearly seen. These rocks were later covered by thick layers of sandstones. The clarity of these rock relationships made it the perfect place for Hutton to start to unravel the mysteries of what later became known as 'deep time'.

Nowell Donovan

There is a small car park at the start of the access track and interpretation boards to help visitors appreciate the significance of the place. The site can be more safely accessed by way of a very pleasant and geologically interesting coastal path from Cockburnspath.

8 Slighhouses is now a farm in private ownership, but it can be viewed from afar without intrusion or disturbance. This is the place where Hutton first took notice of the natural world around him and began to improve the land to create his model farm.

9 Nether Monynut is another working farm in private ownership. Visiting the general area where the farm is located on the southern slopes of the Lammermuir Hills gives a clear indication of the challenges Hutton faced in making a living from these rough pastures.

10 Galashiels hosts the visitor centre that is permanent home to the 'Great Tapestry of Scotland'. Look out for the panel on James Hutton and the other Scottish Enlightenment figures.

11 Allar's Mill, Jedburgh, is a disappointment today in terms of what can be seen of the geology. Vegetation now obscures the view but, periodically, the greenery is pared back and the geological section temporarily revealed.

12 Jedburgh hosts a modern art installation that mimics the Allar's Mill unconformity. Vertical strata of Silurian age are topped by flat lying sandstones.

Jedburgh

Artistic representation in stone sculptural form of the unconformity at Allar's Mill.

Mike Browne

Perthshire

13 Glen Tilt in Highland Perthshire is a good hike up the glen from Blair Castle. Permission is required from the estate for vehicular access. It is well worth the journey back in time to share Hutton's joy at finding conclusive evidence for granite's true place in the scheme of things.

14 Hutton's Dyke near Crieff (on the road to Auchterarder) is a prominent landscape feature that Hutton chanced upon during his travels. It is now used by climbing clubs as a 'nursery wall', but is also available for geologists to view.

15 Campsie Linn near Perth is a continuation of the dyke feature near Crieff that was also visited by Hutton. This time, the dyke is exposed courtesy of the River Tay

Isle of Arran

16 Cock of Arran at the north end of the island near Newton Point is the place to find Hutton's unconformity. It exposes Old Red Sandstones overlying Dalradian schists. The Arran Geopark website gives details of the best access route. The Lochranza Interpretation Centre is located nearby.

17 Goat Fell is the highest point on the island. It is made from the granite that Hutton specifically wanted to study. His understanding of the way in which the granite was intruded from below indicated that he had a good grasp of how molten rock rises through the crust, powered by the Earth's heat engine. The junction of the granite with the surrounding rocks can be seen in North Glen Sannox and Glen Rosa.

Further reading and watching

James Hutton and The Scottish Enlightenment

BAXTER, S. (2003): *Revolutions in the Earth: James Hutton and the True Age of the World* (Weidenfeld & Nicholson, London).
Excellent evocation of Hutton, the man and his achievements.

BROADIE, A. (2010): *The Scottish Enlightenment* (Birlinn Edinburgh).
Very readable overview of the Scottish Enlightenment.

BUCHAN, J. (2006): *Adam Smith and the pursuit of perfect liberty* (Profile Books, London).
Very readable celebration of the life and achievements of one of Hutton's closest friends.

BUCHAN, J. (2007): *Capital of the Mind: How Edinburgh Changed the World* (Birlinn, Edinburgh).
Excellent overview of The Edinburgh Enlightenment.

BUTCHER, N. E. (1997): 'James Hutton's house at St John's Hill, Edinburgh', in *Book of the Old Edinburgh Club*, **4**, pp 107–12.

CHAMBERS, R. (1912): *Traditions of Edinburgh*, Illustrated by James Riddel (W. & R. Chambers, Limited, Edinburgh).

CRAIG, G. Y. and J. H. HULL (eds) (1997): *James Hutton – Present and Future*, Geological Society, London, Special Publications, **150**.

CRAIG, G. Y, D. B. McINTYRE and C. D. WATERSTON (1978): *James Hutton's Theory of the Earth: The Lost Drawings* (Scottish Academic Press, Edinburgh).
For the Hutton connoisseur. Very small print run produced, so copies are scarce.

DAICHES, D., P. JONES and J. JONES (eds) (1996): *The Scottish Enlightenment, 1730–1790* (Saltire Society, Edinburgh).
Excellent portrait of the Edinburgh Enlightenment and its main players, including a chapter on Hutton.

DEAN, D. R. (1992): *James Hutton and the History of Geology* (Cornell University Press, Ithaca, NY).
The most academic of the books on Hutton. Informative and rigorous, but not an easy read.

DEVINE, T. (2015): *Recovering Scotland's Slavery Past: The Caribbean Connection* (Edinburgh University Press, Edinburgh).

EYLES, V. A. and J. M. EYLES, J. M. (1951): 'Some geological correspondence of James Hutton', in *Annals of Science*, **7** (4), 316–39.

FRY, M. (2009): *Edinburgh: A City of History* (MacMillan, London).
Very readable account of history of Edinburgh through the ages.

GEIKIE, A. (1905): *The Founders of Geology* (MacMillan and Co. Limited, London).
First exhaustive historical review of the subject, surprisingly readable.

GORDON, H. (2021): *Notes from Deep Time: A Journey Through Our Past and Future Worlds* (Profile Books, London).
Excellent read that helps to put Hutton's work into a historical perspective.

GOULD, S. J. (1988): *Time's Arrow, Time's Cycle* (Penguin, London).
Gould's must-read classic book on geological time.

HERMAN, A. (2001): *The Scottish Enlightenment: The Scots' Invention of the Modern World* (Fourth Estate, London).
Fulsome account of this period of history.
HUTTON, J. (1785): *Abstract of a Dissertation … Concerning the System of the Earth, its Duration, and Stability* (reprinted by Edinburgh University Library by Scottish Academic Press in 1977).
HUTTON, J. (1788): 'Theory of the Earth; or an INVESTIGATION of the Laws observable in the Composition, Dissolution, and Restoration of Land upon the Globe', in *Transactions of the Royal Society of Edinburgh*, **1** (2), 209–305.
HUTTON, J. (1794): 'Observations on Granite', in *Transactions of the Royal Society of Edinburgh*, **3** (2), 77–85.
HUTTON, J. (1794): 'Of the Flexibility of the Brazilian Stone', in *Transactions of the Royal Society of Edinburgh*, **3** (2), 86–93.
HUTTON, J. (1795): *Theory of the Earth with Proofs and Illustrations*, Volumes I and II (William Creech, Edinburgh).
Publication that secured Hutton's reputation as the founder of modern geology.
HUTTON, J. [GEIKIE, A. (ed.)] (1899): *Theory of the Earth with Proofs and Illustrations*, Volume III (Geological Society, London)
JONES, J. (1982): 'James Hutton and the Forth and Clyde canal', in *Annals of Science*, **39** (3), 255–63.
JONES, J. (1983): 'James Hutton: Exploration and Oceanography', in *Annals of Science*, **40** (1), 81–94.
Unexpected facet of Hutton's interests.
JONES, J. (1984): *Scottish Men of Science: James Hutton (1726–1797)* (Scottish Cultural Heritage, Edinburgh).
Very readable short pamphlet on Hutton's life and achievements.
JONES, J. (1985): 'James Hutton's Agricultural Research and His Life as a Farmer', in *Annals of Science*, **42** (6), 573–601.
KIRWAN, R. (1793): 'Examination of the Supposed Igneous Origin of Stony Substances', in *Transactions of the Royal Irish Academy*, **5**, 51–87.
Paper that galvanised Hutton to complete and publish first two volumes of *Theory of the Earth*.
MADDOX, B. (2017): *Reading the Rocks* (Bloomsbury Publishing, London).
Largely about advances in geological thought made during Victorian times, but acknowledges Hutton's contribution – excellent book.
McINTYRE, A. I. (ed) (2014): *McIntyre's Parcel of Fine Herrings: A life of learning, love and laughter – Donald B. McIntyre 1923–2009* (Fastprint Publishing, Peterborough).
Miscellany of writings, anecdotes and stories about Donald McIntyre's life and times.
McINTYRE, D. B. (1963): 'James Hutton and the Philosophy of Geology', in C. C. Albritton Jr (ed.) *The Fabric of Geology* (Geological Society of America, MA, pp 1–11).
Philosophical slant on Hutton's work.
McINTYRE, D. B. (1997): 'James Hutton's Edinburgh: a precis', in CRAIG and HULL (eds), pp 1–12.
Fascinating background to the Enlightenment and Hutton's place within it.
McINTYRE, D. B. and A. P. McKIRDY (2012): *James Hutton: The Founder of Modern Geology* (NMS Enterprises Ltd – Publishing, Edinburgh).
Previous edition of this book.
McKIRDY, A. P. (2016): *Edinburgh: Landscapes in Stone* (Birlinn, Edinburgh).
Account of the geology of Edinburgh including reference to Siccar Point and Hutton's life in the city.
MELVIN, E. (2017): *The Edinburgh of John Kay* (Eric Melvin, Edinburgh).
Fascinating and beautifully written account of the city that John Kay came to know, which included James Hutton and many of his contemporaries.
MOFFAT, A. (2013): *The Great Tapestry of Scotland* (Birlinn, Edinburgh).
Each panel of the tapestry reproduced in colour with accompanying description.
MONRO, S. K. and A. J. CROSBIE (1997): 'The Dynamic Earth Project and the Next Millennium', in CRAIG and HULL (eds), pp 157–68.
Account of the Dynamic Earth project inspired by James Hutton.
PLAYFAIR, J. (1802): *Illustrations of the Huttonian Theory of the Earth* (Cadell & Davies, London, and William Creech, Edinburgh).
Essential research source for the serious student.
PLAYFAIR, J. (1805): 'James Hutton and Joseph Black', in *Transactions of the Royal Society of Edinburgh*, **5**.
Excellent biographical material on Hutton.

PROTHERO, D. R. (2018): *The Story of the Earth in 25 Rocks: Tales of Important Geological Puzzles and the People Who Solved Them* (Columbia University Press, NY).
Places Hutton's key localities in the context of other important geological sites worldwide.

RIDER, M. and P. HARRISON (2019): *Hutton's Arse: 3 Billion Years of Extraordinary Geology in Scotland's Northwest Highlands* (Dunedin Academic Press, Edinburgh).
Informative and amusing account of the geology of the Northern Highlands.

REPCHECK, J. (2003): *The Man who Found Time: James Hutton and the Discovery of the Earth's Antiquity* (Pocket Books, London).
Informal account of Hutton's life and times.

RUDWICK, M. (2012): 'James Hutton – the Earth's stable system', in Robinson, A. (ed.), *The Scientists: An Epic of Discovery*, pp 78–81 (Thames & Hudson, London).
Describes Hutton's achievements in the context of all the other significant scientists of the last two hundred years.

STEWART, I. and BRITISH BROADCASTING CORPORATION (2010): *Men of Rock*.
Excellent television programme that describes Hutton's life, times and achievements.

SZATKOWSKI, S. (2017): *Enlightenment Edinburgh: A Guide* (Birlinn, Edinburgh).
Beautifully illustrated and written guide to Enlightenment Edinburgh.

TOMKEIEFF, S. I. (1948): 'James Hutton and the Philosophy of Geology', in *Proceedings of the Royal Society of Edinburgh*, Section B. Biology, **63** (4), 387–400.
Interesting but challenging read.

WHITE. G. W. (ed) (1973): *James Hutton: Contributions to the History of Geology*, Volume 5 (Hafner Press, New York, NY).
Compilation of some of Hutton's writings and Playfair's biography in one volume.

WITHERS, C. W. J. (1994): 'On Georgics and Geology: James Hutton's "Elements of Agriculture" and Agricultural Science in Eighteenth-Century Scotland', in *Agricultural History Review*, **42** (1), 38–48.
Academic review of Hutton the farmer.

Wider geological and agricultural topics

BLACK, G. P. (1966): *Arthur's Seat: A History of Edinburgh's Volcano* (Oliver & Boyd Edinburgh).
Technical geological account of Arthur's Seat volcano.

FRIEND, P. (2012): *Scotland: Looking at the Natural Landscapes*, Collins New Naturalist Series (Harper Collins, London).
Account of the geology and landscapes of Scotland suitable for students.

GILLAN, C. (2013): *Geology and landscapes of Scotland* (Dunedin Press, Edinburgh).
Excellent introduction to the geology of Scotland, albeit for the slightly more advanced reader.

LYELL C. (1830): *Principles of Geology* (republished as a Penguin Classic in 1997, London).
Classic text, arguably the first comprehensive modern geology textbook to be published anywhere in the world.

McKIRDY, A. P., J. E. GORDON and R. CROFTS (2012): *Land of Mountain and Flood: The Geology and Landforms of Scotland* (Birlinn, Edinburgh).
Well-illustrated introduction to the subject for readers with no real background in the subject.

McKIRDY, A. P. (2015:) *Set in Stone: The Geology and Landscapes of Scotland* (Birlinn, Edinburgh).
Good introduction to the subject for those with no background in geology.

McKIRDY, A. P. (2016–22): *Landscapes in Stone*.
Individual titles cover the following areas: Skye; Arran; Edinburgh; The Cairngorms; Mull, Iona and Ardnamurchan; Argyll and the Islands; The Outer Hebrides; Lochaber and Glencoe; The Northern Highlands; Orkney and Shetland; Central Scotland; South of Scotland; and The Small Isles (Birlinn, Edinburgh).
Series of regional geological guides to thirteen different areas of Scotland for those with no prior knowledge of the subject.

TREWIN N. H. (ed.) (2002): *The Geology of Scotland*, 4th edition (Geological Society, London).
Finest scientific account of the geology of Scotland currently available. Also the gateway to all the significant geological papers published during the last one hundred and fifty years.

Acknowledgements and image credits

I thank National Museums Scotland for commissioning this book, which is their third rendering of a work on the life and times of James Hutton. I worked closely with Lynne Reilly and Lesley Taylor from NMS Enterprises Ltd – Publishing throughout the publication process and I thank them for their direction and support. Mark Blackadder's cover design was up to his usual very high standard. The James Hutton Institute supported the publication of this book financially and in many other ways. Professor Colin Campbell FRSE, Lorraine Robertson and Anne Pack BEM, all from The James Hutton Institute, played important roles in making sure the project happened. Professor Stuart Monro OBE FRSE and Moira McKirdy MBE read and commented on the manuscript at various stages and both suggested many helpful improvements and corrections. Professor Alan Werritty FRSE provided well-observed insights on Hutton's agricultural activities and writings, as did Denise Walton, Borders farmer and Hutton enthusiast. Professor Nowell Donovan, Dr Stuart McKirdy, Jane Dalgleish, Angus Miller and Eric Gordon also made valuable comments on the draft. Jeanne Donovan and Les Mitchell assisted with aspects of genealogical research on Hutton. Adrian Shaw commented on the religious and social context of the period. I am very grateful to them all for their input. But any remaining mistakes and omissions are mine and mine alone.

The Scottish Borders, where James Hutton spent 14 years of his life, was also my home as a young man. Over 200 years after Hutton, I too worked on this land as a schoolboy and student, doing contract work on many farms around Slighhouses and across the Scottish Borders before I turned to the study of geology, chemistry, soil science and zoology at the University of Aberdeen. It is the strong sense of fellowship and admiration I feel for Hutton that made me want to write this book and previous works that celebrate the life, times and achievements of this genius of the stones and the soil.

I am now a freelance writer publishing mainly on geological topics where I've tried to make the extraordinary story of Scotland's geology and landscapes accessible to a wider public including books for children, written with Moira, on geology and the environment. For too long, it's been the exclusive preserve of the academic and the expert. Prior to my retirement, I worked for 36 years in conservation; firstly with the Nature Conservancy Council in Newbury and Peterborough and then with Scottish Natural Heritage (now NatureScot) in Edinburgh and finally at Battleby near Perth. With SNH, I was initially Head of Earth Sciences, Habitats and Species and later took on the challenge of Head of Knowledge and Information Management. This latter role was not nearly as boring as it sounds. Data, information and knowledge are the key to understanding most of the issues that excite, advance and trouble the world today.

All images and photographs are credited individually on the page. Every attempt has been made to contact copyright holders for permission to use material in this book. If any source has been inadvertently overlooked, please contact the publisher.

Thanks are due to:

THE ABBOTSFORD TRUST
For the Charles Martin Hardie painting, *Meeting of Robert Burns and Sir Walter Scott at Sciennes Hill House,* on page 75.

KEITH ADAM (BLAIR ADAM)
for the portrait of John Clerk of Eldin by Archibald Skirving on page 27.

BIRLINN LIMITED
for the illustration on page 143.

MIKE BROWNE
for the photographs on pages 18, 42 (x2), 46 (x2) and 148.

SIR ROBERT CLERK OF PENICUIK
The late Sir John Clerk of Penicuik, Bt gave permission to reproduce drawings by John Clerk of Eldin in the previous editions of this book. In 2021 Sir Robert Clerk of Penicuik, Bt generously reaffirmed permission for this edition. The drawings are reproduced on pages 84, 91, 93, 94, 97, 100, 118, 134 (x2) and 134–35.

NOWELL DONOVAN
for the photograph on page 147.

LORNE GILL/NATURESCOT
for photographs on pages 23, 83 and 102 (x2).

JOHN HEPNER
for the portrait of James Lind by Sir George Chalmers on page 62.

HISTORIC ENGLAND ARCHIVE
for the painting on page 128.

MRS ALMA HOWARTH-LOOMES
for the photograph on page 130 from The Howarth-Loomes Collection at National Museums Scotland.

INTELLIGENT GROWTH SOLUTIONS & JAMES HUTTON LTD
for the photograph on page 47.

THE JAMES HUTTON INSTITUTE
for artwork from which the illustrations on pages 8, 9, 12, 13, 14, 16, 17, 25, 35, 40, 41, 43, 52, 64, 77, 90, 105, 127 and 144 (x2) were based and the photograph on page 138.

JIM LEWIS
for the illustration on page 86.

IAN MACDONALD
for the photograph on page 145.

PATRICIA & ANGUS MACDONALD/
AEROGRAPHICA

for the photograph on page 80.

DONALD B. McINTYRE

for the photographs on pages 18, 85, 87 (x2), 91, 93 and 117.

McINTYRE FAMILY

for the photographs on pages 10 and 11.

ALAN McKIRDY

for the photographs on pages 59, 60 (x2), 65, 67, 85, 99, 119, 125, 129 and front cover.

GRAEME McKIRDY

for the photograph on page 32.

MOIRA McKIRDY

for the photograph on page 145.

STUART MONRO

for the photograph on page 96.

NATIONAL GALLERIES SCOTLAND

for Sir Henry Raeburn's portrait of James Hutton on pages 2–3 and 132 and detail from William Brassey Hole's Processional Freize on page 17.

NATIONAL LIBRARIES SCOTLAND

for the map on page 41.

NATIONAL MUSEUMS SCOTLAND

for the illustration on page 63 and photographs on pages 1, 63 and 132.

NATIONAL RECORDS SCOTLAND

for the registry entry on page 125.

NATURESCOT

for the illustrations on page 96 (x6).

ROBERT NELMES

for the illustrations on pages 82 and 136.

ROYAL SOCIETY OF EDINBURGH

for the photograph on page 15.

LYNNE REILLY

for the photographs on pages 30 (x2) and 146.

HEATHER ROSS, URBAN DESIGN
& DISPLAY LTD

for the illustration on page 98.

SCOTTISH CANALS/ PETER SANDGROUND

for the photograph on page 55.

SHUTTERSTOCK

for Norfolk countryside [ID:710251006]
by BBA Photography on pages 36–37;
for the Needles [ID:1152220433]
by Liz Miller on page 38;
for horseman [ID:1061865308]
by Tony Marturano on page 38;
for Picardy [ID:790497916]
by vvoe on page 39;
for five-arched bridge [ID: 475141399]
by douglasmack on page 49;
for sea cliffs [ID:1393668578]
by Alan Morris on page 51;
for canal lock gates [ID:1392173342]
by Dave Thom on page 53;
for Arthurs Seat [ID:1100070254]
by Harald Lueder on pages 58–59;
for monsoon image on page 73 [ID: 1796890474]
by Mukesh Kumar Jwala;
for cross-bedded channel sandstones
[ID:1388880800] by Studio Karel on page 79;
for the Royal Society of Edinburgh building
[ID:229785322] by clivewa on page 139.

US GEOLOGICAL SURVEY

for José F. Virgil's illustration on page 137.

WIKIMEDIA COMMONS

for St Salvator's Chapel on page 19
Andy Hawkins, CC BY-SA 2.0
<https://creativecommons.org/licenses/
by-sa/2.0>, via Wikimedia Commons.

for Playfair's Monument on page 28
dun_deagh, CC BY-SA 2.0 <https://creativecommons.org/licenses/by-sa/2.0>, via Wikimedia Commons.
for Benjamin Franklin on page 48
After Joseph-Siffred Duplessis, Public domain, via Wikimedia Commons.
for Aristotle on page 72
After Lysippos, Public domain, via Wikimedia Commons.

WELLCOME COLLECTION

for the illustration on page 66.

Thanks also to STEPHEN KEARNEY and GERHARD OTT for photographs as credited.

Index

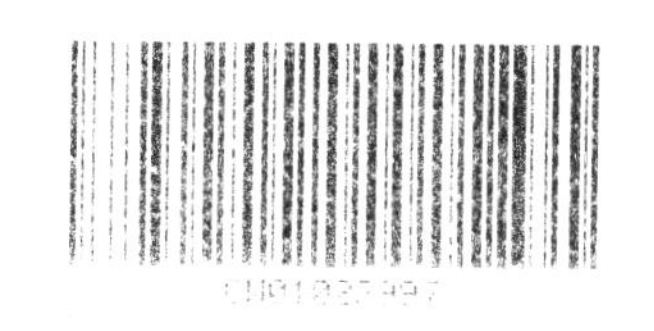

OCR GCSE History A Schools History Project

Germany, 1919–45

RICK ROGERS

Heinemann is an imprint of Pearson Education Limited, a company incorporated in England and Wales, having its registered office at Edinburgh Gate, Harlow, Essex, CM20 2JE. Registered company number: 872828

www.heinemann.co.uk

Heinemann is a registered trademark of Pearson Education Limited

Text © Pearson Education Limited 2009

First published 2009

13 12 11 10 09
10 9 8 7 6 5 4 3 2 1

British Library Cataloguing in Publication Data
A catalogue record for this book is available from the British Library

ISBN 978 0 43550144 0

Edited by Kim Vernon
Proofread by Julie Jackson
Designed by Pearson Education Limited
Typeset by Wearset Ltd, Boldon, Tyne and Wear
Produced by Wearset Ltd, Boldon, Tyne and Wear
Original illustrations © Pearson Education Limited 2009
Illustrated by Wearset Ltd, Boldon, Tyne and Wear and Tek-Art, Crawley Down, West Sussex
Cover design by Pearson Education Limited
Picture research by Q2AMedia
Cover photo/illustration © Getty Images/Gary Cralle
Printed in Spain by Graficas Estella

Acknowledgements
The author and publisher would like to thank the following individuals and organisations for permission to reproduce copyright material:

Page 3 Source C La Belle Epoch website. **Page 13 Source E** H.J. Gordon *Hitler and the Beer Hall Putsch*. 1972 Princeton University Press. **Page 21 Source B** Jonathan Wright *Gustav Stresemann: Weimar's Greatest Statesman* 2002. By permission of Oxford University Press. **Page 24 Source A** A. Turnbull Scott Fitzgerald *My Lost City* 2001 Grove Press New Directions Publishing Company. **Page 25 Source F** K. Von Ankum (ed) *Women in the Metropolis: Gender and Modernity in Weimar Culture*, 1997, University of California Press. **Page 25 Source C** K. von Ankum (ed) *Women in the Metropolis: Gender and Modernity in Weimar Culture* 1997 University of Carolina Press. **Page 26 Source A** A. McElligott *The German Urban Experience 1900-45: Modernity and Crisis*, 2001 Routledge. **Page 26 Source B** History Learning Site website. **Page 42 Source A** Reproduced by kind permission of the publisher from The Young Hitler I Knew by A. Kubizek published in English by Greenhill Books, London 2006. **Page 59 Source C** From *The Nazis: a Warning from History*, by Laurence Rees, published by BBC Books. Reprinted by permission of the Random House Group Ltd. **Page 63 Source C** F. Hillenbrand *Underground Humour in Nazi Germany* 1995 Routledge. **Page 66 Source A** Michael Russell Publishers. **Page 66 Source D** D. Guerin. *The Brown Plague: Travels in Late Weimar & Early Nazi Germany*, Copyright, 1994, Duke University Press. All rights reserved. Used by permission of the publisher. **Page 67 Source E** F. Hillenbrand *Underground Humour in Nazi Germany* 1995 Routledge. **Page 77 Source B** R. Bytwerk *Bending Spines* 2004 Michigan State University Press. **Page 80 Source A** H. Bergmeier and R. Lotz *Hitler's Airwaves* 1997 Yale University Press. **Page 82 B** F. Hillenbrand *Underground Humour in Nazi Germany* 1995 Routledge. **Page 89 Source D** D. Guerin. The Brown Plague: Travels in Late Weimar & Early Nazi Germany, Copyright, 1994, Duke University Press. All rights reserved. Used by permission of the publisher. **Page 90 Source A** H. Sunker and H. Otto (Eds.) Education and Fascism 1997 Routledge. **Page 91 Source C** I. Scholl *The White Rose*, 1970, Wesleyan University Press. **Page 93 Source D** H. Sunker and H. Otto (eds) Education *and Fascism*, 1997 Routledge. **Page 105 Source C** R. Baden Powell *Scouting for Boys* (1908) 2005. By permission of Oxford University Press. **Page 105 Source D** German Propaganda Archive http://www.calvin.edu/academic/cas/gpa/pt36frau.htm. **Page 124 Source B** from The Venlo Incident by Captain S. Payne Best, published by Hutchinson. Reprinted by permission of the Random House Group Ltd.

The author and publisher would like to thank the following individuals and organisations for permission to reproduce photographs:

Page 2 Bettmann/Corbis. Page 3 Corbis. Page 5 Henry Guttmann/Stringer/Hulton Archive/Getty Images. Page 7 Classic Image/Alamy. Page 10 German Photographer (20th Century)/Private Collection/Peter Newark Pictures/The Bridgeman Art Library. Page 12 Bundesarchiv, Bild183-J0908-0600-005. Page 16B Private Collection/Archives Charmet/The Bridgeman Art Library. Page 16T Bettmann/Corbis. Page 17 Interfoto Pressebildagentur/Alamy. Page 19 Hulton Archive/Getty Images. Page 20 Interfoto Pressebildagentur/Alamy. Page 24 Michael Ochs Archives/Stringer/Getty Images. Page 25 Musee National d'Art Moderne, Centre Pompidou, Paris, France/Lauros/Giraudon/The Bridgeman Art Library. Page 27 Universum Film (UFA)/Ronald Grant Archive. Page 28 Hulton-Deutsch Collection/Corbis. Page 31T Régis Bossu/Sygma/Corbis. Page 31B David Bathgate/Corbis. Page 32T Bundesarchiv, Bild102-01915A. Page 32B Hulton Archive/Getty Images. Page 36 Snap/Rex Features. Page 37BL Interfoto Pressebildagentur/Alamy. Page 37T Getty Images. Page 37BR Hulton-Deutsch Collection/Corbis. Page 39L Light/Alan Spencer/Alamy. Page 39R Hulton-Deutsch Collection/Corbis. Page 40 Mary Evans Picture Library. Page 42 akg-images. Page 44T Mary Evans Picture Library. Page 44B Interfoto Pressebildagentur/Alamy. Page 45B Bettmann/Corbis. Page 45T Austrian Archives/Corbis. Page 47 Imagno/Contributor/Hulton Archive/Getty Images. Page 51 New York Times Co/Hulton Archive/Getty Images. Page 52 Corbis. Page 53 Austrian Archives/Corbis. Page 54 Private Collection/Peter Newark Military Pictures/The Bridgeman Art Library. Page 55T Private Collection/Peter Newark Pictures/The Bridgeman Art Library. Page 55B Imagno/Hulton Archive/Getty Images. Page 63 bpk/Bayerische Staatsbibliothek/Heinrich Hoffmann. Page 66 The Print Collector/Alamy. Page 67 Hulton-Deutsch Collection/Corbis. Page 68 Hulton-Deutsch Collection/Corbis. Page 71 Mary Evans Picture Library/Alamy. Page 73 Sidney 'George' Strube/Daily Express on 3rd July 1934/British Cartoon archive. Page 75T Popperfoto/Getty Images. Page 75B Associated Press. Page 76 Hulton-Deutsch Collection/Corbis. Page 80 Corbis. Page 83 German School (20th century)/Private Collection/The Bridgeman Art Library. Page 84 Hulton-Deutsch Collection/Corbis. Page 86 New York Times Co./Contributor/ Hulton Archive/Getty Images. Page 88 Keystone/Stringer/Hulton Archive/Getty Images. Page 89 Max Rossi/Reuters. Page 91 Mary Evans Picture Library. Page 92 akg-images. Page 95B Deutsches Historisches Museum, Berlin. Page 95T Bettmann/Corbis. Page 97 Mary Evans Picture Library. Page 100 FPG/Hulton Archive/Getty Images. Page 101T Bettmann/Corbis. Page 101B Popperfoto/Contributor/Getty Images. Page 102 Topfoto. Page 105 FPG/Hulton Archive/Getty Images. Page 107 akg-images/ullstein bild. Page 109B Bundesarchiv, Bild183-2005-0530-500. Page 109T Deutsches Historisches Museum, Berlin, Germany/© DHM/The Bridgeman Art Library. Page 110 bpk Berlin. Page 113 bpk Berlin. Page 116 Corbis. Page 117 Bettmann/Corbis. Page 119T Dpa/Corbis. Page 119B © National Archives and Records Administration. Page 120 The Jacob Rader Marcus Center of the American Jewish Archives. Page 121 The U.S. National Archives and Records Administration. Page 123 Arnd Wiegmann/Reuters. Page 125T Bettmann/Corbis. Page 125B Ira Nowinski/Corbis.

Websites
There are links to relevant websites in this book. In order to ensure that the links are up to date, that the links work, and that the sites are not inadvertently linked to sites that could be considered offensive, we have made the links available on the Heinemann website at www.heinemann.co.uk/hotlinks. When you access the site, the express code is 1440P

For Petra

Contents

Get ready for your Study in Depth: Germany, 1919–45

How this book can help

This book is designed to prepare you in two ways for your Depth Study of Germany 1919–45:

1 It provides you with all the important information which you will need in order to answer the questions you will face in the exam.
2 It explains the different types of questions you have to answer *and* gives you tips and practice to help you improve your performance so that you can reach the highest levels.

Understanding the mark scheme

When you try to answer the questions in this book – and in your exam – it is useful to know how your teachers and examiners will mark your answers. There is a mark scheme for each question – the marks are divided into bands or levels, with each level representing a level of skill or understanding. The more marks available for the question, the more levels there will usually be. Some of the questions you will answer in this OCR History exam have six levels. The examiner marking your answer has to decide which level it fits – the higher levels will be given to those answers which answer the question set *and* display the specific skills needed for that question. So if the question is a Why? Question, which asks you to explain something (i.e. give reasons why), it's no good just describing what happened and leaving it up to the examiner to pick out the bits that are relevant! In such a case, they will have to award a low level – no matter how plentiful and accurate the facts – as the answer would *not* be doing what the question has asked.

Essential exam skills: the hierarchy of response

Questions and answers can take various forms and varying degrees of difficulty. In the exam, recognising what a question requires can often help you to give the correct form of answer. This will obviously lead to higher marks and a better grade.

The hierarchy of response is a way of trying to understand what kind of questions make up an exam paper. Like all generalisations, it will not fit exactly, but if you can successfully produce answers for each category, you will be prepared for the demands of the examination paper.

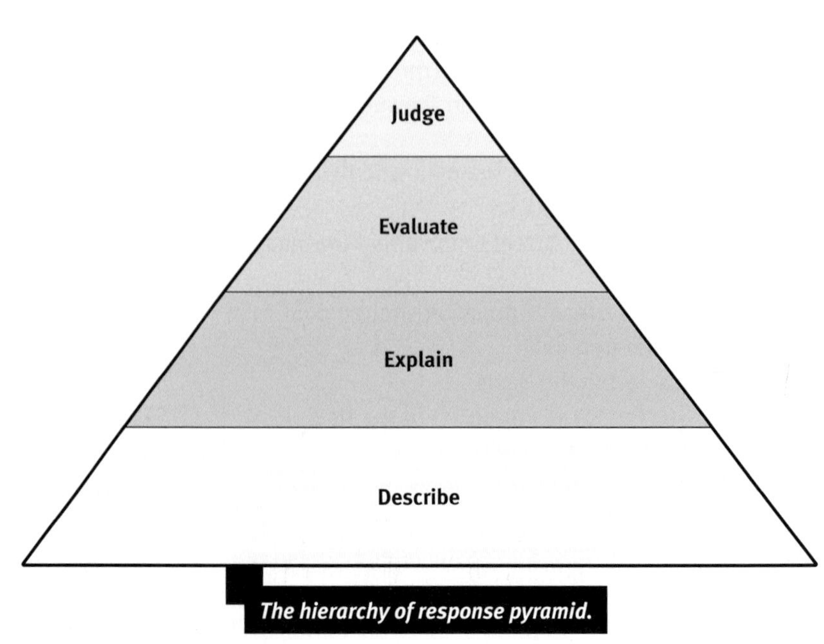

The hierarchy of response pyramid.

Non-source questions – Describe

'Describe' questions might begin with 'briefly describe...' or 'what' or 'how'. When answering describe questions, you may need to identify different aspects of a situation or describe the course of an event.

Non-source questions – Explain

This involves a more developed response and answers 'why' questions. Responses will contain words and phrases like 'because', 'this means that' or 'this shows us that'. Remember that the explanation has to relate very closely to the question.

Source questions – Evaluate

Some questions will be based on sources. Some of these will ask you to explain the meaning of sources e.g. 'What impression does this source give of...?', 'What is the message of this source?' With these questions, it is important to go beyond the surface details of the sources and to make inferences from them. Using your knowledge and understanding of the topic will help you to do this.

Some questions will ask you to evaluate sources. These will ask about the usefulness of sources or about their reliability. For usefulness questions you should concentrate on working out what you can learn from sources and on what sources do not tell you. To test the reliability of sources you should use your knowledge to test what the source is saying or to consider who has written or drawn the source and whether they have a purpose in what they have written or drawn.

Non-source questions – Judge

Sometimes part (c) questions of the structured essays require you to reach and support a judgement. They come in a variety of forms, for example: 'Was X the most important reason...?', 'Which was the more important reason X or Y?', 'To what extent was X...?', 'X was successful – how far do you agree?' or 'X and Y were very similar. How far do you agree?'

In most (but not all) questions the important thing for you to do is to explain the strengths or arguments of one side (factor) and then explain the strengths or arguments for the other side. For full marks you need to either explain why the arguments on one side are stronger than those on the other side, OR explain how for example, the two factors they have been asked to compare in terms of importance were equally important. This must be based on argument not simply a statement.

Describing

Explaining

Evaluating

Judging

GradeStudio

Helping you to write better answers

Throughout each chapter, you will find Grade Studio activities, which include practice questions to help you develop the skills necessary to answer the six different types of questions in the exam. Each Grade Studio activity is accompanied by Examiner's tips. In the Grade Studio at the end of each chapter, you will find an exam-style question. This explains the mark schemes the examiners have to apply to each type of question, and then gives you a typical sample answer with Examiner comments that include precise tips and advice on how the candidate could have pushed their answer into the top levels. You will then have the chance to produce your own – better! – answer.

Chapter 1

Was the Weimar Republic doomed from the start?

This chapter deals with the Weimar Republic, a democratic Germany that lasted from 1919 to 1933. It was a period of political instability and great social and economic problems. It led to the rise of the Nazis, and many historians have claimed that, from the beginning, it was inevitably going to fail. During the years before 1924, the Republic survived several crises before enjoying a period of stability. After 1929, a world economic crisis caused more problems than could be solved and the Republic proved too weak to survive.

Before the First World War...

Germany under the rule of the Emperor, Kaiser Wilhelm II, was the success story of Europe. A relatively new country – it was only founded in 1870 – it represented all that was modern and progressive in Europe of the time. Germany had its industrial revolution later than other countries such as Britain, and so its factories were more modern. By 1913, Germany had overtaken Britain in industrial production and contributed 17 per cent of world output. Scientists and engineers like Albert Einstein, Gottlieb Daimler, Robert Koch and Sigmund Freud, philosophers such as Freidrich Nietzsche and Karl Marx, and musicians like Wagner and Mahler, put German culture on a world footing (see Sources C and D). The events of the summer of 1914 would alter all this and sweep in a radical new order at the end of what was known at the time as the 'Great War'.

SOURCE A

People looked to the Kaiser (Emperor) for guidance. He was the supreme authority in Germany.

SOURCE B

The Socialist question could have at one time been solved by using the police; now it will be necessary to use the army.

Otto Von Bismarck, leader of the German government, speaking in the early 1890s.

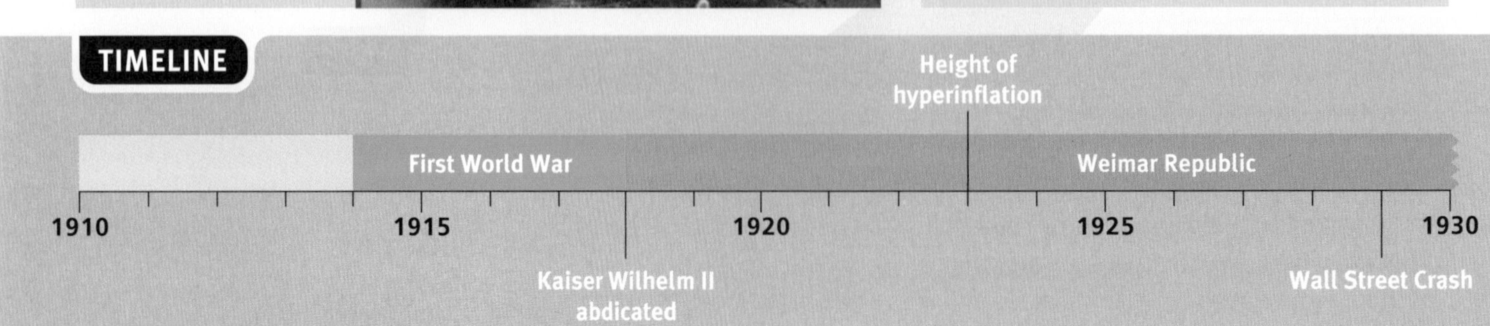

After the First World War…

Germany in the 1920s was a much darker place. Economic difficulties were normal and shortage of food had become commonplace. The old rulers had fled the country to be replaced by a new democratic government that faced revolution from both left and right and seemed to have the support of only a few Germans (see Sources B and F). Millions of ex-servicemen who had fought in the First World War felt betrayed by the leaders who had negotiated the surrender of Germany in 1918 and had signed the hated 'Treaty of Versailles'.

SOURCE E

Socialist Friedrich Ebert was the first elected President of the Weimar Republic.

SOURCE C

The years between 1871 and 1914 represent one of the most fascinating periods in the European history. As far as we know, there was nearly no other period during which so many artists and scientists were contemporaries. Arts and sciences developed with an incomparable speed and intensity.

From the website La Belle Epoque.

SOURCE F

Long live the republic! Whose cornerstone is Democracy – the Democracy that leads to Socialism!

From *Memoirs of a Social Democrat* by Philipp Scheidemann, published in 1929.

SOURCE D

Wondrous and eloquent are the statistical revelations of Germany's bounding growth in population, of Imperial Berlin's rise to metropolitan splendour, of the empire's colossal foreign trade, of the amazing expansion of national wealth… of triumphs countless in the realms of science, art and industry, which combine to make the German name synonymous with progress and power.

F.W. Wile, an English writer, from a book about Germany published in 1913.

ACTIVITIES

1. Briefly describe the situation in Germany immediately before the First World War.
2. Briefly describe the situation in Germany after the First World War.
3. Study Sources A and E. How did the government change? Use the sources and your own knowledge to explain your answer.
4. Study Sources B and F. How did the power of socialists change? Use the sources and your own knowledge to explain your answer.
5. Study Sources C and D. What was positive about Germany in the pre-war period? Use the sources and your own knowledge to explain your answer.
6. Study Source D again. What is ironic about this source? Would the author have said the same things in 1919? How might his book have changed?

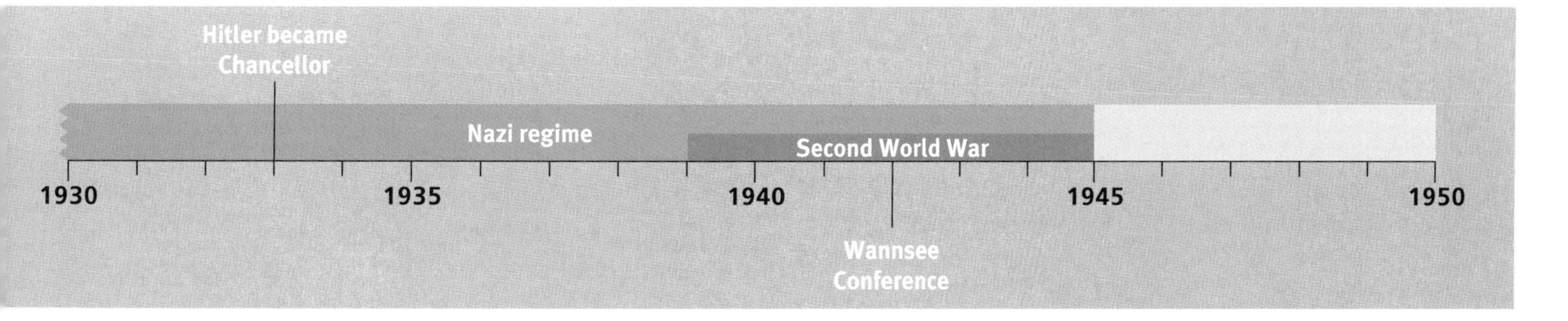

1.1 Background: Why did Germany become involved in the First World War?

LEARNING OBJECTIVES

In this lesson you will:

- learn about Germany's motives for entering the First World War
- practise extracting material from sources in order to answer exam-style questions.

KEY WORDS

Empire – *group of territories ruled by another country.*

Nationalists – *people who support their country, often to excess.*

Decisions for war

Leaders of countries will nearly always say that in declaring war they had no choice – that events had created a situation that meant they had to fight a war. Others would argue that leaders always have a choice and that they make the choice for war because it suits them at the time. With the First World War, we need to consider how far the leaders were forced into the war, or whether they had a choice. If they had a choice, why did they choose war and what did they think would happen?

Causes of the First World War

Traditionally, historians point to several factors coming together like a roomful of gunpowder barrels set off by a trigger cause, and starting the First World War. These are some of the factors:

- Militarism – the major powers of Europe were building up their armed forces. Britain and France pointed to Germany's military tradition and accused it of provoking a war.
- Imperialism – the European powers each wanted to have a large **empire**. Britain had the largest empire, with France a close second. When Germany started to look for an empire, the best parts of Asia and Africa were already controlled by Britain and France.
- Nationalism – a wave of **nationalist** pride had swept across Europe. Men and women were eager to show that their country was the best. The French in particular were looking for revenge after being defeated by Germany in 1871 (see Source B).

SOURCE A

The European empires in Africa at the beginning of the First World War. Nearly all the land was taken after 1870.

- Defeating socialism – many governments were afraid that socialists would soon take over their countries. Some leaders believed that, in a war, people would be loyal to the governments and that socialists would lose support.
- The naval race – Britain started to build modern dreadnought battleships in 1906. Wilhelm II was a keen sailor and wanted a large navy, so Germany started building dreadnoughts in 1908. In response, Britain built even more. By 1914, Britain had 29 dreadnoughts, Germany 17.

SOURCE 

It depends entirely upon the attitude of the German victor to determine whether this war [Franco-Prussian War of 1870] has been useful or dangerous. If they take Alsace-Lorraine, then France with Russia will arm against Germany. It is not necessary to point out the disastrous consequences.

From a letter by Karl Marx to the Communist Committee in Braunschweig in 1871.

SOURCE C

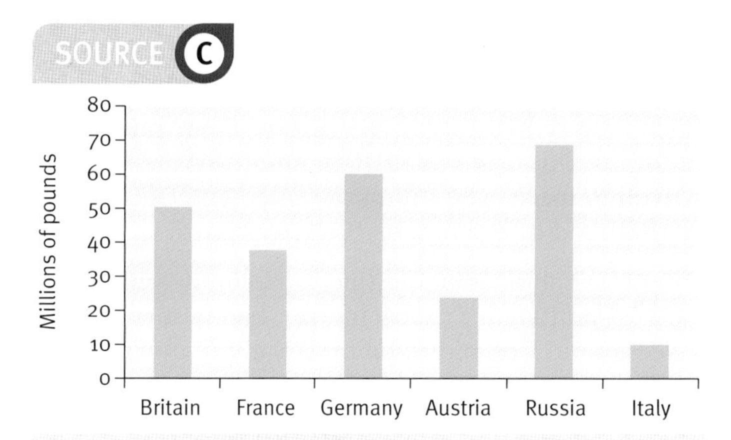

Military spending of the great powers, 1913–14.

The trigger for war was the assassination of the heir to the Austrian throne, Archduke Franz Ferdinand. This caused Austria to start a war with Serbia, which led to Russia declaring war on Austria, Germany declaring war on Russia, and France and Britain declaring war on Germany.

It is important that you try to understand the German point of view. Germany believed that it had a right to behave as Britain and France had with regard to their empires, and that Britain and France had provoked a war in order to defend their position. In addition to this, the Germans believed that the war would be over quickly and that a rapid French surrender would soon be followed by a negotiated peace with Britain and Russia.

ACTIVITIES

1. Explain why the First World War started in 1914.
2. Study Source A. Which countries were most actively building up their empires between 1870 and 1914? Use the source and your own knowledge to explain your answer.
3. Study Source B. How far could this have contributed to the start of the First World War? Use the source and your own knowledge to explain your answer.
4. Study Source C. Of the two alliance blocks (Austria and Germany, or Britain, France and Russia), which spent the most on their armed forces? Is this important? Use the source and your own knowledge to explain your answer.
5. Study Sources C and D. To what extent do these sources support the view that Germany was a militaristic state? Use the sources and your own knowledge to explain your answer.

SOURCE D

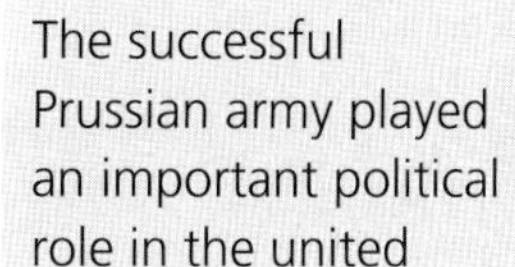

The successful Prussian army played an important political role in the united Germany.

Fact file

Socialism was a political idea that societies should be more equal. Governments, elected by everybody, had a duty to care for the weak and the sick and to provide work or benefits for all. In the Reichstag (German parliament), the Socialists (SPD) were the largest party after the First World War.

1.2 Background: Why did Germany lose the First World War?

LEARNING OBJECTIVES

In this lesson you will:

- learn why Germany lost the First World War
- get practice in writing answers that describe, explain, evaluate, judge.

GETTING STARTED

Write down three words that sum up the First World War.

Germany had hoped that the war that started in 1914 would be a short one. It attacked France but was stopped just before it reached Paris. Great trench systems were dug and attacks from both sides made very small gains at the cost of thousands of lives. As the war dragged on, Germany faced many problems:

- War on two fronts – it was fighting Britain and France on the Western Front and Russia on the Eastern Front.
- Naval blockade – Britain's bigger navy was able to sail battleships close to Germany to stop supplies getting through (see Source A). This meant that Germans had to deal with shortages of food and goods.
- Economic strength – Britain was a far richer country than Germany.
- Manpower – Germany and its allies had fewer people than their enemies.

The two main turning points in the First World War came in 1917. Firstly, the United States entered the war on the side of Britain and France – the **Allies** – and secondly the Russians, now with a communist government, surrendered.

The Germans saw that they had the possibility of a quick victory before the tide turned. They launched an Spring Offensive of 1918, before the Americans arrived in force. The offensive failed and Germany surrendered in November 1918 (see Source C).

The Kaiser abdicated and fled to Holland, and the socialist politician Friedrich Ebert had to form a government. The blockade on Germany meant that millions faced starvation and the soldiers returning from the war made the situation worse. Germans had once been proud of their strong and wealthy nation and were now left bitter and angry.

SOURCE A

At the beginning of the war, England started the war of starvation against Germany and Austria-Hungary. In 1915, England declared her intention of seizing all neutral ships entering or leaving Germany. All goods intended for Germany or exported from there, or owned by Germans would be then seized by the Royal Navy.

German General Ludendorff, writing in his memoirs published in 1933.

KEY WORDS

Allies – *countries that fight together against a common enemy.*

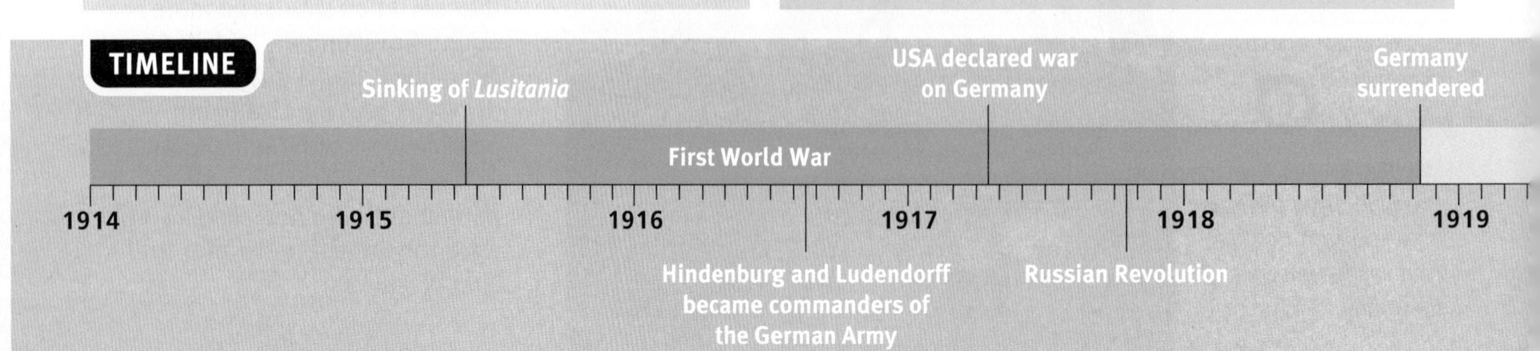

SOURCE B

The German Army still stands firm and successfully wards off attacks. But the situation becomes daily more critical and may force the supreme command to take very important decisions. It is desirable in the circumstances to break off the battle in order to spare the German people and its allies useless sacrifices. Every day wasted costs thousands of brave soldiers their lives.

Field Marshal Paul von Hindenburg, in conversation with Prince Max of Baden in October 1918.

Fact file

Paul von Hindenburg was the Commander-in-Chief of the German Army during the later years of the First World War and virtually ran the country on behalf of the Kaiser. When the Social Democrat president, Friedrich Ebert, died in 1925, Hindenburg became the President of the Weimar Republic. Though he did not belong to a political party, he was very traditional and believed firmly in the traditions of nationalism. He remained president until his death in 1934.

SOURCE C

The sinking of the passenger ship, the *Lusitania*, upset the Americans and played a part in bringing them into the First World War.

ACTIVITIES

1. Briefly describe the course of the First World War.
2. Explain why the Russian Revolution in October 1917 was a turning point in the First World War.
3. Was economic strength the most important reason that the Germans lost the First World War?
4. 'The Germans lost the war, the moment that the Spring Offensive of 1918 ground to a halt.' How far do you agree with this statement?
5. Study Sources A and B. How similar are these sources? Use the sources and your own knowledge to explain your answer.
6. Study Source C. How useful is this source in explaining why Germany lost the First World War? Use the source and your own knowledge to explain your answer.

GradeStudio

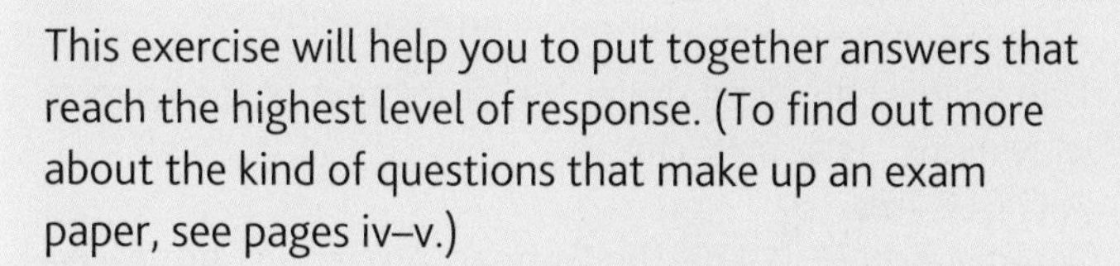

This exercise will help you to put together answers that reach the highest level of response. (To find out more about the kind of questions that make up an exam paper, see pages iv–v.)

If we take the question, 'Why did Germany get involved in the First World War?', we can write an answer using the points below. Decide which one is description, which is explanation, and so on. When putting together your answer, try to make sure that the writing flows.

It felt that it needed a big army because it felt threatened. The alliance between France, Britain and Russia had it surrounded.	This threat was a factor to an extent but others must be considered. The ambition of certain German politicians was also an important reason.
This was important because Germany felt it needed to fight to reduce the threat of invasion from two sides. It also saw that the other states had large empires and Germany did not want to be left behind.	Germany was a very big country in 1914 with a large army.

Now, answer the question, 'Why did Germany lose the First World War?' in the same way.

1.3 What did the Treaty of Versailles mean for Germany?

LEARNING OBJECTIVES

In this lesson you will:

- learn about the Treaty of Versailles
- practise extracting evidence from sources in order to answer exam-style questions.

KEY WORDS

League of Nations – *international organisation of countries devised to aid cooperation and to prevent war.*
National self-determination – *the right of people of the same nationality to live in their own country.*
Reparations – *money paid by Germany to France and Britain to compensate them for their losses from the First World War.*
Treaty – *agreement between nations.*

The First World War was ended by a **treaty** that, it was hoped, would sort out all the problems caused by the war. The meeting to decide the contents of the treaty took place in Paris in early 1919. The Germans were allowed to attend the meeting but only to observe, not to take part.

The aims of the winners

The victorious powers – Britain, France and the USA – wanted different things from the treaty. The aims of each of the 'big three' are outlined below.

The French wanted to keep Germany weak and to make it pay for the damage caused by the war.

The British also wanted to punish Germany but not as harshly as the French. They wanted to reduce the size of the German navy and for Germany to lose its overseas empire.

The US president Woodrow Wilson believed that a harsh treaty might lead to further conflict. He came up with 'fourteen points' that he hoped would create a fair peace. These included the right for people to decide which country they wanted to be ruled by and the setting up of an international organisation called the League of Nations which in the future would resolve arguments between countries without them needing to go to war.

VOICE YOUR OPINION!

Was Germany really to blame for the First World War? Why might people think so?

On 7 March 1919, the Allies announced the points of the treaty (see Source A). The Germans had hoped that the peace treaty would not be too harsh (see Source B).

SOURCE A

Clauses of the Treaty of Versailles
ARTICLE 22
German colonies shall be ruled by the **League of Nations**.
ARTICLE 43
In the area around the Rhine, the maintenance and assembly of armed forces is forbidden.
ARTICLE 45
As compensation, Germany gives to France the coal-mines situated in the Saarland.
ARTICLE 49
Germany renounces in favour of the League of Nations, in the capacity of trustee, the government of the Saarland. After fifteen years, the inhabitants will vote for which country they want to belong to.
ARTICLE 102
Danzig will be placed under the protection of the League of Nations, as a 'free' city.
ARTICLE 160
After March 31, 1920, the German Army must not exceed 100,000 men, including officers.
ARTICLE 181
The German naval forces must not exceed: 6 battleships, 6 light cruisers, 12 destroyers, 12 torpedo boats. No submarines.
ARTICLE 231
Germany accepts the responsibility for causing the war imposed by the aggression of Germany.
ARTICLE 232
Germany will make compensation for all damage done.

Some of the most important clauses from the Treaty of Versailles (1919).

SOURCE B

Newspaper cartoon from 1919 showing Germany taking her 'medicine'.

BRAIN BOOST

How can we remember the clauses of the Treaty of Versailles? Using a mnemonic can help. The five main areas that affected Germany were based around taking the **b**lame, losing German **l**and, reducing its **a**rmy, paying **reparations** and losing its **e**mpire 'b-l-a-r-e'.

SOURCE C

The historian, with every justification, will come to the conclusion that we were very stupid men.

Harold Nicolson, one of the British group of diplomats who negotiated the Treaty of Versailles.

ACTIVITIES

1. Briefly describe the purpose of the Treaty of Versailles.
2. Explain why the United States did not want a harsh peace treaty.
3. Study Source A. How would articles 43, 45, 160 and 181 make France safe from attack? Use the source and your own knowledge to explain your answer.
4. Study Source B. Do you think the creator of this cartoon supported the Allies or the Germans? Use the source and your own knowledge to explain your answer.
5. Study Source B and Source C. What do you think Harold Nicholson meant? Use the sources and your own knowledge to explain your answer.

SOURCE D

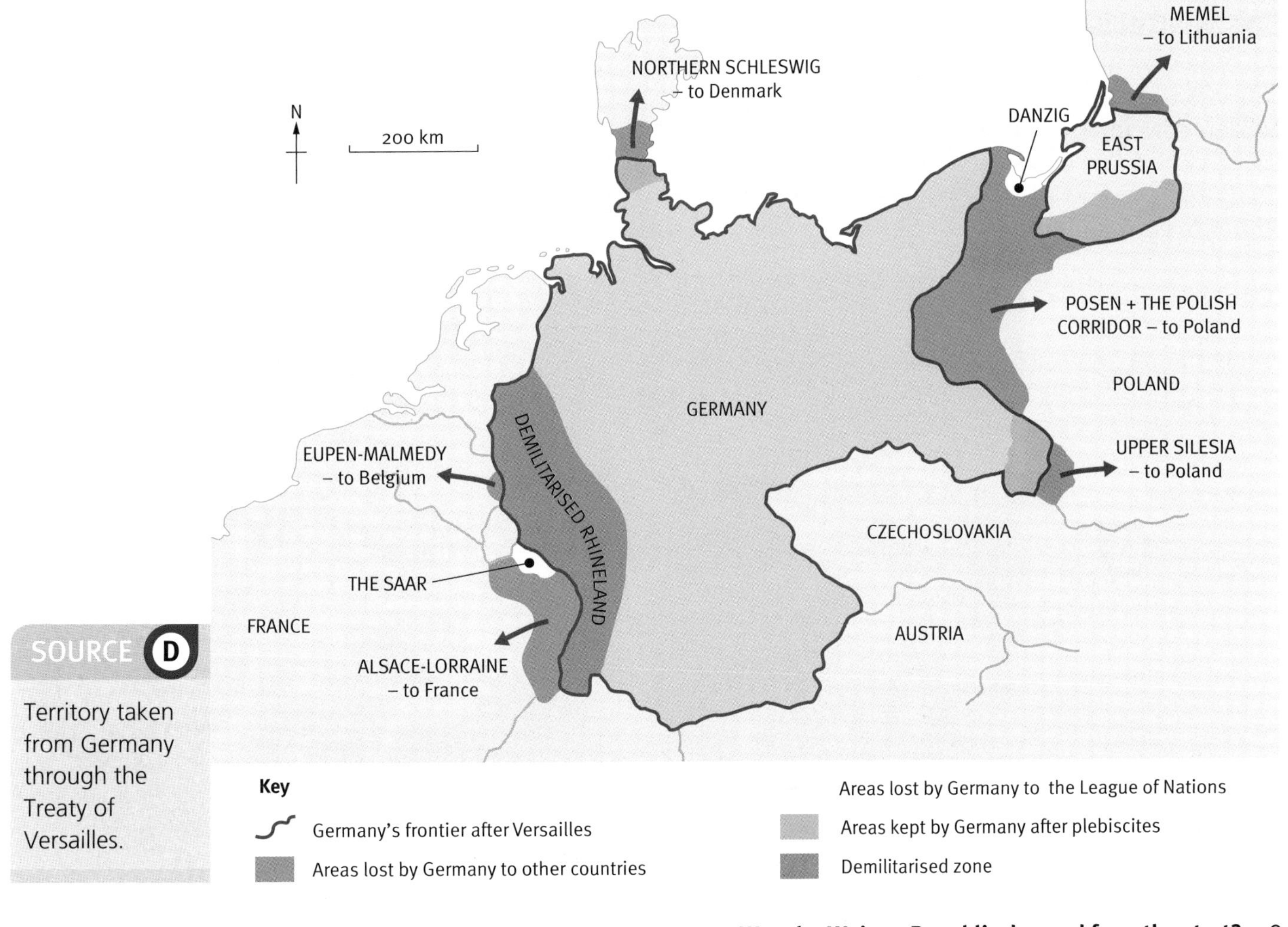

Territory taken from Germany through the Treaty of Versailles.

1.4 Why was the first German democracy declared in a small town near Berlin?

LEARNING OBJECTIVES

In this lesson you will:

- learn about the instability in Germany after the First World War
- practise answering a question that requires description.

KEY WORDS

Communists – *supporters of a system of politics where everybody owns things collectively and gets an equal share.*

Freikorps – *groups of ex-soldiers who remained armed.*

Manifesto – *document produced by a political party showing its policies.*

Power vacuum – *situation without any clear group in control.*

Reich – *German word for empire.*

Reichstag – *German parliament.*

Spartacists – *communist revolutionary group.*

On 9 November 1918, Kaiser Wilhelm II, Emperor of Germany, abdicated. He realised that he could no longer rule Germany having lost the First World War. This left a **power vacuum**, which meant that no one had effective control of the country. The socialists led by Friedrich Ebert formed a temporary government, but other groups had ideas about the future of Germany.

The Spartacists

The **Spartacists** were a group of **communists** who believed that Germany should be run along the same lines as communist Russia, with decisions being taken by councils of workers and not by politicians. They planned to seize power in Berlin and organise a communist system throughout Germany.

The Freikorps

The **Freikorps** were ex-servicemen who remained armed and tried to influence politics. They wanted a nationalist government and many would have preferred a return to the rule of Kaiser. Politicians had limited control over the Freikorps and they came to symbolise the instability of Germany in the years following the First World War.

SOURCE A

Freikorps units like these were a fairly common sight in post-war Germany. They were able to arm themselves with rifles and sometimes even armoured cars!

The Spartacist uprising

In January 1919, the Spartacists saw their chance and started a revolution by seizing important government buildings. They published a **manifesto** to show that they had seized power (see Source B). Lacking soldiers, Ebert asked the Freikorps to help to defeat the revolution.

Following brutal fighting on the streets of Berlin, the Spartacist uprising was defeated by the Freikorps. Germany was saved from a communist revolution, though the situation was far from stable. Ebert took the temporary government away from the danger in Berlin to the small town of Weimar. There, they wrote the constitution of the new Germany, which would become known as the Weimar Republic (see Source C).

SOURCE B

The revolution has made its entry into Germany. The masses of the soldiers, who for four years were driven to the slaughterhouse for the sake of capitalist profits, the masses workers, who for four years were exploited, crushed, starved, have revolted... Workers' and Soldiers' Councils have been formed everywhere.

From the Spartacus Manifesto.

SOURCE C

Article 1: The Germany **Reich** is a Republic. Political authority comes from the people.
Article 22: The delegates [of the **Reichstag**] are elected by men and women over 20 years of age.
Article 50: All decrees of the Reich President must be countersigned by the Reich Chancellor.
Article 123: All Germans have the right to assemble peacefully.

From the Weimar Constitution.

HISTORY DETECTIVE

Where did communism come from? Who thought of it? How popular was it before 1914?

Fact file

Rosa Luxemburg and Karl Liebknecht were journalists and outspoken supporters of Communism. They had both been imprisoned during the First World War as potential enemies of the state. They were seen as the leaders of the Spartacus movement and played a major role in organising the uprising. On the 15th January, they were arrested by members of the Freikorps, but were murdered before ever reaching a legitimate police station.

ACTIVITIES

1. Explain why you think the Kaiser abdicated.
2. Are you surprised that the politicians chose to have their meeting about the constitution away from Berlin? Explain your answer.
3. Study Source A. How useful is this in explaining why the Spartacist uprising failed? Use the source and your own knowledge to explain your answer.
4. Study Source B. Are you surprised by this source? Use the source and your own knowledge to explain your answer.
5. Study Source C, Article 123. How does this help the enemies of the Weimar Republic? Why does it have to be in their constitution?

GradeStudio

In questions that ask you to describe something on the exam paper (6(a) and 7(a) questions), you are often asked to describe a process or situation (see 'The hierarchy of response' on pages iv–v). In the mark scheme, you will be given one mark per point to a maximum of 5 or even 2 or 3 if the point is well described or explained. The question below is a description question. See if you can make five points in order to gain maximum marks.

Briefly describe how Ebert put a stop to the Spartacist uprising.

Examiner's tip

In the exam, questions 6(a) and 7(a) are marked very simply. Examiners award one mark for every relevant point made. If this point is explained, they can award two or three marks. The maximum mark for this question is 5. (See Grade Studio on pages 32–33 for a fuller explanation.)

1.5 How far did the Kapp and the Munich Putsches threaten the new democracy?

LEARNING OBJECTIVES

In this lesson you will:

- learn about the Kapp and Munich Putsches
- practise cross-referencing material in order to improve the quality of answers to source-based questions.

KEY WORDS

Hyperinflation – *out-of-control inflation, causing a country's currency to become worthless in a short period of time.*

Nazis – *slang term for Hitler's political party, the NSDAP.*

Putsch – *revolution.*

The Social Democrats had defeated the first major threat in January 1919 and were able to declare the new republic. The Weimar constitution was officially published in August 1919 and held the promise of a more stable Germany.

SOURCE A

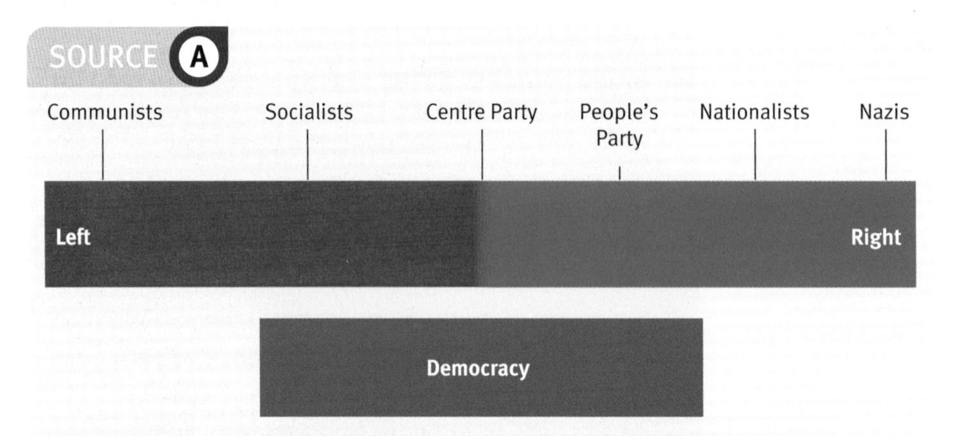

Political parties in Germany.

The 'stab in the back'

In November 1919, the government set up a commission to investigate why the First World War had been lost. One of the key witnesses was the former commander-in-chief Paul von Hindenburg. At the end of his statement, he claimed that the army had been 'stabbed in the back', implying that the new government under Ebert was to blame.

SOURCE B

Strike, stop working, strangle this military dictatorship, fight… for the preservation of the republic, forget all dissension! There is only one way to block the return of Wilhelm II. General strike all along the line! Workers unite!

Government appeal for a general strike to fight against the Kapp Putsch, Berlin March 1920.

SOURCE C

The general strike brought Berlin to a standstill in March 1920.

SOURCE D

I can guarantee that if there is a vote in the Reichstag, the German People's Party will be voting in favour of a general amnesty for those involved in the Putsch.

Gustav Stresemann, leader of the German People's Party, in a letter to vice Chancellor Dr Heinze, August 1920.

SOURCE E

Suddenly a Hitler man who stood left of me fired a pistol and killed Sergeant Hollweg. Before I could give an order, my people opened fire. At the same time the Hitler people opened fire and for twenty or thirty seconds a regular fire fight developed.

Lieutenant Von Godin, whose police company met the Munich Putsch march.

The Kapp Putsch

In March 1920, the Allies insisted that two brigades of Freikorps be disbanded. While the government tried, the brigades themselves refused. One of them, the Ehrhardt brigade led by General Freiherr von Luttwitz, marched on Berlin to be met by the Freikorps leader, Wolfgang Kapp. The Freikorps soldiers took control of government buildings and the government was forced to flee to Dresden. Kapp announced a new 'national' government and raised the flag of the old Second Empire (1870–1918). He hoped that people would welcome a return to the values of the Germany that had existed before the First World War.

Ebert called on the army to put down this revolution, but the army did nothing. 'Troops do not fire on troops,' they said. Ebert tried a different approach and called on all the workers of Berlin to go on strike (see Sources B and C). This was effective immediately. After four days, Kapp and Luttwitz fled from Berlin and the **putsch** collapsed. The government returned to Berlin but did not punish harshly those involved in the putsch (Source D).

The Munich Putsch

The year 1923 was a difficult one for the young Weimar democracy. The money that Germany had to pay to France as reparations for the First World War was crippling the economy. This led to **hyperinflation**, which caused enormous problems for a lot of people. Adolf Hitler saw a chance to try to grab power for his party and organised a putsch to take place on 8 November 1923. It began with the capture of the Bavarian Prime Minister, Gustav Kahr, and then led to a march into Munich. When the police refused to join the **Nazis**, there was some gunfire and the putsch collapsed (see Source E). (To find out more about the Munich Putsch, see Chapter 2, pages 38–39.)

ACTIVITIES

1. Briefly describe the ways in which the role of the Freikorps was similar to the attempted revolutions we have looked at?
2. Explain why the Weimar Republic was under threat in the years 1919 to 1923.
3. Why might Hindenburg like the idea of the 'stab in the back'? Why might the German people like it? Explain your answer.
4. Look at Sources B, C and E. Which Putsch had the better chance of success? Use the sources and your own knowledge to explain your answer.
5. Study Source D. Why might Stresemann not be keen to punish those involved in the Kapp Putsch? Use the source and your own knowledge to explain your answer.
6. Study Sources B and C. How far does Source C support the material in Source B? Use the sources and your own knowledge to explain your answer.

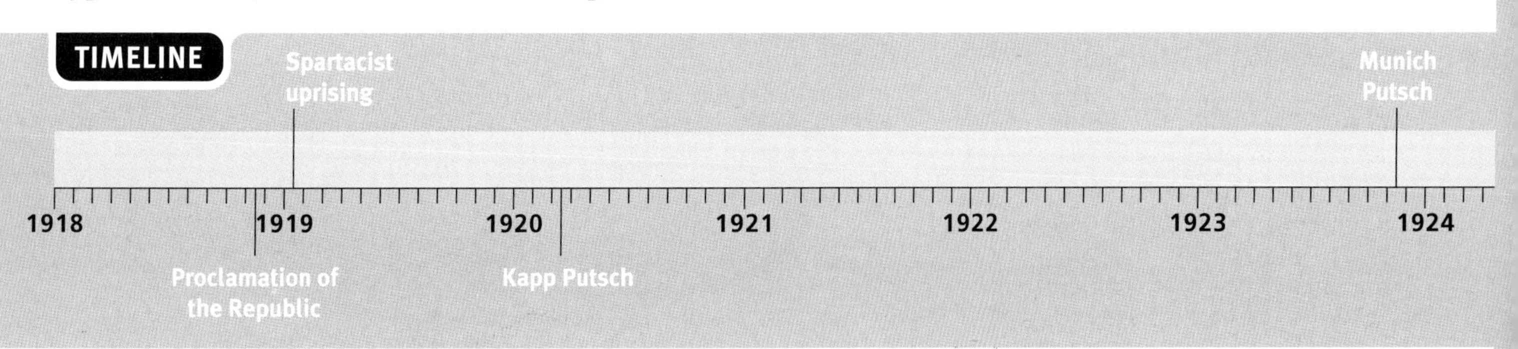

1.6 How did the loss of the First World War affect the German economy?

LEARNING OBJECTIVES

In this lesson you will:

- learn about the economic problems facing Germany in the four years after the First World War
- practise extracting material from sources in order to answer exam-style questions.

Before the First World War, Germany had been the most economically powerful country in Europe and had used its industrial might to fight through four long years of war. The Treaty of Versailles left Germany much weaker. It was faced with a bill for compensation that it would struggle to pay.

The new Germany

As a result of the Treaty of Versailles, Germany lost land, some of which was very important for its economy. Alsace-Lorraine was a wealthy area and would have helped to make money for the new Germany. Very important industrial areas such as the Saarland and Upper Silesia were lost, along with their vast coal reserves. Key industries in Eupen and Malmedy were given to Belgium and the industry and resources of West Prussia went to Poland. In total, Germany had lost 13 per cent of its land and six million people.

The problem facing the major European powers after the First World War was how to pay back some of the vast amounts of money that they had borrowed during the war and thereby reduce the national debt back to manageable proportions. Britain and France faced difficulties and had years of economic problems as a result of the war. For Germany, the situation was made much worse due to the £6,600 million that it was expected to pay in reparations (see Source B).

Confidence and investment

Economies prosper in stable conditions. Countries make money when people are willing to invest in business and those businesses make profit. Parts of these profits go back to investors, who may then invest even more and the economy will make money. This is an upturn. Sometimes when people lack confidence, they don't invest as much and so profits get lower. Returns on investment get lower and investors will then invest less and the economy will make less money. This is a downturn.

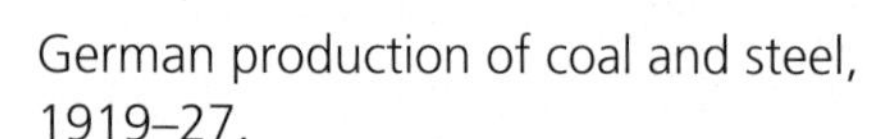

German production of coal and steel, 1919–27.

In the table below, 100 stands for production in 1913; the figures for coal and steel production are a percentage of 1913 production.

Year	Coal	Steel
1919	61	40
1921	72	58
1923	33	36
1925	70	70
1927	81	93

BRAIN BOOST THE INFLATION CYCLE

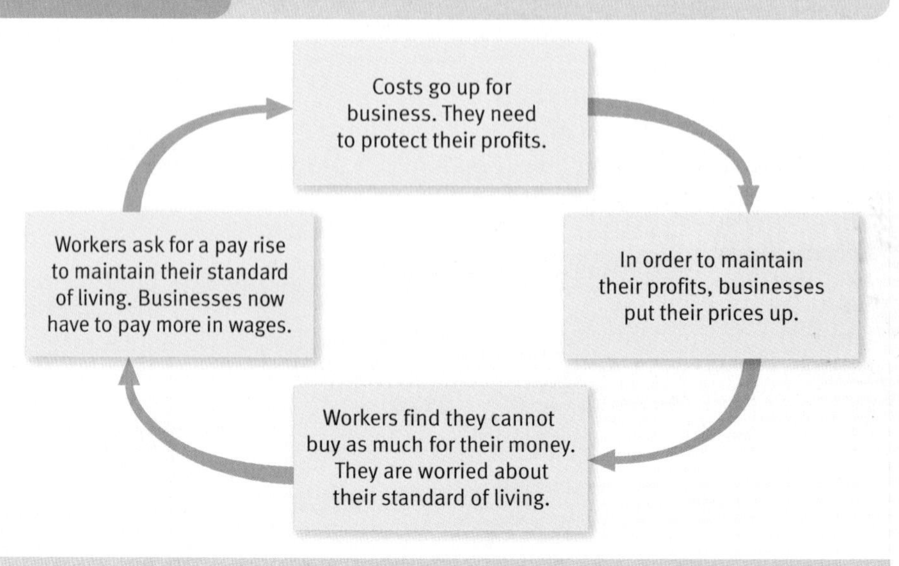

As we have already seen, the early years of Weimar Germany were extremely unstable. This meant that people were worried about investing in business, so profits were down. This also meant that the German government received less in taxes. Thus they faced the problem of how to pay their debts, create confidence among the business community and pay reparations with a tax income that was inadequate even for just one of these tasks.

Loans and payments

The Reparations Commission published its report in April 1921 that set Germany's reparations payments for £100 million each year plus payments equivalent to the value of a quarter of Germany's exports. A proportion of this was to be made every month. Germany had no choice to accept these terms, though few in Germany believed that it was possible to keep up such payments. Indeed, to make the first payments, Germany had to borrow £50 million which she then tried to repay in November 1921.

By the beginning of 1922, it was clear that Germany could not make the reparations payments and it was granted a moratorium (break from making the payments) for January and February. The new French president, Poincaré, took a very anti-German position so that when Germany asked for another moratorium in the summer, the French refused. The economic situation in Germany got worse and was not helped when France threatened to take over the Ruhr coalfields (see Source C). By the end of the year, a financial and political crisis was about to erupt.

SOURCE B

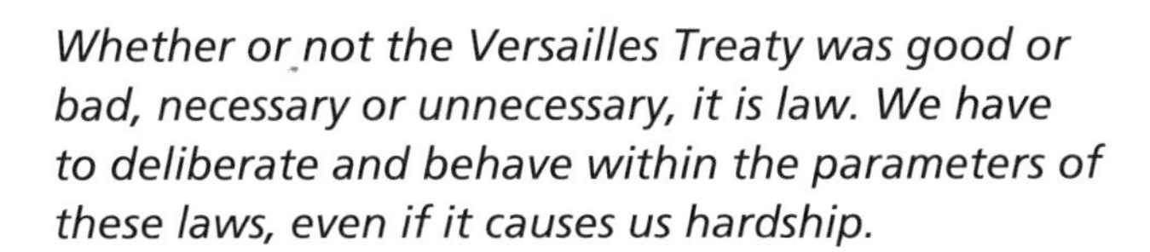

Whether or not the Versailles Treaty was good or bad, necessary or unnecessary, it is law. We have to deliberate and behave within the parameters of these laws, even if it causes us hardship.

Wilhelm Solf, German diplomat writing in 1929.

SOURCE C

That is the German tragedy!

The enemy steals, robs and plunders and will not protect the property and goods of men, women, children and babies; nor will he attend to the sick and the old. On every field and street he commits murder.

Part of a speech delivered at Kulmbach in 1923 by Father Kern. The enemy he refers to is the French.

ACTIVITIES

1. Briefly describe the ways that governments can raise money.
2. Explain why Germany found it difficult to recover economically from the First World War.
3. Why might the French feel that a strict policy towards Germany was justified?
4. Low industrial production, large national debt or reparations: which was the biggest problem facing Germany in 1922? Explain your answer.
5. Study Source A. What effect did the First World War have on industrial production? Use the source and your own knowledge to explain your answer.
6. Study Sources B and C. How useful are these sources in explaining the attitudes of ordinary Germans to the Treaty of Versailles? Use the sources and your own knowledge to explain your answer.
7. Complete the Venn diagram by placing each of the problems in the list in the correct sector of the diagram.

Problems

- **a** The threat of Nationalist revolution
- **b** The threat of Communist revolution
- **c** Reparations
- **d** Weak German economy
- **e** Large German national debt
- **f** The attitude of France

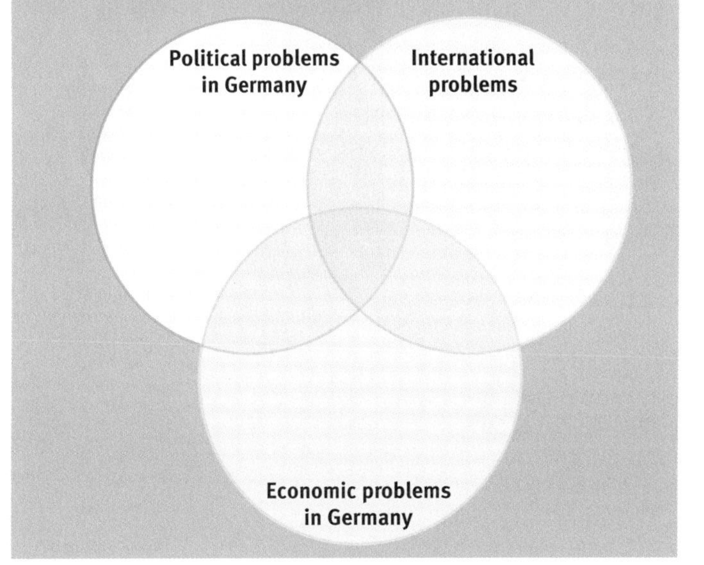

1.7 Who won and who lost in the hyperinflation of 1923?

LEARNING OBJECTIVES

In this lesson you will:

- learn about hyperinflation
- learn how to answer a source-based question.

KEY WORDS

Mark – *German currency.*

GETTING STARTED

Look at Source A. What is happening in the picture?

In February 1923, France occupied the industrial area of the Ruhr in order to use it to pay the compensation owed to them. This led to a crisis of confidence in the German economy and its currency and meant that prices began to rise. By the autumn, inflation was so bad that prices were rising dramatically on a daily basis.

SOURCE B

It was far more efficient for people to use money for cooking or heating rather than buying coal which was very expensive.

Papiergeld! Papiergeld!

„Brot! Brot!“

Letzte Zuflucht

SOURCE A

'Paper Money! Paper Money!'

At the height of the hyperinflation, life for ordinary Germans was difficult to understand. Ordinary day-to-day items were costing billions of **marks** and the government could not print new money quickly enough. This meant that people making normal shopping trips needed a large suitcase or a wheelbarrow to carry enough money to buy their daily essentials. People in restaurants were advised to pay for their meal before they ate it because if they took too long, the price could go up in the time that it took to complete the meal. People actually started to burn money rather than to buy coal to burn (see Source B).

The winners and losers from hyperinflation

Anybody who was in debt could have cleared it during hyperinflation. People who had bought houses with mortgages, businesses that had taken out loans to expand, investors who had borrowed money in order to invest, could easily clear their total debt. People with foreign currency could exchange it for a fortune in marks and buy things they could only have dreamed of. Rich businessmen were able to buy up smaller businesses and increase their market share. Perhaps the biggest winner was the government, which was able to reduce the national debt from 150,000 million marks to less than one.

People who had savings saw them wiped out (see Source D). People with bank accounts or cash savings believing they were safe from the ups and downs of the economy became poor overnight. Those who were living on a fixed income like pensions, could no longer use money to buy what they needed but were forced to swap items. Often, people exchanged their valuable family heirlooms for only a fraction of their value in food. Small businesses that could not keep going through the crisis either went bankrupt or were bought up cheaply by bigger businesses.

ACTIVITIES

1. Briefly describe the reasons for hyperinflation.
2. Explain why certain people might have done well out of hyperinflation?
3. Which do you think is the most important reason for hyperinflation? Explain your answer.
4. Look at Source D. What did Stresemann feel was one of the main results of hyperinflation? What does this suggest about the stability of Weimar during the so-called 'Golden Age'? Use the source and your own knowledge to explain your answer.

Fact file

This is how hyperinflation affected the price of a loaf of bread in Germany following the First World War:

- In 1918, a loaf of bread cost 0.63 marks.
- By January 1921 it had risen to 10 marks.
- Just over a year later in February 1922, a loaf of bread cost 250 marks.
- By September 1923, it cost 1.5 million marks.
- At the height of hyperinflation, in November 1923, a loaf of bread cost 200,000 million marks.

SOURCE C

A picture of a very high denomination bank note.

SOURCE D

The intellectual and productive middle class which was traditionally the backbone of the country, has been paid for the utter sacrifice of itself to the state during the war by being deprived of its property and being made working class.

Gustav Stresemann, speaking in 1927.

VOICE YOUR OPINION!

Are we right to be concerned with inflation? Would it be better if prices went down? Is there an answer to the problem?

1.8 Why did the French invade the Ruhr in February 1923?

LEARNING OBJECTIVES

In this lesson you will:

- learn about the French invasion of the Ruhr
- practise answering source-based questions.

KEY WORDS

Moratorium – *delaying something with everybody's agreement.*

Separatist – *someone who wants their local area to become independent.*

Under the conditions of the Treaty of Versailles, Germany had agreed, reluctantly, to pay compensation to France and Britain for the damage caused by the First World War. A committee called the Reparations Commission set the figure at £6,600 million, payable by annual instalments of £100 million. In 1921, Germany just managed to make the payments but it was clear to most that the country could not sustain the repayment schedule in the face of widespread economic problems.

The moratorium of 1922

In January 1922, it was clear that Germany would be unable to make the payments. The Reparations Commission granted them a **moratorium** which meant that they could delay making the payments. The reaction of the two countries who were owed the money was different. Britain was willing to accept the delay as they wanted Germany to recover so that they could benefit from trade with Germany. France, on the other hand, was less happy. Their new Prime Minister, Raymond Poincaré was unhappy with the agreement and insisted that Germany should make the payments at the time specified. When Germany asked for a further moratorium in August 1922, Poincaré insisted that the Commission refuse. They did and the tension between France and Germany grew.

The invasion of the Ruhr

In January 1922, the Commission declared that Germany had failed to deliver shipments of timber to France that were part of the compensation package. This was the excuse that France needed and soon French troops were pouring over the border. They had targeted the richest industrial area of western Germany named after the river Ruhr, which ran through it. The French said that their purpose was to put pressure on the German government so that it would pay or failing that, the French would take the industrial output of the area as payment in kind (see Source A).

SOURCE A

If anyone will read the complete report of the speech that was made by M. Poincaré at Dunkirk, they will find the opening sentences of that speech contained no reference whatever to Reparations. He pointed out that just as England would take every step within her power to protect her frontiers were they threatened by sea, so the French are bound to take every step that opportunity offers them to see that their frontiers are protected by land. It is certainly not surprising that they take that view.

From a speech made in the House of Lords, Westminster, 20 April 1923.

The German response

When the French army entered the Ruhr, there was little practical action that the German government could take to oppose it. The army which had been limited to 100,000 soldiers could not hope to take on the French and the large groups of Freikorps which had populated Germany after the war had been disbanded. The German government called for passive resistance to the occupiers (see Source B), which most Germans gladly took part in. This meant that workers in key areas went on strike and their wages were covered by the German government. To counter this, the French brought in their own workers for some of the key industries, which in turn caused violent clashes between German strikers and French troops. Some German nationalists went so far as to commit acts of sabotage to prevent the French from removing goods and raw materials from Germany.

The results of the French invasion

Initially, the arrival of French troops helped to unify German feeling (see Source C) but after a few months cracks began to appear. Politicians in some areas, notably Bavaria, the Rhineland and the Palatinate started to work against the government in Berlin and planned to remove their states from Germany and become independent. Both the Rhineland and the Palatinate declared independence and functioned as independent republics for a short time. The French supported these **separatists** and tried to undermine the German government. For the most part though, most Germans wanted to remain part of Germany and resented the French occupation.

SOURCE 

Germany will follow a programme of 'moral resistance' which will be completely passive and non-aggressive against any future French aggression in order to bring round world opinion.

Wilhelm Cuno, German Chancellor, 1922–23.

SOURCE C

French troops and German civilians during the French occupation of the Ruhr in 1923.

BRAIN BOOST

There were four key results of the French occupation of the Ruhr, from which you can make an appropriate mnemonic – MUSH.

M – Munich Putsch
U – Unity of the German people
S – Separatists
H – Hyperinflation

VOICE YOUR OPINION!

Plan a debate. Half the class argue for the French, half for the Germans explaining the reasons behind their attitudes towards the invasion.

ACTIVITIES

1. Briefly describe the events that led to the French occupation of the Ruhr.
2. Explain why Germany did not actively resist the French invasion.
3. Study Source A. Would the speaker agree with the French view that the invasion of the Ruhr was entirely to do with financial matters? Use the source and your own knowledge to explain your answer.
4. Study Source B. How useful is the source in understanding the attitude of the Germans to the French invasion? Use the source and your own knowledge to explain your answer.
5. Study Source C. Why would German newspapers publish pictures of this kind? Use the source and your own knowledge to explain your answer.

1.9 How far was Stresemann the hero of Weimar?

LEARNING OBJECTIVES

In this lesson you will:

- learn about Gustav Stresemann
- practise answering questions that require explanation.

KEY WORDS

Coalition government – *government formed by more than one party.*

Fact file

Gustav Stresemann was a German politician and leader of the German People's Party. He was appointed Chancellor (the German equivalent of Prime Minister) in 1923 during the hyperinflation crisis. Despite solving the problem of hyperinflation, he was replaced as Chancellor and given the role of Foreign Minister, a post he held until his death in 1929.

In August 1923, President Ebert appointed Gustav Stresemann as Chancellor. Stresemann was the leader of the small German People's Party and so had to rely on the powerful members of other parties to fill the important roles in the government. This is called **coalition government**. Such were the problems facing Germany that most politicians were willing to forget their differences and work together. Stresemann had to take some difficult decisions.

Solving hyperinflation

Stresemann called off the strike in the Ruhr and removed some state governments that he knew would cause problems. In October, with the help of a new bank and a new Commissioner for Currency, Hjalmar Schacht, Stresemann issued a temporary currency called the Rentenmark. By doing this, he was able to knock all the noughts off prices and re-set them at sensible levels. Also, the German government very carefully started to control the amount of money being printed. Stresemann cut back government spending and the number of government workers was reduced – those that stayed in work had their wages cut. Despite calls for more money to be printed, Schacht refused and by the beginning of 1924, confidence in the German economy was on the way to being restored and the economic crisis, at least in its extreme form, was over.

The last problem, which was not going to go away, was reparations. Foreign soldiers were still in the Ruhr and France was insisting that payments should begin again as soon as the hyperinflation crisis was over. Fortunately for Stresemann, the USA was willing to help and in January 1924, a committee led by US General Charles Dawes met with the aim of solving Germany's economic problems (see Source A). Both Britain and France agreed to the Dawes Plan.

SOURCE 

The Dawes Commission consisted of a number of experienced men whose aim was the restoration of economic peace for the benefit of the whole of the civilised world. It is also to convince the Germans that it is worth making the effort to repay the money owed under the Treaty of Versailles to bring about this peace.

Professor Max Sering, from his book, *Germany under the Dawes Plan*, written in 1928.

Fact file

The Dawes Plan was a scheme to rescue the German economy. It was devised in 1924 by a team led by Charles Dawes, a US banker and politician. It provided US loans to help the German economy, also enabling it to continue paying reparations to the French and British.

Stresemann becomes Foreign Minister

Once the crisis was over, parties in the Reichstag who had supported Stresemann began to distance themselves from him. Those on the far Right, thought him too liberal and those on the left, thought him too right wing. He was replaced by Wilhelm Marx as Chancellor, though he carried on as Foreign Minister. He was credited by most Germans as the man who solved the economic crisis and it is true that all the measures in Germany were all starting to work by the time that he was replaced as Chancellor. The only measure that needed to be in place was an agreement with other countries, particularly the United States. As Foreign Minister, it was Stresemann who was responsible for these negotiations.

The 'Golden Age' of Weimar

The stability in Weimar that lasted from 1924 to 1929 was a time when Germany seemed to regain its place in the world. The country was culturally stronger, economically more buoyant and politically more stable. Gustav Stresemann had tackled the problem of hyperinflation and negotiated loans that led to German prosperity. He had brought Germany back into the international community and had signed new treaties with all the major powers of Europe (see Source B). His reputation was kept intact by the fact that he died just three weeks before a stock market crash in the US (see page 46) plunged Weimar Germany into another economic crisis, one that would only be resolved with the rise to power of Adolf Hitler.

SOURCE 

The Stresemann government left a solid record of achievement. A new and stable currency was introduced and the democratic government survived...The foundations were laid for the relative stability of the Republic in the years that followed.

From a biography of Stresemann, published in 2002.

ACTIVITIES

1. Briefly describe how Stresemann ended hyperinflation.
2. Explain why Stresemann was unable to continue as Chancellor for very long.
3. Look at Source A. Explain why other countries were important in stabilising Germany in 1924. Use the source and your own knowledge to explain your answer.
4. Look at Source B. Why is Stresemann remembered as the most successful politician of the Weimar era? Is this a fair judgement? Use the source and your own knowledge to explain your answer.

GradeStudio

Examiner's tip

Making ideas maps is a useful way to summarise material. Below is an example of the four factors that helped solve hyperinflation.

Hyperinflation

- Support from the army strengthens the regime.
- The Rentenmark stabilises the currency.
- An end to the strike gets production going again in the Ruhr.
- The Dawes Plan provides money to help the German economy.

1.10 How high were living standards under the Weimar Republic?

LEARNING OBJECTIVES

In this lesson you will:

- learn about living standards under the Weimar Republic
- extract material from sources to answer questions requiring evaluation and judgement.

KEY WORDS

Standard of living – *the quality of food and goods you are able to buy.*

Welfare – *state support for the very poor.*

It is a generalisation to say that the Weimar Republic experienced years of poverty 1918–23, years of wealth 1924–29 and years of poverty again 1929–32. The evidence supports this general trend, though there will always be exceptions. Poor working-class people would have always been poor even during the middle years, though the extent of their poverty may not have been so bad on the whole. Similarly, wealthy people whose wealth was not based in money or stocks and shares will have lived through the Weimar Republic with few financial problems.

Living standards during the First World War and after

Towards the end of the First World War, food shortages became common, due to the British naval blockade (see page 6), and some people hoped that an end to the war would improve the situation. This was not the case, and a deadly outbreak of Hispanic influenza that killed more people worldwide than had been killed in the war meant a continuation of suffering for the people of Germany. The political instability that followed and the crisis year of 1923 kept many people struggling to get by and nearly everybody feeling nervous about their **standard of living** and the future (see Source A).

SOURCE A

I went onto the docks almost every day. I was irresistibly drawn there; it ruined my shoes...but it was worth it, for there was often something or other to be had. Almost always as I went out with my sack and pickaxe my mother would say 'Don't ever take anyone else's property. Son, don't bring shame on us.'

Ludwig Turek, who grew up in Hamburg during and immediately after the First World War.

How golden was the 'Golden Age'?

German people compared the time 1924–29 with the period immediately before it and decided that it was a great improvement. Historians made a comparison with the period immediately after it and came to a similar conclusion. Certainly the general political stability and the new Dawes Plan did allow the German economy to grow. Wages went up and so did industrial production. Reparations payments were manageable and the amount of goods being exported grew every year up to 1929.

It is, however, too simplistic to see the years between 1924 and 1929 as an economic boom. Although exports were up, so were imports and only in 1926 did Germany export more than it imported. Unemployment was significantly higher in the years 1924–29 than it had been in the years before and though wages were higher overall, this was a reflection of working-class wages going up while, in real terms, wages for middle-class jobs went down. The economy was still not very strong (see Source B).

SOURCE B

Germany is dancing on a volcano. If the short-term credits are called in, a large section of our economy would collapse.

Gustav Stresemann in 1928.

To protect people against the problems of poverty, Germany had a **welfare** state to provide unemployment benefit for those out of work, and shelter and food for those who had nowhere to live. This welfare system came at a price and spending on social matters, which had accounted for 15 per cent of the state income in 1913, had risen to 26 per cent in 1929 (see Source C).

SOURCE C

Many Germans are unhappy with the way that our welfare system is developing. They see an ever increasing proportion of the population going onto welfare and cannot see any indication that people will again become self reliant.

From a speech by the General Secretary of the German League for Free Welfare Organisations in 1927.

GradeStudio

Sometimes sources can be statistical. These need to be handled with care as they can be misleading. Like other sources they need contextual knowledge to make sense of them. See page 30 for an explanation of contextual knowledge. If you examine Source D, you may ask questions like 'Why were women losing their jobs?' or 'Was it only in the government sector that this was happening?' Contextual knowledge that might prove useful in using this sources might be that the government was trying to cut spending in 1923 and 1924 and that in the 1920s it was still easier to sack women than men. Statistics are often limited and for a higher level answer you need to challenge these limitations.

HISTORY DETECTIVE

What items of 'modern technology' might people have had in their homes in the 1920s?

ACTIVITIES

1. Briefly describe the problems that people faced in Germany during the First World War and the period of Weimar up to 1924.
2. Briefly describe the problems that were still there during the period 1924 to 1929.
3. Explain why people might have thought that the period 1924 to 1929 was a 'golden age'. How far do you agree with this view?
4. Study Source A. How useful is this in understanding living conditions in the years immediately after the First World War? Use the source and your own knowledge to explain your answer.
5. Study Source B. What was Stresemann's fear about the German economy? Use the source and your own knowledge to explain your answer.
6. Study Source C. Are you surprised by this view? Use the source and your own knowledge to explain your answer.
7. Study Source D. How do these figures help us to understand the government's attitude to women in the 1920s?

SOURCE D

Female employees	Total	October 1923		Total	April 1924	
		Married	% of the total married		Married	% of the total married
Reich ministries	13,980	689	4.9	8259	153	1.9
Reich post	66,293	2824	4.3	53,084	21	0.04
Reich railways	3057	145	4.7	2353	19	0.7

The reduction in female employees in Reich employment October 1923 to April 1924.

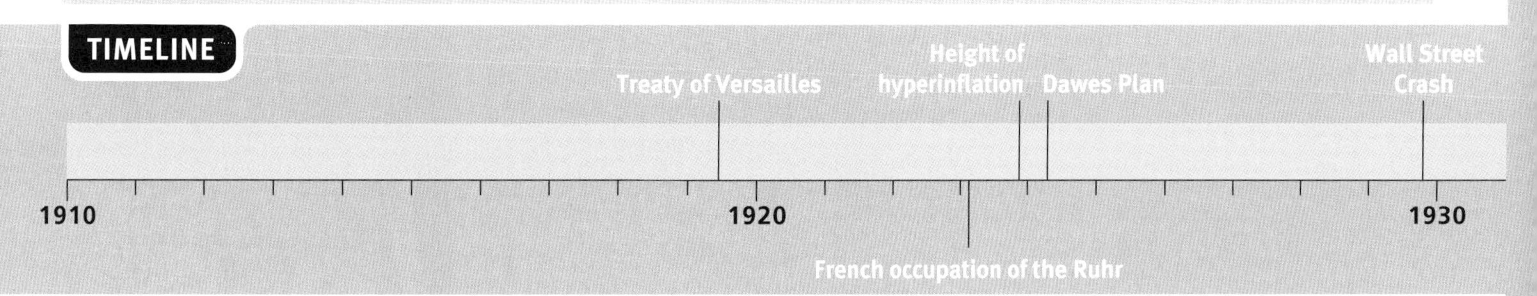

1.11 Case study: How far did art reflect the Zeitgeist of Weimar Germany?

LEARNING OBJECTIVES

In this case study you will:

- learn about the arts in Weimar Germany
- use independent research skills to gain a better understanding of the importance of the arts in 1920s Germany.

In this case study, you should try to work out what the **Zeitgeist** of Weimar Germany was during the middle years. You can use the sources on these pages and your own research to support your work. At the end of the study, you should make a short film, or radio documentary, or computer presentation or a large montage poster to show your findings. You will need to think about:

1. What was the feeling of German people at the start of 1924? What had they lived through in the previous decade?
2. Do the arts reflect people's opinions or influence them?
3. What aspects of Weimar Germany do the arts put emphasis on?
4. Why were the arts particularly important during the 1920s?

The Roaring Twenties

The 1920s was a time of modernity. The US took the lead in creating the first truly modern technological advanced industrial nation and the richer states of Europe were trying to match the Americans. The German experience of the 1920s took a slightly different and darker path but has left us with very vivid images of life in Weimar Germany, and it was this cultural explosion, rather than any economic upturn that gives us the image of the 'golden age' (see Source A).

GETTING STARTED

Study Source D. Write three words to sum up the picture.

KEY WORDS

Zeitgeist – *the spirit of the times; things that symbolise those times to people in future generations.*

SOURCE 

The parties were bigger...the pace was faster, the shows were broader, the buildings were higher, the morals were looser.

American writer, F. Scott Fitzgerald, writing about the 1920s.

The nightclubs of Berlin

By the mid-1920s, Berlin had become the most vibrant city in Europe (see Source C). Its nightclub scene was the most exciting in Europe. The nightclub acts were adventurous for the time and included jazz music, risqué songs, striptease acts and bawdy comedians.

SOURCE 

American jazz dancer, Josephine Baker, made several visits to Berlin to perform in nightclubs, where she was a smash hit.

SOURCE 

The hustle and bustle of the metropolis [Berlin] is simply breathtaking. Just like on the express train, you don't have the leisure to follow a thought through to the end or to finish looking at something since your attention is immediately caught up by something else.

A female traveller writing about Berlin in the 1920s.

SOURCE D

Portrait of Sylvia von Harden by Otto Dix. Having a portrait done in a modern style would often flatter the person being painted.

Art: new objectivity and Bauhaus

German painting of the 1920s found new experimental directions. The 'new objectivity' movement led by George Grosz and Otto Dix believed that art should reflect society, though its style still took something from expressionism and surrealism. Pictures showing the uglier side of society became very popular and even portraits emphasising the uglier aspects of a person were popular (see Source D). Bauhaus was a movement inspired by Walter Gropius, which used bold and unusual shapes, mainly in the design of furniture and buildings.

Music

New directions in classical music were led by German composers like Schoenberg and Webern, who wrote using a harsh sounding ten note scale. Operas of the time began to move away from the German legends that had inspired Wagner and began to reflect modern concerns. The operas produced at the Kroll theatre, for example, looked at modern issues from a left wing point of view. Jazz from America was becoming popular and the new affordable radios were bringing the new music into people's houses.

Literature, film and theatre

The publishing boom in Weimar Germany was led by writers like Thomas Mann ad Arnold Zweig. *All Quiet on the Western Front*, a novel by Erich Maria Remarque, which challenged the idea of the 'stab in the back' sold half a million copies in the first three months after it was published. Fritz Lang directed *Metropolis* one of the most advanced films of the decade and Marlene Dietrich became a world famous film star. In the theatre, the direct and very challenging style of Berthold Brecht became popular and his collaborations with composer Kurt Weil were successful worldwide (see Source E).

SOURCE 

Art is not a mirror held up to reality, but a hammer with which to shape it.

The epic theatre's spectator says: I'd never have thought it – That's not the way – That's extraordinary, hardly believable – It's got to stop – The sufferings of this man appall me, because they are unnecessary – That's great art; nothing obvious in it – I laugh when they weep, I weep when they laugh.

Bertolt Brecht's view of the arts and the 'epic' theatre.

SOURCE 

Cities are no longer forbidden spaces... But in the streets we continue to move strategically, always alert to having to justify our presence. We practice the aim orientated walk... which is to demonstrate we are on our way to a secure location, to a job to a clearly defined aim – and that we are not just loitering around.

A female traveller writing about Berlin in the 1920s.

1.12 Get your sources sorted!

How good was life under the Weimar Republic?

LEARNING OBJECTIVES

In this lesson you will:

- learn about the quality of life under the Weimar regime
- get practice in answering questions that ask you to consider how useful a source is.

KEY WORDS

Utility – *how useful a source is.*

What is a utility question?

Utility questions ask you to explain what you can learn from a source. However, some utility questions ask you to do more than this. They require you to use your knowledge to explain what a source does not tell you about a particular topic. In other words, you have to explain ways in which a source is not useful.

It is important that you recognise which type of utility question you are faced with.

Straightforward utility questions

These are the ones that ask you what you can learn from a source e.g. 'What does this source tell you about the Weimar Republic?', or 'Explain how this source is useful as evidence about the Weimar Republic?' You will have noticed that these questions ask you to explain how a source is useful about a particular topic – in this case the Weimar Republic. Look at Source A. If a question asks you 'Explain what Source A tells you about living conditions in the Weimar Republic?' you can see that it tells us quite a lot – living conditions sound very poor because people were crowded together in filth, they were sick and many children did not have a bed of their own. This is what you need to explain to the examiner – reach a view about living conditions e.g. were they good or bad? Then support your view by using details from the sources.

Slightly more complicated utility questions

Sometimes a question will be more general and will leave it to you to decide what a source tells you about e.g. 'In what ways is this source useful?' or 'Would an historian find this source useful?' You can see with these types of questions that you need to work out what the source is telling you about. However, this is not as easy as it sounds. You need to be a bit more careful with these questions because although Source A might tell us a lot about living conditions in the Weimar Republic, it also tells us something about the person who wrote the source. It tells us that he was angry about living conditions – look at the language he is using. It also suggests something about his purpose in writing the source – he wants to get something done about the

SOURCE 

Every fifth child of the German cities is without a bed of its own; it has to live amid poverty and sickness, immorality, dirt, and coarseness. Thus millions of people exist in conditions of bitter horror, in half lit dungeons, where six to eight or even fourteen or more human beings are crowded together amid rats and filth.

Eugen Diesel, a German writer, writing in 1931.

SOURCE 

Most, though not all, of the unemployed were male. These men were almost certainly family men who could see no way ahead with regards to providing for their families. Money was required for food, heating a home, clothes, etc. With no obvious end to their plight under the Weimar regime, it is not surprising that those who saw no end to their troubles turned to the more extreme political parties in Germany – the Nazi and Communist Parties.

Taken from the History Learning Site website.

SOURCE 

They say the Apaches of Paris...were descended from the youth that went bad during the war of 1871. Considering difficulties of the last war and the state of war that exists even in peacetime, we could get a species of Apaches in Berlin that would make the Paris ones pale by comparison.

***Berliner Tageblatt*, the Berlin daily newspaper in 1923, warning of the dangers of youth crime on the streets. By 1930, estimates put the number of young men in gangs in Berlin at between 10,000 and 16,000.**

terrible conditions. So in answer to the second question you could say that an historian would find the source useful because it tells us that there were people who were angry about conditions in the Weimar Republic and wanted something to be done about it. Details from the source should be used to support these points.

Even more difficult utility questions

Some utility questions are worded rather differently e.g. 'How useful is this source as evidence about why the Weimar Republic was unpopular in 1931.' The word 'how' is the important word here. It is asking you to come to a judgement about how useful the source is. You need to do three things in answering these questions. Firstly, use the evidence in the source to explain how it is useful. Secondly, use your knowledge of the topic to explain other reasons (not mentioned in the source) why the Weimar Republic was unpopular e.g. hatred of Versailles, political instability. Finally, explain to the examiner that the source is useful to some extent but its usefulness is limited because of the reasons for Weimar's unpopularity that it does not tell us.

SOURCE D

Scene from a German nightclub of the 1920s.

SOURCE E

President Ebert as a horse being ridden by the Nazis and the Communists.

ACTIVITIES

1. Look at Source A. What can we learn about the amount of poverty in Weimar Germany from this source?
2. Look at Source B. What we can learn from this source about the lives of young people and those they lived with under the Weimar regime? Use the source and your own knowledge to explain your answer.
3. Look at Source C. In what ways can we use this to explain the rise in street crime during the early 1930s? Use the source and your own knowledge to explain your answer.
4. Study Source D. What can we learn about the quality of life of ordinary Germans from this photograph? Use the source and your own knowledge to explain your answer.
5. Study Source E. How useful is this in showing us attitudes to the Weimar government? Use the source and your own knowledge to explain your answer.

1.13 How significant was Hitler in the history of the Weimar Republic?

LEARNING OBJECTIVES

In this lesson you will:

- learn about Hitler during the Weimar period
- practise answering source-based questions on utility.

Fact file

Adolf Hitler was born in Austria and was leader of Germany from 1933 to 1945. He served in the German army during the First World War, where he was decorated for bravery. After the war, he became the leader of the National Socialist German Workers' Party and was appointed Chancellor in 1933. He is often personally blamed for the start of the Second World War and the mass murder of European Jews.

SOURCE A

A photograph taken of the crowd in Munich following the declaration of war in 1914. The person circled is allegedly Adolf Hitler.

KEY WORDS

Retrojection – *judging historical figures with the use of unreasonable hindsight.*

Significance – *importance.*

The Weimar Republic failed because it led to the rise of Hitler and an evil one-party state. This is often the view put forward by historians. It is because of this that Hitler's fortunes during the years of Weimar are well documented. Even when Hitler became a fringe figure and even when he was completely ignored, he still seems to stand in the wings, waiting for events to bring him into the picture. Looking back, it is of course easy to give Hitler a greater **significance** during Weimar because of what we know came after. This is called **retrojection**.

Hitler as a stereotype

The First World War created a large body of men with a grudge against the Weimar government and, one might argue, the world around them. The idea of nationalism was popular at that time and during the First World War had held the army together and kept it going. Many soldiers took defeat in 1918 personally and were deeply hurt by it. Hitler felt it as keenly as anyone (see Source B). When Hindenburg introduced the notion of the 'stab in the back' (see pages 12–13), this found a very receptive audience in the soldiers who had fought in the war.

Hitler as unique

As an Austrian living in Germany, Hitler was technically a foreigner, though eventually he became a citizen of Germany. He would have had, at least in the early years, a slightly different accent and spoken a different dialect to those around him. He had piercing blue eyes and a personal intensity that some found intimidating and others fatally attractive. His ability as a public speaker was what gave Hitler his edge as a politician and his uncanny instinct for identifying people's concerns about the Weimar Republic, at least, during times of crisis (see Source C).

Hitler and the Golden Age

After the Munich Putsch of November 1923 (see pages 40–41), Hitler was put on trial for treason but so impressive was his public speaking that he was only sentenced to five years. He used his trial to attack the Weimar Republic and it is, perhaps, due to the sympathy that the judges had for his views that he was let off lightly. In the end, he only served nine months in an open prison, where he was free to dictate his book, *Mein Kampf*. It is ironic that it was Hitler's ability to express the broadly felt dissatisfaction with the regime that got him off so lightly. Despite his popularity, the Nazi Party was not popular during the Golden Age of Weimar (see Source D).

SOURCE B

There was a man in their midst who was addressing them without a pause and with growing passion in a strangely guttural voice. I saw a pale, thin face beneath a drooping, unsoldierly strand of hair, with a closely cropped moustache and strikingly large light blue eyes coldly glistening with fanaticism.

Professor K.A. Von Muller, writing in 1919. The man was Adolf Hitler.

SOURCE C

The masses prefer a ruler to a weakling and are filled with a stronger sense of mental security by a party that will not allow opposition than a system that gives them a choice. They only see the ruthless force and brutality of the strong party and will always give in to it in the end.

Adolf Hitler, *Mein Kampf*.

Hitler and the failure of Weimar

The Weimar Republic is ultimately judged on the fact that it allowed a non-democrat to come to power by democratic means and then abolish the very democracy which had given him power. We have seen through this chapter that the democracy was never far from a serious threat and that perhaps sooner or later, it would be destroyed. It was, perhaps, the underlying economic weakness of the Republic that let people like Hitler prosper, rather than any political or social problems.

SOURCE D

In spite of their well prepared and thoroughly organised propaganda...this party is not going anywhere. Today it is a numerically insignificant revolutionary splinter group.

A government report on the Nazis from 1927.

ACTIVITIES

1. Briefly describe the first two phases of Weimar Germany, 1918–24 and 1924–29.
2. Explain why Hitler did better during the first phase (1918–24) than the second (1924–29).
3. To what extent was Hitler an important figure before 1929? Explain your answer.
4. Study Sources A and B. How far do these explain how Hitler was able to become the leader of a political party?
5. Study Source C. How useful is this in understanding why different groups tried to overthrow the Weimar republic by force?
6. Study Source D. How useful is this in explaining attitudes to the Nazis during the Weimar period? Explain your answer.

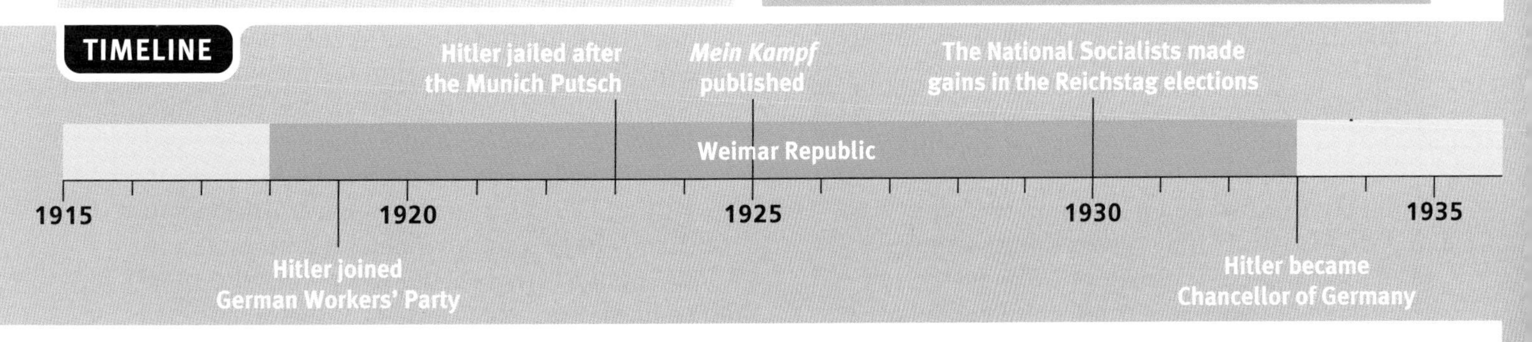

1.14 What did Weimar really achieve?

LEARNING OBJECTIVES

In this lesson you will:

- learn about the achievements of Weimar
- practise extracting material from sources in order to answer questions that require evaluation and judgement.

SOURCE 

The Constitution of the German Republic is the freest constitution in the world. The weakest spot – and it still exists – is that people have not yet made it a thing of life. Everything is learnt in time. A nation without national unity, that has been broken into feeble small states...must first learn how to enjoy freedom and take advantage of its constitutional rights.

Written by Weimar politician Philipp Scheidemann, in his book, *Memoirs of a Social Democrat*, in 1929.

Was Weimar a failure?

If Weimar is judged at the point at which it ceased to exist (arguably March 1933), then it achieved the rise of a regime considered to be the most evil in history. If Weimar is judged 12 years later when a devastated Germany was on the brink of losing the Second World War, the judgement will be even harsher. Critics would say that it was incompetence to let Hitler in and criminal negligence to let him do what he did. This narrow perspective condemns Weimar; a more balanced view comes from a bigger picture.

Weimar from a broader perspective

Unlike many of the other large states of Europe (Britain, France, Russia), Germany has not been a single state for very long. Unified in 1870, it has been a monarchy, a democracy, a dictatorship, a divided state consisting of democracy in one half and a communist dictatorship in the other half, and finally, from 1990, unified into a single democratic state. If we judge Weimar by the standards of today's Germany and consider the circumstances of its birth, it becomes a far more impressive period than if we simply dismiss it as causing the rise of Hitler.

SOURCE 

When discussing the shape of the Federal Germany keep referring to the 'mistakes of Weimar'. No subject about the politics in the free German state, proportional representation, state assemblies can be mentioned without some mention of the 'mistakes of Weimar'.

From an American Diplomatic report written just after the end of the Second World War.

Weimar as a cultural phenomenon

The fact that certain aspects of Weimar culture are still instantly recognisable is testimony to its power and success. The longevity of Bauhaus and the paintings of Dix and Grosz and the continuing popularity of Brecht and Weil reinforce the point. That a modern singer of international acclaim – Ute Lemper – can still build a career singing German songs of the 1920s is further testament to the enduring strength of Weimar culture.

Weimar as a modern state

By looking at the modern German state, it is possible to see how Weimar provided the model for the current government. The structure of government departments and the way that politicians are elected are all based upon the Weimar model and the governments themselves are similar in make up to those of the Weimar Republic. During Weimar, no one party had an overall majority and so the state was governed by consensus, which means that parties had to work together and form coalition governments. This is true of modern day Germany and is part of the reason that Germany has developed into a liberal and tolerant country. The welfare system under Weimar has also provided a model for systems of welfare in Germany and other countries around the world. Weimar's achievement was to pioneer a model democratic state in what were the most difficult of circumstances.

SOURCE C

Bauhaus has influenced architecture and design up to the present day.

Was the Weimar Republic doomed from the start?

In many ways, the failures of the revolutions up to 1923 indicate that perhaps it was not. Also, it is perhaps reasonable to speculate that had the world not gone into depression, Weimar would have continued. In this chapter, we have seen the problems that the Weimar Republic experienced and how it was able to survive. In the next chapter, we will see how it died and perhaps be better placed to answer this key question.

SOURCE D

Angela Merkel, first female Chancellor of Germany, leader of a coalition government, including the Social Democrats.

ACTIVITIES

1. Identify one reason that people might see Weimar as a failure.
2. Study Sources A and B. How far do the two sources agree on the achievements of Weimar? Use the sources and your own knowledge to explain your answer.
3. Study Source C. How useful is this source for understanding the success of Weimar culture? Use the source and your own knowledge to explain your answer.
4. Study Source D. What links a modern leader like Merkel with the Weimar Republic? Use the source and your own knowledge to explain your answer.
5. This chapter mainly put a case for Weimar as a success. Can you construct a more balanced argument? Making a balance sheet, positive and negative, and putting points for and against the idea of a successful Weimar might help you to clarify your thoughts. You could then use this as the basis for an essay on the question.

1.15 Was Weimar doomed from the start?

LEARNING OBJECTIVES

In this lesson you will:

- learn about the problems of Weimar
- be able to explain the two sides of the argument.

The Weimar Republic was certainly born against a background of instability. Having lost the First World War, Germany was in turmoil. That the government had to leave the capital Berlin in order to write a constitution in the small town of Weimar is an indication of these problems. When we consider whether Weimar was doomed from the start, we have to think of the two broad arguments; 'yes it was' and, 'no it was not'.

Philipp Scheidemann was the first Chancellor of the Weimar Republic and a strong supporter of it.

Argument One: It was doomed

These points support the argument that it was doomed:

1. Germany had no tradition of democracy before 1919. Since unification in 1870, Germany had been ruled by a powerful elite led by the Emperor. This government was identified with the success of Germany before 1914, people looked back and longed to return to those years of prosperity.
2. The Treaty of Versailles was universally loathed by German people. The Weimar government was seen as the regime that allowed the Treaty of Versailles to happen. It was representatives of the Weimar government that signed it. It was this connection that made the Weimar government so unpopular.
3. Reparations payments kept Germany dependent on other states. Firstly Britain and France had to agree in the early stages to accept delayed payments. In 1923 when France refused to accept any more delays in payments, they invaded the Ruhr which in turn led to hyperinflation. After 1924, the United States, through the Dawes Plan kept the German economy afloat. When the United States recalled their loans after the Wall Street Crash, Weimar was doomed.
4. Coalition governments could only be maintained by cooperation between parties. Some of these parties had very little in common. When people believed that decisive action was needed, the coalition governments could not agree. This led to the Chancellor and the President ruling by decree, which ended democracy in Weimar Germany.
5. The revolutions from left and right demonstrated how unpopular the regime was. Eventually either left or right was bound to replace the Weimar government.

As leader of the Communist Party, Ernst Thaelmann worked against the Weimar Republic in much the same way as Adolf Hitler and the Nazis.

Argument Two: It was not doomed

These points support the argument that it was not doomed:

6 After recovering some form of economic prosperity in 1924, the Weimar government did well. People voted for mainstream democratic parties and the extremists, the Communists and Nazis, lost a lot of support.

7 It was not inevitable that the Chancellor would be unable to form a working coalition government in 1930. It was only the protest vote in the elections that gave massive influence to the Communists and Nazis and made it difficult. Had the democratic parties continued to dominate the Reichstag, a solution would probably have been found because it had been found before.

8 A democratic state even with a coalition government was the preferred option of most Germans. Though there were many attempted revolutions between 1919 and 1923, they all failed. In 1932, Hindenburg, the existing President of Weimar Germany, beat Hitler in the Presidential election. Even at this late stage, most people voted for the 'Weimar' constitution and against the extremists.

9 The economic situation had reached its lowest point in 1932. The Nazi Party had reached its highest. Had the Weimar regime been able to last a little longer, the economy would have improved and the political situation stabilised. The bankrupt Nazi Party would have lost support.

SOURCE B

You have to consider the feelings of the people who ran German big business. They considered that it was better to be an SA man and have discipline and order than a member of the Communist Party.

A German banker writing about his feelings in the early 1930s. [Quoted in J. Hite and C. Hinton, *Weimar and Nazi Germany*, John Murray 2000.]

SOURCE A

The collapse of the Weimar Republic was a complex process with many separate strands all of which played a separate part in the tragedy. The crisis of German democracy was not peculiar to that country but a reflection of a more general crisis. The general drift away from democracy was speeded up by the Great Depression. In short, the tragic death of German democracy can be properly understood only as part of a wider canvas.

A historian writing in 1985. [From William Carr, *Germany 1815 to 1985*, Edward Arnold 1985.]

HISTORY DETECTIVE

In Source A, it says that 'the tragic death of German democracy can be properly understood only as part of a wider canvas.' Which other countries experienced a crisis of democracy? Was there situation similar or different to that of Germany.

ACTIVITIES

In this lesson there are nine points of argument. Copy and complete the table below. In the second column give the argument a value based on the strength of the argument; 10 for very strong, 1 for very weak. In the explanation column try to explain why. In the end, it may help you to decide whether Weimar was doomed or not.

Point	Strength	Explanation
1		
2		
3		
4		
5		
6		
7		
8		
9		
10		

Putting it all together

You have now completed this unit, which has focused on whether the Weimar Republic was doomed from the start. You have also had practice in answering questions designed to prepare you for your exam. Below is an example of one type of exam question, with some hints to help you write a top-scoring answer.

a Briefly describe the main clauses of the Treaty of Versailles. **[5 marks]**

Examiner's tip

The part **a** question on the exam paper will ask you to describe something. These questions are marked very simply. One mark is awarded for every relevant point made, plus 2–3 marks if that point is explained, up to a total of 5 marks.

Fact file

In the exam, you will be asked to answer two questions from Section B, the Depth Study: a source-based question and a structured question. The structured question is divided into three parts – **a**, **b** and **c**. In this Grade Studio, we'll be looking at how to produce a top-level answer for the **a** type of question.

Below are three answers to the question above. How many marks would you give each of them?

Answer 1

The Treaty of Versailles restricted the German Army to 100,000 soldiers. It blamed Germany for the war and made them pay compensation. Germany also lost its empire and could not put soldiers in the Rhineland.

Answer 2

The Treaty dramatically reduced the German military. This meant that it would not be able to start a war again. It also lost its colonies in Africa and therefore no longer had an overseas empire. These colonies were given by the League of Nations to Britain and France to rule under the mandate system.

Answer 3

The Germans were forced to pay reparations to France and Britain. The idea of this was to compensate them for the damage done during the war. The German Navy was dramatically reduced. This was so that they could not challenge British power on the seas or threaten the British Empire. The Germans also lost land on their borders. Some of this was due to new countries like Poland or Czechoslovakia being created or because Germany had taken land after winning previous wars.

Below are three more questions. Use the following table to create a top-mark answer for each of them.

1 Briefly describe the problems caused by hyperinflation.

2 Briefly describe what life was like in Berlin in the mid-1920s.

3 Briefly describe the events of the Kapp Putsch.

People on a fixed income could not afford to live in 1923.	In the end, the new government was brought down by a strike. All services in Berlin were suspended and the city was brought to a halt.	In March 1920, Freikorps units took control of government buildings in Berlin and proclaimed a new 'national' government.
People were very excited about the modern developments in art, music and theatre.	The Berlin nightclub scene was very popular. This meant that people from abroad saw Berlin as a tourist destination which made some Germans proud.	Ordinary Germans lost faith in a government that could allow such an economic catastrophe to happen.
Big businesses were able to buy up smaller businesses that were in financial trouble.	President Ebert asked the army to intervene but they refused saying that 'soldiers do not fire on soldiers'.	People's savings became worthless overnight.
American loans meant that Germans enjoyed a strong economy. Unemployment was therefore not such a problem and the vast majority of people did not have to live with the threat of poverty.	People had to carry their money in wheelbarrows to buy even basic items like bread.	Many German soldiers in the Freikorps believed the idea of the 'stab in the back'. This made the government very unpopular with them and made them more likely to oppose the government.

Revision tips

Factual recall

Remembering information is a key skill for all the questions but particularly for part (a) questions. There are lots of techniques to aid factual recall, some of which are given below.

- **Repetition** – It can help you retain information. What you should avoid though, is simple copying because this entails dealing with text a phrase at a time and you don't really get the benefit of reading and understanding the whole thing.
- **Kinaesthetic and visual learning** – Putting information on cards and sorting it out can be useful. This can be information about different groups or individuals or events and sorting them into different categories such as important/not important, useful/not useful. You can also colour-code them or number them and make up games. For example, colour-code the cards into groups of six. Deal the cards and try to collect sets by correctly guessing what is on the cards that your opponents hold. You can use the cards that you have to narrow down the possibilities.
- **Audio reinforcement** – Record yourself speaking some of the vital information. Play it back to yourself on your MP3 player.

Remembering as fun

It is important to make all these exercises that focus on factual recall as enjoyable as possible. It you are tense or bored, the brain will not focus as well and the learning will not be as effective. Doing revision with friends and playing games with the information are good ways of learning and remember, learning something and being able to remember it, is a real achievement.

Try out these description questions for yourself, using Chapter 1 to help you:

1. Briefly describe the important developments in the arts in Weimar Germany.
2. Briefly describe the achievements of Gustav Stresemann.
3. Briefly describe the events immediately following the First World War.
4. Briefly describe the achievements of the Weimar Republic.

Chapter 2

How was Hitler able to come to power in Germany?

GETTING STARTED

What kind of people do you think the Nazis were?

KEY WORDS

Gauleiters – *regional Nazi Party leaders.*

***Sturm Abteilung* (SA)** – *the paramilitary wing of the Nazi Party.*

Weimar at its height

In 1929, when Philipp Scheidemann expressed his opinion that the Weimar Republic had 'the freest constitution in the world' (see page 32), it was probably at the peak of its achievement. American loans had helped to stabilise the economy and even the unemployed enjoyed the safety net of a welfare state. Industrial production had just about reached its 1913 level, which was taken by some as a sign that the disastrous effects of the First World War were over.

Stresemann's successful foreign policy had taken Germany back into the international community and the wound of reparations and the war guilt clause was starting to heal in people's minds. The strength of German culture restored pride and gave people the feeling that, once again, life could be enjoyed. The lure of the new cities, bustling and cosmopolitan, went beyond the German borders and attracted people from all over the world.

Stresemann warned of the consequences of basing the economy on American loans in 1928 (see page 24) and historians, with the benefit of hindsight have identified weaknesses with the German economy. These included the reliance on American money, but unemployment and low prices for farm produce were also problems that were apparent even at the height of Weimar's achievements. The cultural freedom that attracted people to the cities during Weimar was not universally popular and many, particularly those living in the country disapproved and saw the new culture as a sign of a corrupt and immoral regime.

The Nazi State

By the end of 1933, Germans were starting to see a much better economic situation. Thanks to the Nazi's job-creation schemes, unemployment was cut and workers were starting to enjoy the benefits of belonging to the German Workers' Front. Hitler tore up the Treaty of Versailles and so worries about reparations became a thing of the past. A new strong leader and a stable unified government had restored Germans' pride in their country and Germany was looking forward to a more prosperous future.

The price of this upturn in fortune was, for many, not really an important issue. For others, it was the only important thing about the Hitler government. All other political parties had been banned and their activists had been imprisoned in concentration camps or went abroad. People who spoke out against the Nazis were dealt with harshly. Attacks on Jewish people were on the increase and rather than protecting citizens from violence, it seemed that the state was encouraging violence.

President von Hindenburg was ill and powerless after the Reichstag had voted powers to Adolf Hitler that made him a dictator. The institutions of government, though still in existence, were ignored as

SOURCE 

Liza Minelli in the film *Cabaret* from 1972.

Hitler governed through his network of local chiefs, called **gauleiters** or imposed his will through the violence of the SA, whose three million members ruled the streets with a rod of iron. Every possible avenue of communication poured forth Nazi propaganda from the radio and cinema to the school curriculum, relentlessly driving home the Nazi message of racial conflict and total obedience.

The question that puzzled Nazi opponents at the time and historians afterwards and will be the focus for the rest of this chapter is: how was Hitler able to come to power and why did the people of Germany vote to end their own freedom?

SOURCE C

German women and girls in 1925: members of a Jewish sports club wearing the Star of David as their club logo.

SOURCE B

Typical Nazi women fulfilling a typical Nazi role!

SOURCE D

Jews being forced to scrub the street clean by Nazis in Austria in 1938.

ACTIVITIES

1. Briefly describe the situation under the Weimar Republic.
2. Briefly describe the changes that took place under the Nazis.
3. Study Source A. How useful is this source in explaining the popularity of the Weimar Republic? Use the source and your own knowledge to explain your answer.
4. Study Sources A and B. How different is Source B to Source A? Use the sources and your own knowledge to explain your answer.
5. Study Sources C and D. How different are these sources? Use the sources and your own knowledge to explain your answer.

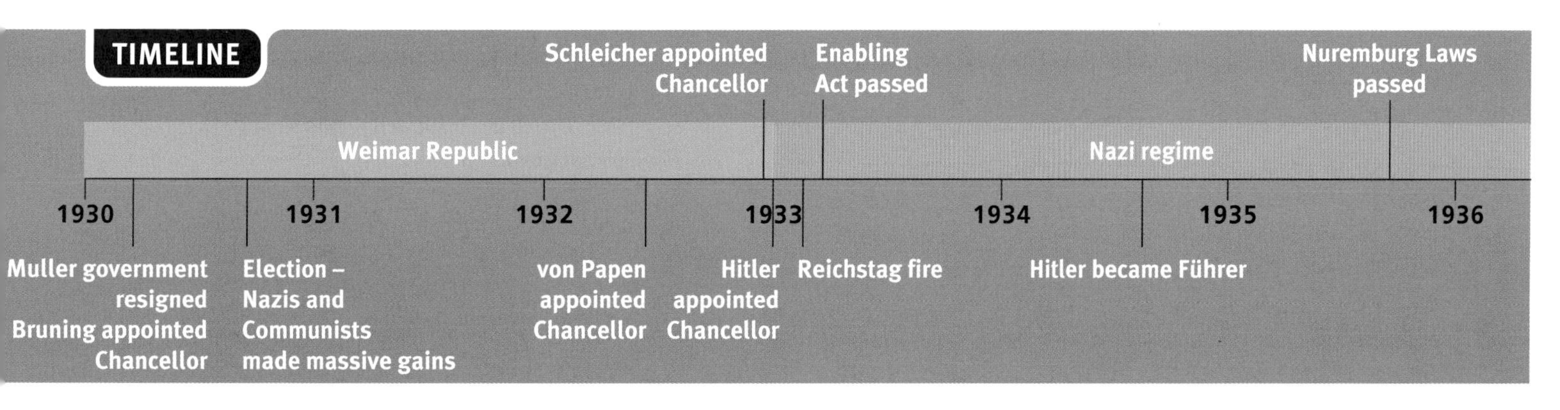

2.1 Where did the Nazi Party come from?

LEARNING OBJECTIVES

In this lesson you will:

- learn about the early development of the Nazi Party and the importance of Adolf Hitler
- gain experience of answering a description-based question.

KEY WORDS

Anti-Semitism – *hatred of Jews.*

Nationalism in Germany

Before the First World War, there were right wing parties, or nationalists. They supported the Kaiser and the government. When Germany lost the First Word War, the nationalists were devastated. Democracy gave them a far greater say in the Reichstag-based government, but still they yearned for the good old days of the Second Reich and the rule of the Kaiser.

The German Workers' Party (DAP)

The Nazis had not existed before the end of the First World War. In many ways, there was no reason for them to exist. In 1919, the situation was far less settled and nationalists, deeply hurt by the defeat, looked for ways to express themselves. Some joined existing nationalist parties, some joined the Freikorps and fought those who they thought were the enemy. In Bavaria, a man named Anton Drexler started a new nationalist party – the German Workers' Party (DAP) – and some nationalists joined it.

The NSDAP

Adolf Hitler, nationalist and **anti-Semite**, became a member of DAP in 1919. He was influential in changing the party's name to the National Socialist German Workers' Party (NSDAP) and helped draft 'The 25-point Programme' (see Source A). As an extraordinary public speaker and a gifted propagandist, he became the focal point for party members, and in 1921, he became the party leader.

SOURCE A

Extracts from the 25-point Programme:

- We demand the union of all Germany.
- Only those of German blood may be members of the nation. Accordingly, no Jew may be a member of the nation.
- We demand that the Treaty of Versailles be declared null and void.
- We demand extra land for settlement of our surplus population.
- The right to vote on the State's government and legislation shall be enjoyed by the citizens of the State alone.
- We demand the nationalization of all businesses which have been formed into corporations.

His first steps as leader were to create the **Sturm Abteilung (SA)** and to launch its own newspaper, the *Volkischer Beobachter* (see Source B).

Hitler's Party

Following the failed Munich Putsch in November 1923, Hitler was put in prison and the NSDAP banned. But Hitler only served a year in prison and, by the time he was released in December 1924, he had become a national figure. His book *Mein Kampf* (My Struggle) was a bestseller. He began to reorganise the party around him as the leader and got rid of those who opposed him. During this time, Hitler introduced the red flag with the swastika symbol and the straight-armed salute.

SOURCE B

Following Hitler's speech, Dietrich Eckart, the enthusiastic pioneer, expressed thanks to the men who had made the party a success; Anton Drexler, the founder and trusted leader and Adolf Hitler, the tireless propagandist.

From an article in the Nazi newspaper, the *Volkischer Beobachter*, 3 March 1921.

VOICE YOUR OPINION!

Do you think that people nowadays would follow someone like Hitler?

What the Nazis stood for

The Nazi Party was above all a nationalist one. It wanted a Germany that was strong and powerful. This also meant excluding those people who the Nazis believe were not pure Germans. The Jews were the group that were clearly identified by the Nazis as being non-German but there were others. The Nazis preached race hatred against these groups and encourage attacks on them.

The Nazis also believed that state control was important. They wanted a system where the country only had one party and that the party controlled all aspects of life. In education, work and leisure all the activities of the people would be organised by the party. As Hitler himself declared, there would never be a time when a person 'is left entirely alone to himself '(see Source A on page 100).

The Nazis, like most Germans, felt that the loss of the First World War and the Treaty of Versailles were a great injustice. It was the aim of the party to right these wrong as they saw them. As early as 1920, the Nazis talked about increasing German territory in order to gain living space in the East for their expanding population (See Source A)

Fact file

The word 'Nazi' was first applied to Hitler and the NSDAP by a Bavarian journalist. Originally, it was the shortened form of the name 'Ignatz' and was Bavarian slang for a person who was foolish or clumsy. The nickname soon stuck to refer to Hitler and his party, though they always referred to themselves as 'National Socialists'.

SOURCE C

The Nazi flag.

GradeStudio

Briefly describe the way that Hitler took control of the Nazi party.

Examiner's tip

The beliefs of the Nazis could form a part (a) question (see Grade Studio, pages 32–33). Remember, to gain full marks, you will need to identify five points. You could make sure of full marks by trying to explain some of them.

ACTIVITIES

1. Explain why other nationalists might tolerate the Nazi Party.
2. How important was anti-Semitism in the thinking of the Nazi Party? Explain your answer.
3. Study Source A. How useful is this source in understanding the ideas of the Nazi Party? Use the source and your own knowledge to explain your answer.
4. Study Source B. In what ways would Hitler's role in 1921 prepare him to be the leader of the Party? Use the source and your own knowledge to explain your answer.
5. Study Sources C and D. How effective was the swastika as a symbol of National Socialism? Use the sources and your own knowledge to explain your answer.

SOURCE D

A Nazi rally sometime in the 1920s.

2.2 Did the Munich Putsch pose a threat to the regime?

LEARNING OBJECTIVES

In this lesson you will:

- learn about the Munich Putsch
- practise cross-referencing material.

GETTING STARTED

Why do people start revolutions?

KEY WORDS

Martyrdom – *dying for a cause.*
Treason – *crime against the state.*

The Munich Putsch of November 1923 was mentioned briefly on pages 12–13. If Hitler had not come to power, it would remain a brief note in a period of stability. In 1929, Social Democrat politician, Philipp Scheidemann, published his memoirs. In the book, he devoted a whole chapter to the Kapp Putsch and five words ('then came the Hitler Putsch') to the Munich Putsch. It is the events after 1929 that make the Munich Putsch slightly more significant to us than it was to Scheidemann.

Hitler's confidence

By the autumn of 1923, Hitler had reason to believe that a National Socialist revolution had a chance of succeeding. He considered the following.

- Germany had suffered a year of hyperinflation, and confidence in the government was at an all-time low.
- There were French troops in the Rhineland, and Stresemann had given in to French pressure and called off resistance.
- Nazis were strong in Bavaria. A revolution that gained a lot of support in Bavaria could gather the momentum to overthrow the government in Berlin.
- The Bavarian state government was very right wing and had been plotting against the Reich government.
- Hitler had support from General Erich von Ludendorff and believed that he would be able to convince the army to join with the Nazis.

SOURCE A

Nazis congregate during the Munich Putsch.

The Munich Putsch

Hitler used the SA (see pages 52–53 for a fuller explanation of the SA and their role within the Nazi Party) to take over at gunpoint a political meeting run by Gustav Kahr, the Prime Minister of Bavaria, and made him agree to support the Putsch (see Source D). Once things had got moving, Kahr was allowed to go home and soon changed sides. The Nazis carried on regardless and marched into Munich. When they arrived in the centre, their path was blocked by policemen and a brief gunfight started despite the presence of General von Ludendorff. Hitler and the other Nazi leaders were soon arrested.

The aftermath of the Munich Putsch

Hitler and the other leaders were tried for **treason** in February 1924. The trial was to prove a triumph for Hitler. Although found guilty and sentenced to five years imprisonment, he used the publicity surrounding the trial to push his message. It made him a nationwide celebrity and his **martyrdom** was used by Nazi propagandists. Ludendorff who claimed that he had only been at the putsch 'by accident' was acquitted but left the court with far less credibility than Hitler.

Landsberg prison

The sympathy for Hitler's cause from the judge at the trial was clear from the start. He received five years, which was a very lenient sentence for treason, a crime that usually carried the death penalty. Hitler was sent to Landsberg prison and kept in a very spacious and comfortable room. He was allowed visitors whenever he wanted and had full access to books and writing materials. It was in prison that Hitler dictated his book, *Mein Kampf*.

ACTIVITIES

1. Briefly describe the events of the Munich Putsch.
2. Explain why the Munich Putsch failed.
3. Study Source A. Why do you think the revolutionaries chose to wear military uniforms? Use the source and your own knowledge to explain your answer.
4. Study Sources B and C. How far does Source B support Hitler's accusation in Source C? Does this make it true? Use the sources and your own knowledge to explain your answer.
5. Study Source D. Why, according to Strasser, did Kahr not support the Putsch? Use the source and your own knowledge to explain your answer.

SOURCE B

Cartoon showing Kahr's double position, at the same time supporting Hitler but also stopping him.

SOURCE C

Lossow, Kahr and Seisser had the same goal that we had... to get rid of the Reich government... If our enterprise was actually high treason, then during the whole period Lossow, Kahr and Seisser must have been committing high treason along with us, for during all these weeks we talked of nothing but the aims of which we now stand accused.

Hitler's defence during his trial for high treason, January 1924.

SOURCE D

How were they to gain von Kahr, General von Lossow and Seisser the Chief of Police? If these three could be won over, Hitler felt sure of victory. When von Kahr asked him who would take power in Germany, Hitler said, 'myself'. von Kahr was naturally hostile to such a proposal.

Former Nazi Otto Strasser, writing in his memoirs published in 1940.

HISTORY DETECTIVE

Find out who were the key individuals involved in revolutions in the early years of the Weimar Republic. What happened to those on the Left? What happened to those on the Right? What does this tell us about the Weimar Republic?

2.3 How important was Hitler in the success of the Nazis?

LEARNING OBJECTIVES

In this lesson you will:

- learn about Hitler's view of the world
- extract material from sources to explain Hitler's character.

SOURCE B

Painting by Adolf Hitler from his Vienna period.

KEY WORDS

Bolsheviks – *Russian Communists.*

Social Darwinism – *application of Darwin's idea about the survival of the fittest to different groups of people.*

Hitler was born in the north of Austria in 1889. His childhood was fairly normal and he was an average student. By the age of 15, both his parents had died and he had moved to Vienna and tried to gain entrance to the Academy of Art. He was unsuccessful and spent his early adulthood struggling to make a living. In Vienna, he learned about different kinds of politics and became a nationalist and an anti-Semite (see Source A). In 1914, he joined the German Army and fought in the First World War. He enjoyed life in the army and found a ready and agreeable audience for his extremist views.

Hitler and the development of the Nazis

Hitler joined the German Worker's Party because he had been asked to spy on them for the German Army. He soon began to take an active role and with the leader, Anton Drexler, it was Hitler who wrote the 25 point programme which was the basis of the party's ideas (see page 38). It was also Hitler's suggestion to change the name of the party to the National Socialist German Worker's Party, which led to the diminutive, 'Nazi'. Drexler was soon replaced by Hitler as the leader.

In the mid 1920s, two things brought the Nazi Party onto the national stage. The first was the Munich Putsch, which although a failure, brought the attention of the nation to Adolf Hitler and the Nazis. Hitler was able to use the trial to put forward his ideas, which were then reported in the press. This led to the second, Hitler's book, *Mein Kampf*. Although lacking in structure and coherent ideas, *Mein Kampf* became a bestseller and thereby the ideas of Hitler and the Nazis had a widespread audience.

SOURCE A

The obvious social injustice which caused him almost physical suffering also aroused in him a demoniacal hatred of that unearned wealth, presumptuous and arrogant, which we saw around us. Only by violently protesting against this state of affairs was he able to bear his own 'dog's life'. To be sure it was largely his fault that he was in this position but he would never admit it to himself.

August Kubizek, a friend who shared a room with Hitler during his stay in Vienna, writing in the 1930s.

SOURCE 

Before the court at Munich you grew before us into the figure of a leader. What you said there is the greatest statement spoken in Germany since Bismarck's death. God gave you the words to describe what is ailing Germany. You began at the bottom like every true great leader. And like every leader you grew greater as your tasks grew greater.

Josef Goebbels in a letter to Hitler. [Quoted in Maclean, French 2000 Quotes from *Hitlers' 1000 Year Reich* published by Schiffer in 2007.]

Fact file

Hitler's world view

By the time that Hitler became the leader of the National Socialist party, he had a very clear world view. In the mid-nineteenth century, Charles Darwin had introduced the idea of the survival of the fittest in his book about evolution. Hitler believed that this also applied to people, an idea known as **Social Darwinism**. In his eyes, the struggle for survival took place between different races and different political groups. Racially, in his view, the divide was clearly between Aryans (humans), Slavs (sub-humans) and Jews (anti-humans) and politically the struggle was with the Communists. It became convenient for him, as time went on, to link the Communists with the Jews and refer to the Jewish-Communist conspiracy.

How important was Hitler to the Nazis?

Without Hitler the Nazi Party would have been a very different organisation. The founder, Anton Drexler was far more moderate in his views than Hitler, and would have pursued a far less radical course of action. Through his personal action, Hitler took the Nazis onto the national stage, he organised the party and then reorganised it after the failure of the Munich Putsch. By the mid twenties, the Nazi Party and Hitler were indistinguishable.

Up to 1929, the Nazi Party were seen as a joke by many. They were different to the mainstream parties and as such had little support. It was this difference that gave them the edge when crisis struck. After 1929, people looked for something different because they believed that mainstream politics had led them to disaster. What stood the Nazis apart from other parties were the ideas of Adolf Hitler.

Hitler was the public face of the Nazi movement through his ability as a public speaker. His passionate speeches which had appeared so comical in the mid 1920s, found a new audience in those made poor by the Great Depression and those fearful of that fate. Hitler's simple messages of hope are what caused the shift in support.

The Nazi Party itself was Hitler's party. He inspired loyalty among party activists, who worked tirelessly for the cause and, as many saw it, for Hitler personally. Men like Goebbels, Himmler and Goering followed Hitler's lead blindly and in turn led groups of men to follow him. It was the personal relationships that Hitler had built up during the 1920s with all the leading figures of the Nazi Party that shaped the movement and contributed significantly to its success.

ACTIVITIES

1. Briefly describe Hitler's early life.
2. Explain Hitler's role in the Nazi party.
3. Which was more important in the success of the Nazis, Hitler himself or the party organisation?
4. Study Source A. How might this explain Hitler's work in the Nazi party? Use the source and your own knowledge to explain your answer.
5. Study Source B. Why did Hitler produce this painting? Does it help us to understand what kind of person he was? Use the source and your own knowledge to explain your answer.
6. Study Sources C and D. Why might Goebbels and Streicher make these statements? Use the source and your own knowledge to explain your answer.

HISTORY DETECTIVE

Find out what Zionism was. Why might Zionism have made some people think that Hitler was right?

I heard your speech. I can only be a helper but you are the born leader.

Julius Streicher speaking in 1922. [Quoted in Maclean, French *2000 Quotes from Hitlers' 1000 Year Reich* published by Schiffer in 2007.]

GradeStudio

The language of your answer is often the key to doing the kind of things that the examiner is looking for. By thinking of how to use certain words, the quality of the answer can be raised. In the table below are some phrases that may help you to raise the quality of your answer and shape the response in a way that the examiner can reward.

Explaining	Evaluating	Judging
X happened because of Y	X is important because...	X is more important than Y because...
X was largely due to Y because...	The significance of X is...	The most important factor is...
For the most part, X was a result of Y. This is because....	The role of X is crucial because....	If X had not happened then Y would not....

2.4 Case study: Who were the men who helped Hitler gain power in Germany?

LEARNING OBJECTIVES

In this lesson you will:

- learn to describe the role of Hitler's main lieutenants
- develop independent research skills.

KEY WORDS

Lieutenant – *an assistant to the leader.*

Though Hitler was the absolute leader of the Nazi Party and later Germany, he could not have risen to power without the help of large numbers of willing Nazis to do the work on the ground. Among these were the few with whom Hitler had a special relationship – they got the most important jobs. Below are fact files about four of them and the names of some more. This will form the basis of an enquiry. You will need to find extra information on the first four and basic information on the other four. At the end of the enquiry, you should be able to assess their relative importance, place them in rank order and be able to explain why you have placed them in this order.

Look for information on background, date joining the Nazis, strengths and fate. Also ask yourself, why were these four important? Did they achieve anything? Were their achievements any better or more significant than the others?

BRAIN BOOST

'Hitler has only got one ball,
Goering has two but very small,
Himmler has something similar,
And Josef Goebbels has no balls at all.'

This was a popular marching song with British soldiers during the Second World War and a very good, if a little vulgar, way of remembering the key Nazi leaders.

Fact file

Hermann Goering

Background: From a wealthy family. Goering fought in the First World War as a fighter pilot and was awarded many medals for bravery.

Joined Nazis in: 1922

Strengths: The acceptable face of National Socialism to people from the higher classes due to his family background, war record and personal charm.

Fate: Killed himself by taking poison in his jail cell at Nuremberg after being sentenced to death.

Extra information needed:

- What responsibilities did he have?
- What were his personal problems?
- Why did Hitler like him?
- How did he fall out of favour with Hitler?

Fact file

Josef Goebbels

Background: Born with a club foot and therefore did not fight in First World War. A doctor of German Literature and unsuccessfully pursued a career as a writer.

Joined Nazis in: 1922

Strengths: Gifted journalist and talented propagandist. Next to Hitler, the best Nazi public speaker.

Fate: Killed himself in the bunker, after giving poison to his wife and children in April 1945.

Extra information needed:

- What were his nicknames?
- How did his relationship with Hitler change in the early days?
- What important evidence has he left us?
- How did his importance increase as the war went on?

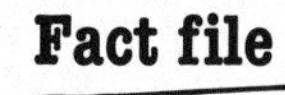

Fact file

Ernst Rohm

Background: Career soldier. Served in the First World War as an officer.

Joined Nazis in: 1919

Strengths: Tough and ruthless. Good leader of soldiers.

Fate: Murdered by the SS in 1934

Extra information needed:

- Why did Rohm enjoy being in the Freikorps and the SA?
- What was his role in the Munich Putsch?
- How important was he during the elections between 1929 and 1933?
- Why did he and Hitler eventually fall out?

Fact file

Heinrich Himmler

Background: The youngest of the leading Nazis – Himmler only just joined the army in time to see some action in the last weeks of the First World War. Tried to make a go of chicken farming during the 1920s.

Joined Nazis in: 1923

Strengths: Extremely efficient and hard working. Showed a high level of care for those under him.

Fate: Took poison when he was captured by the Allies in 1945.

Extra information needed:

- What responsibilities did he have?
- What was his role in the extermination of the Jews?
- How did he feel about Hitler?

Fact file

Other Leading Nazis

Use the Internet and Library resources to find out about these other leading Nazis. Though not as important as the other four, they all played a major in the way that the Third Reich developed.

- Albert Speer
- Rudolf Hess
- Joachim von Ribbentrop
- Martin Bormann
- Robert Ley
- Alfred Rosenburg
- Reinhardt Heydrich
- Fritz Todt

ACTIVITIES

Find out what the charges were at the Nuremburg trials and what the sentences were for those who were sentenced. Imagine that all of the leading Nazis, including Hitler were present (Todt, Himmler, Goebbels and Rohm were dead and Bormann was missing). Decide what the charges would have been for those who were not present at the trial and what the sentences would have been. You have to justify your sentence. What about the sentences that were passed at Nuremburg, were they fair? Would you change any of them and, if so, how?

BRAIN BOOST

Often you will see abbreviations of things connected with Nazi Germany. Here are some of the most important and what they stand for:

NSDAP – National Socialist Party
KPD – Communist Party
SPD – Socialist Party
DAF – Germany Workers Front
HJ – Hitler Youth
BDM – League of German Girls
SS – Schutz Staffeln
SA – Sturm Abteilung.

2.5 How did the Wall Street Crash affect Germany's economy?

LEARNING OBJECTIVES

In this lesson you will:

- learn about the Wall Street Crash and its effect on Germany
- use sources to explain the relationship between the USA and Germany.

GETTING STARTED

Why do people buy shares in companies?

KEY WORDS

Economic depression – *period where confidence in business is low and unemployment is high.*

Economy – *the interaction of everything connected with money.*

Shares – *documents giving part-ownership of companies.*

After the First World War, the United States had the strongest **economy** in the world. Confidence in American business reached an all time high in the late 1920s and **share** prices reflected this optimism. Investors in shares could easily make thousands of dollars and many had made fortunes buying and selling shares and had been able to borrow large sums of money with their shares providing the security.

SOURCE A

The business of America had become business. Paper wealth in the stock market was booming. One of the decade's best-selling books referred to Jesus as the first businessman, and people believed!

An American writer writing about the boom of the 1920s.

Shares prices can also go down

By 1929, some people were beginning to question the value of their shares. Was the USA really as strong as people believed? American investors lost confidence very quickly in the value of their shares. On 24 October 1929, people began to panic sell – the start of the Wall Street Crash. Share prices went down rapidly and billions of dollars were wiped off share prices. Thousands of people in the USA became bankrupt overnight. As a result of this, the whole world went into an **economic depression**.

SOURCE B

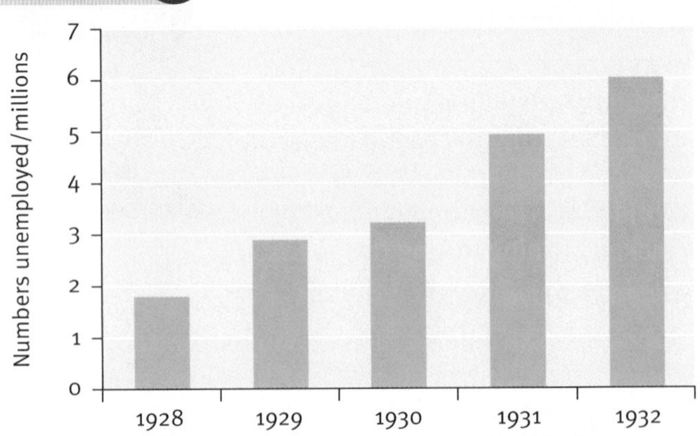

Raw totals of the unemployed in Germany 1928–32.

SOURCE C

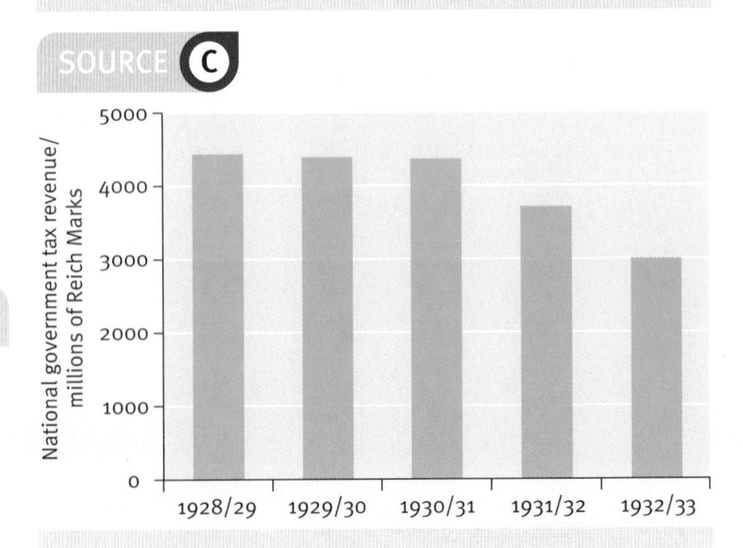

National government tax revenue in millions of Reich marks.

An unemployed musician selling postcards in Berlin, 1930.

The Wall Street Crash and Germany

In Germany, the Wall Street Crash and the economic depression had particularly catastrophic effects. The loans that had supported the economy during the golden years of the Weimar Republic were stopped and outstanding debts called in. Without the support of US finance and in the atmosphere of worldwide depression, the German economy was going to struggle badly. Gustav Stresemann had died three weeks before the Wall Street Crash and so never saw his warning come true (see Source B on page 22).

Without US loans, there was no way that Germany could meet reparations repayments and there was a fear of further French invasions. In the end, the French were having their own problems dealing with the Great Depression and so Germany was left alone. All agreed that reparation repayments be temporarily suspended. International demand for German goods suddenly dried up and with little money at home to stimulate production, many companies went out of business. The German farming industry suffered the same fate as the US one and many agricultural workers lost their jobs and moved to the cities to look for work. Unemployment, which was already high during the golden years, went even higher, factory workers were laid off, with young people suffering particularly.

The welfare state, of which the Weimar politicians were so proud, could not cope with the millions of extra people who were unemployed. The government, whose income was cut dramatically, reduced the amount of unemployment benefit. This, in turn, led to a slump in the housing market, as people could not afford to build houses or to pay rent. Shanty towns grew up in all the major German cities. With the collapse of the economy, the mood had changed dramatically. The party was over and many began to look for new and radical solutions to Germany's problems.

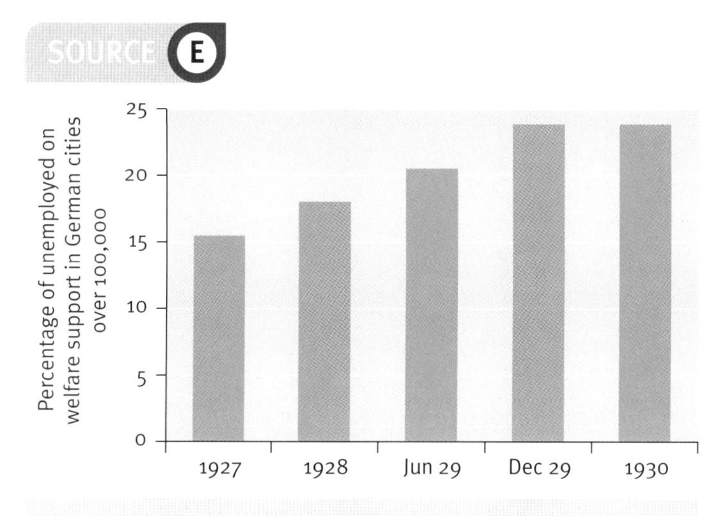

Percentage of unemployed on welfare support in German cities of over 100,000 people.

ACTIVITIES

1. Briefly describe what happened in Wall Street in October 1929.
2. Explain why the Wall Street Crash was significant for Germany.
3. Study Source A. Why might Germans have liked the idea that in the USA, business was very successful?
4. Study Sources B and E. How far do they support the idea that the Wall Street Crash caused all Germany's economic problems?
5. Study Source C. Why were these figures particularly problematic for the German government?
6. Study Source D. How useful is this in telling us what it was like for ordinary Germans during the Great Depression?

2.6 How did the Great Depression change politics in the Weimar Republic?

LEARNING OBJECTIVES

In this lesson you will:

- learn about the rise of the Communists and the Nazis
- practise answering source-based questions on utility and typicality.

KEY WORDS

Nationalisation – *where the state takes control of important industries.*

The rise of the Communists

The German Communist Party (KPD) had maintained a steady percentage of the vote in national elections in the years between 1924 and 1929. From a high of 12.6 per cent in 1924, it had only dropped to 10.6 per cent in 1929. Following the Wall Street Crash, its support increased to 16.9 per cent. People were attracted to its message of the **nationalisation** of large industries and jobs guaranteed for all. Would-be Communist supporters were able to look to the Soviet Union and see that the turmoil caused by the civil war was over and that Communism was seemingly working. The brutal excesses of Stalin were yet to come.

Fact file

Ideologies

Different people have different ideas about how societies should be organised. For example, capitalists believe that everybody should be free to earn money in line with their abilities and that things should be privately owned. Communists believe that earning should be roughly equal and that things should be collectively owned. National Socialists believed in a mix of these but were mainly committed to obeying their leader and creating a racially pure society.

Germany suffered more than most other countries in the Great Depression. Germans blamed the Weimar government and looked for other solutions to the problems.

The rise of the Nazis

The Nazi message, like the Communist one, made promises of bread and jobs for all and found a similar eager audience. Unlike the Communists though, the Nazis couched their message in a new way, playing on similar fears but widening out both the blame and the solutions. They brought back the idea of the 'stab in the back' (see page 16) and Hitler said he would tear up the Treaty of Versailles. Hitler's 'world view', that the civilised world was being undermined by a Communist-Jewish conspiracy, became very popular. While the Communists blamed capitalism in general, the Nazis blamed the Weimar Republic and made it clear that, if they were voted into power, they would replace the whole system of government with a one-party dictatorship.

SOURCE A

'Berlin is Red and is staying red!' Communist graffiti from the early 1930s.

SOURCE B

This means nothing less than the first attempt to press forward, little by little, into the strongest and most important bulwarks of Communist domination...to undermine them and to soften them up...National Socialists...devote their energies to the conquest of the German worker.

From a speech by Josef Goebbels made in 1930.

Old and new fears

With the collapse of confidence, old insecurities began to resurface. People remembered the year of hyperinflation in 1923 or the attempted revolutions of 1919/20. The occupation of the Rhineland was only just over in 1929 and the injustice of the Treaty of Versailles was remembered with particular anger. Young people suffered from lack of opportunities and gang violence in the cities became a major problem. It was perhaps a significant point in the demise of Weimar Germany that the only politician who had the stature and the trust of the people, Gustav Stresemann, had died in 1929.

SOURCE C

Hitler will undoubtedly return to political life. He proposes to return to his party but to act within the law in order to gain power. During his ten months under detention, he has undoubtedly become more mature and calm. When he returns to freedom, he will not seek revenge against those who opposed him and frustrated him in November, 1923.

From a report on Hitler while he was in prison in 1924.

VOICE YOUR OPINION!

Is it reasonable to assume that economic problems lead to more radical politics?

Fact file

Franz von Papen and Kurt von Schleicher, the last Chancellors of Weimar Germany, were Hindenburg's most important advisers during 1932, the last year of the Weimar Republic. Though neither of them was a member of the Reichstag, they both served as Chancellor, and both found it virtually impossible to rule Germany without the cooperation of the Reichstag. Franz von Papen continued to serve in Hitler's government throughout the Nazi period. Kurt von Schleicher was murdered during the 'Night of the Long Knives' (see pages 70–71).

SOURCE D

I have personally given one million marks to the Nazi Party... Just before the Nazis seized power the big businesses began to give money to the Nazi Party... In all, the amounts given by heavy industry to the Nazis were about two million marks a year.

From Fritz Thyssen, *I paid Hitler*, 1941.

ACTIVITIES

1. Briefly describe how the Great Depression changed German politics.
2. Explain why the Great Depression had a particularly devastating effect on Germany.
3. Which was the more important factor for the Great Depression in Germany, the Wall Street Crash or the loss of the First World War? Explain your answer.
4. Study Source A. What can we learn from this source about the popularity of the Communists in Berlin during the last years of Weimar? Use the source and your own knowledge to explain your answer.
5. Study Source B. Why do you think it was important for the Nazis to 'conquer' the German worker? Use the source and your own knowledge to explain your answer.
6. Study Source C. How far did this report prove to be true? Use the source and your own knowledge to explain your answer.
7. Study Source D. Are you surprised that big businesses gave money to the Nazi Party? Use the source and your own knowledge to explain your answer.

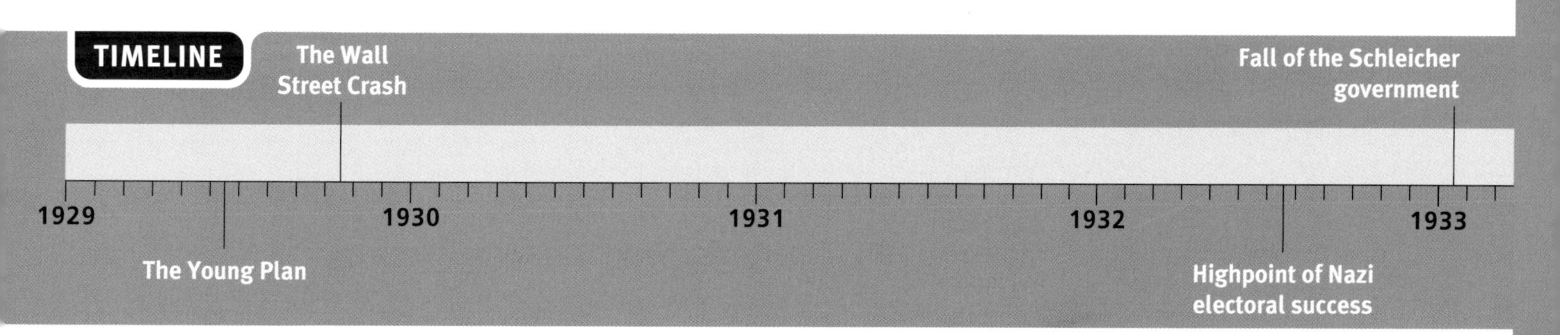

2.7 Who supported the Nazis?

LEARNING OBJECTIVES

In this lesson you will:

- learn to describe the groups that voted for the Nazis
- practice answering source-based questions on utility.

GETTING STARTED

Describe the process of voting in a secret ballot.

KEY WORDS

Manual workers – *a person who may, for example, work in a factory or outdoors and who performs physical work.*

Rural – *in the countryside.*

Democratic elections are conducted by secret ballot. This makes it difficult to know exactly who voted for which party. There is some evidence, however, that may help us understand who supported the Nazis.

Who became a Nazi?

If we break down the membership of the NSDAP between 1930 and 1933 into types of job (see Source A), we see that middle-class professions had a stronger representation in the party than other classes. What drew these people to the Nazis is not totally clear, though it could be argued that the nationalist message would have had a broad appeal, and the anti-Communist stance would have found a ready audience in those other than **manual workers**.

Nazi support

If we examine the voting areas, a clear pattern emerges. Nazis tended to do better in rural, Protestant areas where they gained, in some places, over half the vote. In rural areas like Bavaria, which is mostly Roman Catholic, they did less well, despite the links to Munich from the early days of the party. In cities, the Nazis did badly. In Berlin, for example, they only gained a quarter of the vote at best and they themselves identified the industrial Rhineland as a major problem.

The typical Nazi

From the evidence, the Nazi stereotype was male, under 30, living in a **rural** or semi-rural area. He was middle-class, possibly a white-collar worker or

SOURCE 

	Number of members (1930–33)	Percentage of total members (1930–33)	Estimated percentage of society
Manual workers	233,479	32.5	46.3
White-collar workers	147,855	20.6	12.4
Self-employed	124,579	17.3	9.6
Civil servants and teachers	46,967	6.5	4.8
Peasants	89,800	12.5	20.7
Others	76,766	10.7	6.2
Total	719,466		

Members of the Nazi Party.

SOURCE B

Nazis supporters during the period of the elections.

civil servant. Older members were also often Protestant and may well have owned a small business or a farm. Typical Nazi voters were upper-working or middle-class and equally likely to be male or female.

The Nazi message found an eager audience in these kind of people; staunchly German, proud and nationalistic. They would have been fearful for their jobs or businesses and mindful that a Communist revolution in the cities would lead to the nationalisation of business.

SOURCE C

Working men, women and young voters in the city and the country! On election day give your vote to the Communists...The National Socialist leader gives support to the strike breakers and sends his murdering bands to fight against the improvement of the conditions of the workers.

Wilhelm Pieck, Communist Leader radio broadcast for the election, September 1930.

HISTORY DETECTIVE

Research some individuals who supported Hitler. Try an Internet search for Theodore Eicke, for example – this will give you some websites with information on other Nazi figures. How far do their examples fit in with the ideas in this section?

BRAIN BOOST

Sometimes making a sentence out of key words can help you to remember. If we think of the four main groups who strongly supported the Nazis, we might come up with; white-collar workers, the self-employed, civil servants and teachers. A sentence to help our memory could be something like.

'The **civil teacher** placed him**self** by the **white**board.'

ACTIVITIES

1. Briefly describe the groups that supported Hitler.
2. Explain why it is difficult to know who voted for Hitler and how this problem can be overcome.
3. Study Source A. How can this help us to understand who voted for Hitler? Use the sources and your own knowledge to explain your answer.
4. Study Source B. How typical was this picture in the early 1930s? Use the sources and your own knowledge to explain your answer.
5. Study Sources C and D. How useful are these to a historian studying German politics between 1930 and 1933? Use the sources and your own knowledge to explain your answer.

SOURCE D

They spoke, during those infamous November days of 1918, to our people, particularly the German worker, promising a better economic future. Today, 14 years later, they cannot point to a single improvement in any occupation that their policies have brought about.

Hitler's appeal to the nation, 1932.

2.8 Why was the SA so important to the Nazis?

LEARNING OBJECTIVES

In this lesson you will:

- learn about the importance of the SA to the Nazi Party
- practise comparing and contrasting sources.

KEY WORDS

Paramilitary – *amateur soldiers working for a political party.*

The *Sturm Abteilung* (Storm Unit) – SA for short – was the **paramilitary** wing of the NSDAP. It provided the party with willing workers on the ground and fighters in the streets. It kept security at Nazi meetings and disturbed and disrupted the meetings of others. It carried out marches, distributed leaflets, sang songs and showed to the German public, the unified, disciplined power of the National Socialist movement.

The appeal of the SA

The SA offered young men ready-made friendship groups. For some, it gave them a place to sleep and the offer of a hot meal. In the SA, they could go on training camps, play sports or organise parades. On a very basic level, the SA provided men with the opportunity for a fight. This was not just violence for the sake of it but violence for a purpose, violence with a group who shared the same interest. It was violence that others in the party would justify as necessary. In the eyes of the SA members, it was useful violence.

The SA in public

For many, the SA presented a sympathetic image of the Nazi party. Many Germans were drawn to the smart uniform and the obvious discipline of the SA units. Coming from a country with a strong military tradition, they saw the SA men as continuing that tradition, in a way that the government and the regular army was unable to do. The marches that the SA organised were impressive and often featured a marching band.

SOURCE A

The comradeship in the SA was very appealing to many of its members.

SOURCE B

Since I am an immature and wicked man, war and unrest appeal to me more than good middle class order.

Ernst Rohm, leader of the SA from 1921 to 1923 and from 1930 to 1934.

VOICE YOUR OPINION!

Study Source A. Do you think that the men in the SA were wicked?

The SA in the Great Depression

During the Great Depression, the rise in popularity of the Communists and the Nazis caused clashes, particularly in the cities. Each side knew which areas were safe and which were not but they were still willing to provoke a fight with the other side in order to gain an advantage. In 1932, around the time of the July elections to the Reichstag, hundreds were killed during a seven-week period of extreme street violence. The SA men who died were celebrated by the Nazis as martyrs to the cause.

The end of the SA

By 1934, Hitler did not have the same need for the SA as he had in previous years. Having consolidated power, he wished to make his policies less radical, not more. Ernst Rohm preached the policy of ongoing revolution and wanted to disband the regular army and put the SA in its place. Hitler needed the expertise of the regular army and so, in July 1934, the SA was officially disbanded following the purge of the Night of the Long Knives (see pages 72–73).

SOURCE C

Rohm spent two periods as leader of the SA and became very closely identified with the movement.

SOURCE 

As circumstances required, Adolf Hitler created a new type of combatant: the soldier of the political idea. To these soldiers he gave the red flag with its swastika, the new symbol of the German future, and the brown shirt, clothing of the SA in combat, honour and death. By its colour, the brown shirt distinguishes the SA from the masses. It is this fact which justifies it: it is the distinctive sign of the SA, allowing friends and foe alike to recognise immediately those who profess the National Socialist view of the world.

Ernst Rohm, in a speech to the Diplomatic Corps and Foreign Press, 18 April 1934.

ACTIVITIES

1. Briefly describe the role of the SA.
2. Explain why former members of the Freikorps were so attracted to the SA.
3. How important was the SA in the rise of the Nazi Party? Explain your answer.
4. Study Sources B and C. How far do these sources explain why Rohm rose to be the leader of the SA? Use the sources and your own knowledge to explain the answer.
5. Study Sources A and D. How similar are these sources? Use the sources and your own knowledge to explain the answer.

GradeStudio

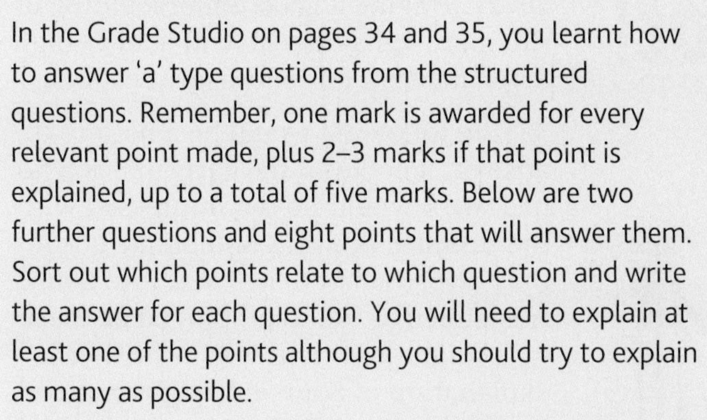

In the Grade Studio on pages 34 and 35, you learnt how to answer 'a' type questions from the structured questions. Remember, one mark is awarded for every relevant point made, plus 2–3 marks if that point is explained, up to a total of five marks. Below are two further questions and eight points that will answer them. Sort out which points relate to which question and write the answer for each question. You will need to explain at least one of the points although you should try to explain as many as possible.

1. Briefly describe how Hitler came to be in Landsberg Prison.
2. Briefly describe the economic effects of the Wall Street Crash on Germany.

Hitler was responsible for the Munich Putsch and was guilty of treason	Some businesses that relied on American money went bust	Hitler was classified as a non-dangerous prisoner and was put in an open prison
Germany was not able to keep up with reparations payments	The judge was sympathetic to Hitler and gave him a light sentence	It meant that American loans to Germany were stopped
Other members of the Putsch, like Erich Ludendorff were too popular to punish and were let off	Tax revenue from a weak economy went down	

2.9 Get your sources sorted!

How did the Nazis use propaganda to win the elections?

LEARNING OBJECTIVES

In this lesson you will:

- learn about the use of propaganda by the Nazis
- learn how to produce answers to source-based questions that address the issue of 'purpose'.

KEY WORDS

Propaganda – *the use of information to make people think in a certain way.*

Purpose – *the reason why something is made.*

Source questions about **purpose** often start with the phrase: 'Why was source X created…?' or even 'What was the purpose of Source Y?'. To gain the highest levels, you need to consider who made the source (its provenance), the reasons why the source was made (its purpose) and link it to some contextual knowledge (relevant information not contained in the source) (see page 26).

SOURCE A

Nazi election poster. *Arbeit* means work and *brot* means bread.

Who created the source?

If the source was created by someone in the political sphere, you need to know the kind of ideas that type of politics had. For example, if a Nazi supporter produced a source that criticises Jews, you will be able to make a couple of general comments about the Nazi attitude to Jews and how they believed that the Jews were responsible for most of their problems.

Why was the source created?

Looking at the source will give you clues about 'why'. There is usually an aspect of persuasion, so you need to ask, who is being persuaded and what is the message? Often during our period, it will be politicians trying to persuade the German people of their point of view. To get the highest mark an answer will need to consider the effect the source was meant to have on its intended audience.

Answering 'purpose' questions in practice

Consider the poster in Source A. If we ask the question 'Why did the Nazis publish this poster?' we might come up with the simple answer 'to get ordinary people to vote for them', but this would not get us many marks. It is the use of contextual knowledge that always gains the higher level for source-based questions, as you saw on pages 26–27. Having a good understanding of the intended audience will lead to higher level answers for 'purpose' questions.

So, the following would be a better answer: 'People in the early 1930s who had work would not be impressed with the promise of 'work and bread' because they already had that. Therefore Source A is aimed at the unemployed or those who might lose their job.' A further explanation of Source A might centre round the Great Depression in the early 1930s and the Nazi desire to appeal to those who were struggling. Contextual knowledge needs to be fully explained in order to gain the higher levels for 'purpose' questions.

SOURCE 

Nazi election poster, the writing says: 'We are for Adolf Hitler!'

SOURCE 

The people that only a few weeks ago were taken in by the flowery speeches of Papen have now turned against him. With the beginning of Hitler's campaign and the deployment of our big speakers, one can see that our people are settling all their hopes on National Socialism!

Josef Goebbels, Head of Nazi Propaganda, in a speech during the November 1932 election campaign.

SOURCE C

LIES! One more stupid and contemptible than the next!

Who took away the civil servant's freedom of expression?

Who has cut his salary with ever new emergency orders?

Who has taken away from him every security for his future?

THE SOCIAL DEMOCRATS AND THE CENTRE PARTIES!

From a Nazi leaflet, published in 1932.

ACTIVITIES

1. Study Source A. Why did the Nazis produce this poster in the early 1930s? Use the source and your own knowledge to explain your answer.
2. Study Source B. Why did the Nazis produce this poster in the early 1930s? Use the source and your own knowledge to explain your answer.
3. Study Source C. Who was the intended audience for this Nazi leaflet in 1932? Why is this important? Use the source and your own knowledge to explain your answer.
4. Study Source D. Why would the Nazis publish a photograph of Adolf Hitler in this pose? Use the source and your own knowledge to explain your answer.
5. Study Source E. Why would Goebbels have made this speech in November 1932? Use the source and your own knowledge to explain your answer.

Adolf Hitler speaking passionately to groups of appreciative Germans formed a major part of the propaganda campaign.

2.10 How far had democracy stopped working by January 1933?

LEARNING OBJECTIVES

In this lesson you will:

- learn about the breakdown of the Weimar Republic
- practise cross-referencing material from sources.

KEY WORDS

Decree – *law made by the leader, not the parliament.*

Coalition government

Some would say that the strength of German politics in general over the last century is that different parties work together. This is because no one party gets a majority of deputies after an election. This means that parties have to work in partnerships called a coalition. In theory, and very often in practice, coalition governments cannot implement extreme policies because the parties act as a check on each other. This makes the current German state a very strong liberal democracy.

SOURCE 

No Government in Germany remained in power longer than a few months, because no single party or coalition of parties could ever muster enough votes to enable them to govern.

Christabel Bielenberg, an Englishwoman living in Germany from 1932 to 1945.

Coalition government fails

Every government in the Weimar Republic was a coalition. Unfortunately, by March 1930, the parties had stopped cooperating. The main problem was that they could not agree on how to deal with the economic crisis caused by the Wall Street Crash. Parties on the left argued that big business should meet some of the costs, whereas parties on the right wanted to cut benefit payments.

Presidential government

In March 1930, President Hindenburg appointed Heinrich Bruning as Chancellor. Bruning was unable to get his laws passed through the Reichstag

SOURCE 

Key to parties: SPD=Social Democrats, DDP=German Democratic Party, Z=Centre Party, DVP = German People's Party, BVP=Bavarian People's Party, DVNP=German Nationalist People's Party.

Appointment	Resignation	Chancellor (Party)	Parties in government
February 1919	June 1919	Scheidemann (SPD)	SPD, DDP, Z
June 1920	May 1921	Fehrenbach (Z)	DDP, Z, DVP
November 1922	August 1923	Cuno (no party)	DDP, Z, DVP, BVP
August 1923	November 1923	Stresemann (DVP)	SDP, DDP, Z, DVP
January 1925	May 1926	Luther (no party)	DDP, Z, DVP,BVP, DNVP
June 1928	March 1930	Muller (SPD)	SPD, DDP, Z, DVP, BVP

Selected coalition governments in Weimar.

and so used Article 48 of the constitution, which allowed President Hindenburg to make laws, known as **decrees**, without going through the Reichstag. The Reichstag protested. Bruning called new elections in September 1930 to get a new Reichstag. He got one but not in the way he had hoped. The two parties who were opposed to democracy (the Nazis and the Communists) made massive gains. There was now no possibility that the Reichstag would support Bruning.

Bruning's government lasted two years, during which the situation became worse. The Nazis and Communists were even more popular and the economic crisis deepened. Finally, in May 1932, Hindenburg sacked Bruning as Chancellor and appointed Franz von Papen. It was clear that Papen could do no better than Bruning, nor could Kurt von Schleicher who succeeded Papen as Chancellor in December 1932. Schleicher resigned in January 1933.

Fact file

Governments in democracies are elected by two methods which can roughly be broken down into two categories: 'first past the post' and proportional representation. The 'first past the post' system is the one used in the United Kingdom. Under proportional representation, the voter votes for a party and at the end of the election that party gets the number of members of parliament, equivalent to the proportion of votes. For example, in the November 1932 election in Germany, the Communists got 16.9 per cent of the vote. This meant they got 16.9 per cent of the deputies in the Reichstag. The argument in favour of the 'first past the post system' is that it creates stable government. The argument for proportional representation is that it is fairer.

SOURCE C

If a state fails to perform the duties imposed upon it by the federal constitution or by federal law, the President may enforce performance with the aid of the armed forces. For the said purpose he may suspend for the time being, either wholly or in part, the fundamental rights described in the constitution.

Article 48.

SOURCE D

The situation was so serious that I considered that the President might be justified in placing the welfare of the nation above his oath to the constitution. I told him I realised that this would be a difficult decision for a man who always placed the value of his word above everything else.

Franz von Papen, writing about the decision that Hindenburg had to take to break the German constitution.

ACTIVITIES

1. Explain why coalition government had caused problems for the Weimar Republic.
2. 'Hindenburg had no choice but to introduce rule by decree.' How far do you agree with this statement?
3. Study Source B. How useful is this in explaining why democracy in Weimar Germany failed? Use the source and your own knowledge to explain the answer.
4. Study Sources A and B. How far does Source B support the claim made in Source A. Use the sources and your own knowledge to explain the answer.
5. Study Source C. Why do you think this clause was put in the Weimar constitution? Use the source and your own knowledge to explain the answer.
6. Study Source D. How far would it be fair to call Hindenburg 'a dictator' at the end of 1932? Use the source and your own knowledge to explain the answer.

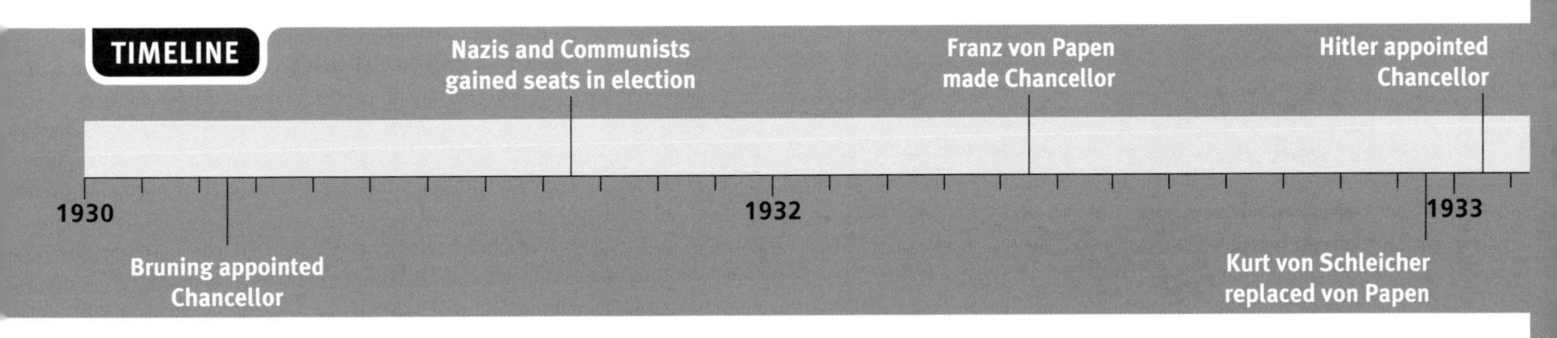

2.11 Why were the Nazis successful after 1929 but not before?

LEARNING OBJECTIVES

In this lesson you will:

- learn about the Nazis before and after 1929
- be able to explain how the changing situation enabled the Nazis to make progress.

KEY WORDS

Totalitarian – *state ruled by one party, often with harsh rules and restrictions on freedom.*

Weimar Germany in the mid-1920s

After the turmoil of hyperinflation and the implementation of the Dawes Plan in 1924, Germany enjoyed a period of relative stability and economic wellbeing. People who after the First World War, had suffered because of lack of work, low wages and/or homelessness were finding that things were much easier. Even for those people unfortunate enough to be without work, the Weimar government had enough money through taxes to be able to pay dole money and fund charitable foundations. At this time of plenty, politics became unfashionable and uninteresting.

Hitler during the Golden Era

Following the Munich Putsch, Hitler spent ten months in Landsberg open prison, where he dictated his book, *Mein Kampf*. The Putsch itself and the trial afterwards, had given Hitler celebrity status and his book was a best seller. People were curious about the Nazi leader but did not take him seriously as a politician. People looked to the ever popular Stresemann to ensure that Germany prospered.

Sales of *Mein Kampf* gave Hitler a source of income and allowed him to spend his time organising the party. He did not mind being seen as separate from normal political parties, indeed sometimes he encouraged it. In 1925, he supported Ludendorff as the presidential candidate, knowing that he was bound to lose to Hindenburg. Being seen as separate from the normal parties was a disadvantage during the 1920s but became a great advantage after the Wall Street Crash.

SOURCE A

I defy you to agitate any fellow with a full stomach.

William Cobbett, 19th century British radical journalist. In this quote, 'agitate' means to persuade someone to take part in some kind of political action.

SOURCE B

The relative wealth of these years was reflected politically in a sharp decline in support for parties on the extreme right and left.

A historian writing in 1987. [William Carr, *Germany 1815 to 1985* published by Edward Arnold.]

The quiet preparation of the Nazi Party

During the mid 1920s, the Nazis did very badly in elections. People did not vote for Hitler and they had very few members elected to either the national parliament in Berlin (the Reichstag) or to the state parliaments. This did not mean that the Nazis were wasting their time.

Hitler gathered around him a group whose loyalty was unfailing. Men like Goebbels and Himmler, who would play a very important role in the success of the Nazi Party after 1929 and in the government of the Third Reich after 1933. Hitler made sure that the Nazi Party had a presence in every region of Germany and that these regions were run by a gauleiter who Hitler both knew and trusted. When the time came, these regional organisations were able to quickly recruit new members and organise very effective political action.

The success of the Nazis

The rise of the Nazi Party began with the Wall Street Crash and the economic catastrophe that followed. Very quickly millions of people were flung into unemployment, poverty and homelessness. People were looking for hope, for someone who would do something to change their lives. They thought that the Weimar government was to blame. The Weimar government had been unpopular since its creation but after 1929 people though they had practical reasons to vote against it.

For desperate people, politics promised the way out of their predicament. The old Weimar parties were all too closely identified with the failure of the Weimar regime. Only the Nazis and the Communists were not associated with this failure. Both parties did well in elections after 1929 but the Nazis did better. Many people in Germany feared that a strong Communist Party would lead a revolution like the one that had taken place in Russia in 1917, and therefore by default favoured the Nazis.

Hitler played a pivotal role in the rise in popularity of the Nazis. His ability as an organiser and a public speaker made him stand out from the other political leaders. People heard his message of hope, stability and strength. They saw the discipline of the Nazi Party members and their uniformed organisations and their loyalty to Hitler which gave them strength and security.

SOURCE C

Today I can only explain it with the poverty the people had been suffering and were suffering...In that context Hitler with his statements seemed to be the bringer of salvation. He said, 'I will get you out of this misery, but you all have to join in.' And everybody understood that.

Jutta Rudiger speaking in the 1990s about the Nazis in the late 1920s and early 1930s. [Quoted in Laurence Rees, *The Nazis: A Warning from History*, BBC Books 1997.]

ACTIVITIES

1. Briefly describe the reasons why the Nazis got very little support in the mid 1920s.
2. Explain why the Nazis were able to exploit the economic crisis caused by the Wall Street Crash.
3. Study Sources A and B. How useful are these sources in explaining why the Nazis made little progress between 1924 and 1929? Use the sources and your own knowledge to explain your answer.
4. Study Source C. Are you surprised by this explanation? Use the source and your own knowledge to explain your answer.

BRAIN BOOST

Learning the sequence of events for any study presents problems. A grid could be used to help with this process. This grid breaks the Weimar period into three stages and asks questions about each stage. Copy it onto a sheet of A4 and try to fill in the relevant information, in chronological order.

What were the major events?	Who ruled Germany?	Who were against the regime?	What was the regime concerned with?
Weimar, putsches and hyperinflation 1918–23			
Hedonism and stability 1924–29			
The Great Depression and street fighting 1930–32			

2.12 Why was Hindenburg so reluctant to appoint Hitler?

LEARNING OBJECTIVES

In this lesson you will:

- learn about the relationship between Hindenburg and Hitler
- practise using contextual knowledge to explain material in sources.

SOURCE B

There was little hint of either domination or genius in his manner or appearance, but he had immense powers of persuasion and an extraordinary capacity for bending individuals and, above all, the masses to his will.

Franz von Papen, writing about Hitler in his memoirs in 1952.

Hindenburg and the Weimar Republic

When the Weimar Republic was created in 1919, Hindenburg distanced himself from politics. His close comrade, General Ludendorff identified himself with the Kapp Putsch and the Munich Putsch and lost credibility. Hindenburg re-entered politics with the presidential election in 1925, where he gained 48% of the vote to become the country's president. Ludendorff in the same election gained 1% of the vote.

SOURCE A

The result of the election is interesting. In the end the great name produced its effect, and brought forth reserves of voters who would hardly have otherwise been available in such numbers if they had not regarded it as their patriotic duty to vote for the great commander in the Great War.

Gustav Stresemann writing in his diary in 1925, after Hindenburg had been elected president.

Hindenburg did not belong to a political party but favoured the right wing German National People's Party. He was an open opponent of the democratic system, though he did abide by its rules while he was president. He had close links with the government before the First World War and even asked the son of the old Kaiser for his permission to become president! As president he took a practical approach to politics, appointing as Chancellor, whichever party leader he felt most able to hold together a working coalition. In some cases, this even meant appointing a Chancellor whose politics he did not much like such as Muller, the Social Democrat.

The breakdown of the Republic

In 1930, Hindenburg appointed Heinrich Bruning to be Chancellor and to lead a coalition government. Bruning worked through the worst years of the depression and found it impossible to pass laws to change the situation. During the time he was Chancellor, the extremist parties gained so many seats in the Reichstag that cooperation was impossible. In May 1932, Hindenburg forced him to resign.

After Chancellor Muller's government fell in 1930, Hindenburg became influenced by two advisers, Kurt von Schleicher and Franz von Papen. It was Schleicher who encouraged Hindenburg to appoint Bruning in 1930 and then to sack him in 1932. In May 1932, Hindenburg appointed Franz von Papen as Chancellor. Papen formed a cabinet without any Reichstag members and ruled exclusively by presidential decree.

SOURCE 

Papen was confident that Hitler could be contained, moved out of the way and fired before government came back to those who believed that it was theirs by right.

A historian writing in 2000 about Papen's role in the appointment of Hitler.

BRAIN BOOST

Lists of key facts are easier to remember if you make a mnemonic.

When you sit the exam, there is certain key information that you will need to remember. For example, some of the factors that led to the rise of the Nazis are:

- **D**emocracy failed after 1930
- **E**conomic problems
- **P**ropaganda
- **S**trong leadership by Hitler
- **E**rnst Rohm and the SA

Using the first letter of each key word to make another word – a mnemonic – is also a way to try and remember. What word could you form using D – E – P – S – E?

Democratic government had now clearly failed. There were two elections in 1932 and in both, large numbers of voters used the election as a show of protest against the regime. This meant that the Reichstag was dominated by extremist parties that actually made matters worse. Hitler, who was the leader of the largest party, argued that the people had made a democratic choice and that he should be Chancellor. Hindenburg resisted and Schleicher became Chancellor in December 1932.

ACTIVITIES

1 Study Source A. Why was Hindenburg so appealing for the German voters? Use the source and your own knowledge to explain your answer.

2 Briefly describe how Bruning, Papen and Schleicher governed Germany.

3 Explain why Hindenburg was ready to turn to Hitler by January 1933.

4 Study Source B. Who did Papen believe that Hitler would be unable to 'dominate'? Who, on the other hand, might be made to bend to his will? Use the source and your own knowledge to explain your answer.

5 Study Source C. Who do you think the historian meant when he wrote 'government came back to *those* who believed that it was theirs by right'? Use the source and your own knowledge to explain your answer.

6 Study Sources B and C. How far does Source B agree with Source C in terms of what Papen believed was the situation in early 1933? Use the sources and your own knowledge to explain your answer.

The Bohemian Corporal

Hindenburg did not like Hitler. He referred to him, mistakenly, as the 'Bohemian Corporal'. (Hindenburg knew that Hitler was not from Germany but Bohemia is in Czechoslovakia, not Austria). He consistently kept Hitler out of government in 1932, despite the Nazis clearly being the largest party in the Reichstag.

It was Papen who persuaded Hindenburg to appoint Hitler. Papen was angry with Schleicher and wanted Schleicher to be replaced as Chancellor. The only alternative was Hitler. Papen told Hindenburg that Germany needed Hitler to get rid of the Communists. Then, Papen argued, the old elite led by Hindenburg, could control Hitler and eventually get rid of him. Hindenburg eventually gave in and Hitler was appointed as the Chancellor of Germany on 30 January 1933.

GradeStudio

Sorting out your source-based questions. You have learnt about two types of source-based question; utility and purpose. Below are three source-based questions. Which of them are 'utility' questions and which are 'purpose' questions? When you have done that you can try to answer them using the sources indicated and the 'Getting your sources sorted!' sections on pages 26 and 52.

1 Study Source A on page 6. Why would Ludendorff describe the British blockade as a 'war of starvation'? Use the source and your own knowledge to explain your answer.

2 Study Source A on page 36. Why did the Nazi Party produce a 25 point programme? Use the source and your own knowledge to explain your answer.

3 Study Sources B and C on page 44. How useful are these sources for a historian studying the rise of Hitler? Use the source and your own knowledge to explain your answer.

2.13 Why was the Reichstag fire so useful to Hitler?

LEARNING OBJECTIVES

In this lesson you will:

- learn about the first part of Hitler's seizure of power
- practise answering a source-based question on 'purpose'.

KEY WORDS

Freedom of speech – *the right to express your opinion.*

Right of assembly – *the right to organise meetings.*

The Reichstag fire

On the night of 27 February 1933, an event happened that shocked the German nation but gave Hitler a wonderful opportunity. The Reichstag building was burned down and the police found a Dutch Communist, who admitted to having started the fire. Hitler acted quickly and within 24 hours, Papen's boast to Hindenburg that he 'could control Hitler' was proved to be an extremely hollow one.

On the morning of 28 February, Hitler persuaded Hindenburg to sign a presidential decree, giving Hitler wide-ranging powers, including the power to deal with the 'state of emergency' that had arisen following the Reichstag fire. Entitled 'The Protection of the People and the State', it gave Hitler the power to rule by decree. It curbed **freedom of speech** and the **right of assembly**. It also gave the police the excuse to arrest Communist leaders. In Prussia alone, Herman Goering's policemen arrested over 4000 Communists in the days following the Reichstag fire.

The Nazi seizure of power

Like Papen had promised, Hitler had dealt with the Communists. Unlike what Papen had promised, Hitler was now out of the control of Hindenburg, Papen and the rich and powerful who usually controlled German politics. Only four weeks after becoming Chancellor, Hitler had got Hindenburg to sign a decree that fundamentally altered the Weimar Constitution because it gave the Chancellor the right to rule by decree. It also made legal the mass arrests of Nazi opponents, by which the Nazis were able to dominate the elections of March 1933. There were other measures that the Nazis needed to take in order to build the National Socialist State under Adolf Hitler, but the first step had been taken.

SOURCE 

Severe depression is everywhere. Party work is proving impossible because of financial difficulties. There is a real danger of the party going to pieces.

Josef Goebbels in his diary, December 1932.

GradeStudio

Study Source D. Why would pictures like this be distributed by the Nazis? Use the source and your own knowledge to explain your answer.

Hint: In answering the question, you will need to decide what the question is asking you to do, then make sure you include something from the source and your own knowledge to gain the higher levels for your answer.

Examiner's tip

This is a 'purpose' question. It is actually asking you about both the Nazis and the situation that the photograph relates to. Thus the Nazis, who are desperate to take total control of Germany, are aided by the Reichstag fire and the fear that it creates of a Communist revolution. You could also bring in some material about the role of Goebbels and the newly created Ministry of Propaganda and their purpose in the Nazi state. To gain the highest level you will write about the impact that the photograph would have had on its intended audience in terms of changing its attitudes towards the Nazis.

SOURCE B

1 There are now restrictions on personal liberty, on the right of free expression of opinion, including freedom of the press, on the right of assembly and the right of association.
2 If any state fails to take the necessary measures to restore public safety and order, the Reich government may temporarily take over the powers of the highest state authority.

Excerpts from the decree written by Hitler and signed on 28 February 1933.

SOURCE C

It is early in 1933. One storm trooper says to the other, 'Have you heard the latest? The Reichstag is on fire!' The other storm trooper hisses, 'Shhh! Not until tomorrow!'

A German joke from 1933.

ACTIVITIES

1 Briefly describe the change in Hitler's rule brought about by the Reichstag fire.

2 Explain why the Reichstag fire was 'a wonderful opportunity' for Hitler.

3 Study Source A. What does this suggest might have happened to the Nazi Party had Hitler not been appointed as Chancellor? Use the source and your own knowledge to explain your answer.

4 Study Source B. How far did this change life in Germany? Use the source and your own knowledge to explain your answer.

5 Study Source C. How useful is this in understanding people's attitudes towards the Nazis? Use the source and your own knowledge to explain your answer.

6 Write an essay to the question: 'How far was Adolf Hitler responsible for the end of the Weimar Republic?'

SOURCE D

The Reichstag after the fire. Pictures like this were released to the world's press in the days following the fire.

GradeStudio

You have now completed this unit, which has focused on how and why Hitler was able to come to power in Germany in January 1933. You have also had practice in answering questions designed to prepare you for your exam. Below is an example of one type of exam question, with some hints to help you write a top-scoring answer.

b Explain why the Nazis lost popularity in the mid-1920s? **[7 marks]**

Examiner's tip

Explanation questions often begin with a simple 'why' or 'explain why', and then add a situation. The question above is actually asking you to explain the factors behind the situation, that is, the reasons why the change or event took place. The most important word in an answer that requires you to explain is 'because'.

Fact file

In the exam, you will be asked to answer two questions from Section B, the Depth Study: a source-based question and a structured question. The structured question is divided into three parts – **a**, **b** and **c**. In this Grade Studio, we'll be looking at how to produce a top-level answer for the **b** type of question, which asks you to explain something. The **b** question has 7 marks.

Candidate's answer

People stopped voting for the Nazis and they did not have many seats in the parliament. The failure of the Munich Putsch, the economic upturn and success in foreign policy also made the Nazis less attractive to ordinary Germans. The Munich Putsch was important because Hitler and other leading Nazis were sent to prison and so the party lost its direction. This meant that other parties offered Germans a more stable option at election time. Once Stresemann and Schacht had sorted out hyperinflation, ordinary Germans enjoyed a period of economic stability. As a result of this, the standard of living improved for many people and they were not so ready to listen to the Nazis message, which relied on people's unhappiness. Also, the treaties that Stresemann was able to negotiate with other European countries moved Germany forward and further away from the frustration felt at the Treaty of Versailles.

Examiner's comment

The first part of the answer (in red) gets the candidate into Level 1. By identifying specific reasons, and then explaining them, the candidate is able to build on their answer so that it reaches the top level.

Simplified mark scheme

Level 1 (1 to 2 marks): General assertions These answers relate to the question but do not show any of the candidate's own knowledge.
Level 2 (2 to 4 marks): Identifies specific reasons The candidate can show own knowledge through mentioning relevant reasons why something happened. The more reasons identified, the higher the mark within the level.
Level 3 (3 to 5 marks): One reason explained By adding an explanation to one of the reasons, the answer moves into Level 3. N.B. The explanation must relate the reason to the question. Merely describing what happened will not be good enough. Hint: linking phrases such as 'This meant that' or 'As a result of this' can help to further develop explanations.
Level 4 (5 to 7 marks): More than one reason explained Two reasons well explained should get close to maximum marks. Again the explanation needs to relate closely to the question.

Now let us construct an answer to the following question.

b Why was the Weimar government able to hold on to power between 1919 and 1923?

Which of the following reasons could you identify in order to move to Level 2?

The factions (Spartacists, Nationalists, Nazis) did not have nationwide support.	Hyperinflation meant that people had problems with money.	In 1919 and 1923, the Army stood by the Weimar government.
Ebert used the Freikorps to break the Spartacist uprising,	People blamed the Kaiser for the loss of the First World War.	Many ordinary Germans were afraid of Communism.

To move onto Level 3, you need to explain one of the reasons.

Suppose you have chosen the reason 'The factions (Spartacists, Nationalists, Nazis) did not have nationwide support'. Which of the following explanations would be the best one to answer the question and ensure that the level is gained? What is the problem with the other one?

The Spartacus uprising took place in Berlin. It was all over by the middle of January 1919. Rosa Luxemburg and Karl Liebknecht were killed. The Reichstag moved to Weimar. The nationalists took power in Berlin but the workers went on strike and the national government collapsed. The Munich Putsch failed when Hitler shouted 'surrender' when faced with a large group of soldiers.	This meant that when they tried something, the government was able to move either the army or the Freikorps to that place and concentrate their efforts and crush the uprising because it was only in one place. For example, if the Nazis had organised a putsch that started in Munich, Berlin, Cologne and Dresden at the same time, it may have been far more effective.

To move to Level 4, you need to repeat that process with another point.

Suppose you have chosen the reason 'In 1919 and 1923, the army stood by the Weimar government'. Which of the following explanations would be the best one to answer the question and ensure that the level is gained? What is the problem with the other one?

The government called on the army when faced with revolutions. The army would shoot the enemies with guns in order to stop them. Sometimes those people would surrender and might go to prison. The government did not change because of this. Revolutions aim to change governments and need lots of men with guns in order to overthrow the governments. In Germany this happened a lot in the years following the First World War and usually the army was involved.	In 1919, the Spartacus uprising was put down by the Freikorps who murdered Rosa Luxemburg and Karl Liebknecht. In 1920, the Army did not stop the Kapp Putsch but the government got the workers to go on strike. The Nazis failed in 1923 because the army shot them and then they ran away.

Try out these explanation questions for yourself, using Chapter 2 to help you.

1 Explain why 1923 was such a difficult year for the Weimar Republic.

2 Explain why more people voted for the Nazis in the years 1929–32.

3 Explain why the Reichstag fire was so useful for Hitler.

4 Explain why the German economy collapsed after 1929.

Chapter 3

How effectively did the Nazis control Germany, 1933–45?

KEY WORDS

Schutz Staffeln (SS) – *a large organisation within the Nazi Party run by Heinrich Himmler.*

Totalitarian dictatorship – *government by a small unelected minority, with one man having absolute power.*

In this chapter, you will learn how the Nazis kept control of Germany. Here are the four key areas and some key questions for each area. As you work through the chapter, you can refer back to these areas and key questions.

SOURCE A

It pleased Hitler immensely to see organisations which dealt with similar issues engage in feuds with one another. For only in such circumstances would he be able to maintain his independence from the specialised ministries. Those who became too powerful he would cut down to size; to those who were stranded out on a limb he extended a hand and helped them back on their feet.

Reinhardt Spitzy, former adjutant to the Nazi Foreign Minister, writing in his book, *How We Squandered the Reich* published in 1997.

SOURCE B

I see the first task of this new ministry as establishing a co-ordination between the government and the whole people…It is not enough for people to be more or less reconciled to our regime, to be persuaded to adopt a neutral attitude towards us. Rather, we want to work on people until they have capitulated to us. The New Ministry has no other aim than to unite the nation behind the ideal of the national revolution.

Josef Goebbels speaking to a press conference on 15 March 1933.

SOURCE C

Adolf Hitler in military uniform.

SOURCE D

In the cities, the Young SA men took over the pavements and paraded about in their new and over-waxed boots and shoulder straps. Around the brown houses, guarded by numerous sentries, there was an intense commotion of comings and goings amongst crowds of sympathizers and onlookers.

French traveller, Daniel Guerin, describing the atmosphere during the July 1932 election.

SOURCE 

Charlie Chaplin is annoyed: 'I can't prevent Hitler from copying my moustache, nor can I help it that Goebbels always imitates the way I walk, but it really makes me furious that people laugh more at Goering than at me!'

Goering likes to take animals for a walk. One day, Hitler looks down and sees him from his office window. 'Hermann!' he shouts, 'why are you taking that tortoise for a walk?' Goering yells back, 'No my Fuhrer, that isn't a tortoise; it's Goebbels wearing a steel helmet!'

Popular jokes among ordinary Germans during the Third Reich.

SOURCE F

The Nazis used the Gestapo to control people by making them afraid.

Political control

National Socialist Germany was a one-party state. This meant that the National Socialists had to change Germany from the multi-party Weimar democracy to a **totalitarian dictatorship.** Eliminating their political opponents was a major part of their early rule. Then they imposed new systems of government at national, state and local level so that National Socialism was able to control all aspects of administration. Key questions are:

- How effectively did the Nazis eliminate political opposition?
- What different ways of governing did the Nazis use?
- How was the **SS** important?
- How total was Nazi control of the Third Reich?

Psychological control

It was important for the Nazis to put across their message. The constant outpouring of propaganda using all types of media had one purpose: to make people believe in the Nazi ideals and have confidence in the regime. In practice, it was less important to get people to actively support the regime than to ensure that the vast majority were, at best, not opposed to the regime. Key questions are:

- How effectively did the Nazis create a 'People's Community'?
- How far did people trust Adolf Hitler as leader?
- How did the Nazis co-exist with organised religion?

Violent control

Violence had been part of politics in Germany since the First World War. In having the SA, their own **paramilitary** wing, the Nazis made it clear that they would attempt to outmuscle any of their opponents. After they gained power, the Nazis continued to use violence to intimidate opponents but also to persuade others that opposition was not worth it. Key questions are:

- How effective was the threat of violence in keeping down opposition to the Nazis?
- Why did Hitler disband the SA?
- Why did violence against the Jews get worse?

Lack of control

Despite the attempts of the Nazis to gain total control of Germany, there were still people who would not be controlled, ranging from people who were actively trying to kill Hitler or to overthrow the regime, people who were outspoken and critical, or people who just would not toe the line and were an irritant to the Nazi regime. Key questions are:

- What sorts of people were opposed to the Nazis?
- How did these people show their opposition to the Nazis?
- How far did opposition pose a threat to the Nazis?

3.1 What did the Enabling Act actually enable?

LEARNING OBJECTIVES

In this lesson you will:

- learn about the Enabling Act
- practise answering source-based questions on typicality and purpose.

KEY WORDS

Civil liberties – *rights enjoyed by ordinary people.*

Decree of the Reich President for the Protection of the People and State

The decree that followed the Reichstag fire gave Hitler some of the powers he wanted. The suspension of **civil liberties** allowed the Nazi-controlled police forces – many of whom drafted in SA men to help – to detain and 'question' Nazi opponents. It also gave Hitler the power to issue decrees on his own without the agreement of the president and to replace state governments if they did not follow the lead of the Reich government.

There were two problems with the decree of 28 February 1933. Firstly, it had given Hitler emergency powers under the old constitution and granted by the president. Hitler wanted to abolish the constitution and wanted to stop Hindenburg taking back what he had given. This meant taking a step further.

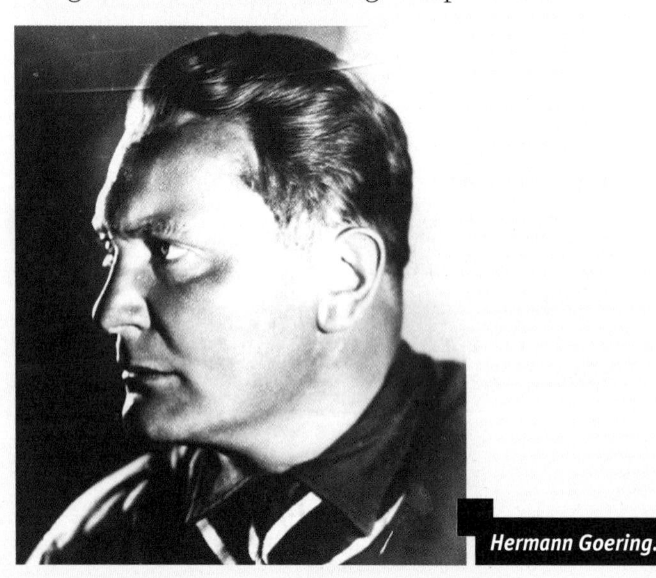

Hermann Goering.

SOURCE A

Hitler's mission is of importance for the history of the whole world, because he took up a war to the death against Communism. The day will come when other countries will be thankful that at the critical moment there was an Adolf Hitler in Germany.

Hermann Goering, writing in 1934.

Dealing with the Communists

After the Reichstag fire, the Communist Party was banned. In the elections of March 1933, therefore, the Communists did not have any seats in the Reichstag. This was good for Hitler in one way but also created a problem for him.

The Communist menace, that Hitler was appointed to deal with, had indeed been dealt with (see Source A). The Communist Party could not take their seats in the Reichstag and most of their leaders had been jailed. If Papen was right, early March was the time to make good his promise to Hindenburg and 'control' Hitler. The best way of doing this would be for Hindenburg to cancel the decree of 28 February.

The Enabling Act

To prevent this happening, Hitler needed to change the constitution and transfer even more power from the President to the Chancellor. This needed an act to be passed through the Reichstag with a two-thirds majority. The first meeting of the Reichstag was to take place in the Kroll Opera House on 23 March 1933.

The problems of rule by Presidential Decree

The major criticism of the Weimar Regime in the last two years is that government had nothing to do with the people. The deduction from this is that the politicians who ruled Germany did not have the interests of the people at heart. This partly explains the popularity of parties like the Nazis and the Communists in the elections of 1930 and 1932.

Though the Nazis were intent on creating a one-party dictatorship, they wanted this based on the

SOURCE B

Law to Remove the Distress of the People and the State (The Enabling Act)

The Reichstag has passed the following law, which, after it has been established that it meets the requirements for legislation altering the Constitution.

Article 1. National laws can be enacted by the Reich Cabinet as well as in accordance with the procedure established in the Constitution. This also applies to the laws referred to in Article 85, Paragraph 2, and in Article 87 of the Constitution.

Article 2. The national laws enacted by the Reich Cabinet may deviate from the Constitution as long as they do not affect the position of the Reichstag. The powers of the President remain undisturbed.

Article 3. The national laws enacted by the Reich Cabinet shall be prepared by the Chancellor. They come into effect, unless otherwise specified, the day after their publication.

Article 4. Treaties of the Reich with foreign states which concern matters of national legislation do not require the consent of the bodies participating in legislation. The Reich Cabinet is empowered to issue the necessary provisions for the implementation of these treaties.

Article 5. This law becomes effective on the day of its publication. It becomes invalid on April 1, 1937; it also becomes invalid if the present Reich Cabinet is replaced by another.

Passed on 23rd March 1933.

broad support of the people. As Goebbels said, the Nazis wanted to 'unite the nation behind the ideal'. It was not enough for people to understand that the Nazis had the power, they had to believe that the Nazis were the right and natural rulers of Germany.

During the meeting, the opera house was full of armed SA men. Hitler made a speech outlining what the Enabling Act was and how it would save Germany from the threat of Communist revolution (see Source B). Nazi delegates cheered. When Hitler had finished, the Social Democrat leader, Otto Wels, made a speech in reply. He spoke as though at a funeral, referring to the end of the Weimar Constitution and the destruction of social democracy. He pledged himself and his party to the principles of a modern liberal democracy (see Source C). For much of his speech, he was heckled by the Nazis. When Hitler stood up to reply, both sides shouted at one another. When the vote was taken, the Enabling Act was passed by 444 votes to 94. Most of the non-Nazi delegates had been intimidated and had voted for Hitler.

SOURCE C

We Social Democrats pledge ourselves to the principles of humanity and justice, of freedom and socialism. We greet the persecuted and the oppressed. We greet our friends in the Reich. Your courage and loyalty deserve admiration.

From the speech by Social Democrat leader, Otto Wels, during the session of the Reichstag that passed the Enabling Act, 23 March 1933.

VOICE YOUR OPINION!

Would you have accepted the Enabling Act? How far is your opinion based on what you know came after?

ACTIVITIES

1. Briefly describe the powers that the Enabling Act gave Hitler.
2. Explain why Hitler was able to get the Enabling Act through the Reichstag.
3. How important was the election of March 1933 in consolidating Hitler's power? Explain your answer.
4. Study Source A. Why would Hermann Goering have written this in 1934? Use the source and your own knowledge to explain your answer. (For more information on Hermann Goering, see page 42.)
5. Study Source B. How far had Hitler become the absolute ruler of Germany? Use the source and your own knowledge to explain your answer.
6. Study Source C. Are you surprised by this source? Use the source and your own knowledge to explain your answer.

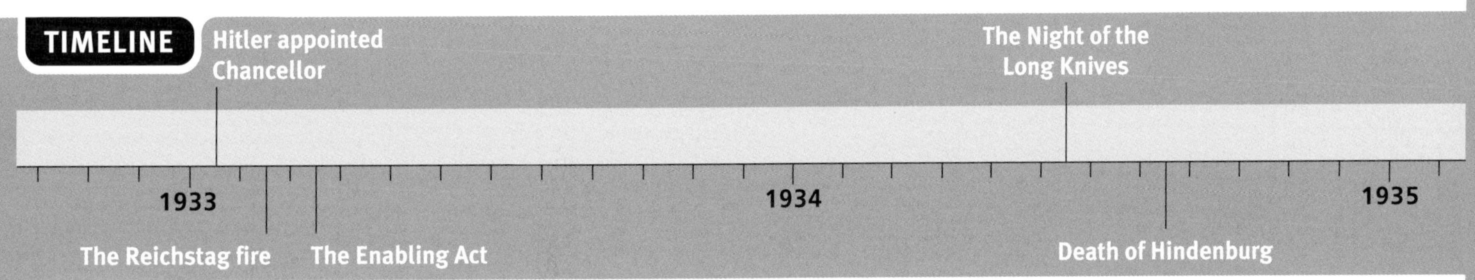

3.2 How did Hitler build the one-party state?

LEARNING OBJECTIVES

In this lesson you will:

- learn about the Nazi one-party state
- practise answering source-based questions on typicality.

KEY WORDS

Dictator – *someone who has absolute control of a country.*

Gleichschaltung – *coordination of all state institutions under Nazi control.*

Purge – *getting rid of unwanted people, usually by murdering them.*

Führer – *German word for leader, adopted by Hitler as his title in place of 'Chancellor'.*

Hitler as Dictator

After the Enabling Act was passed, Hitler was almost the **dictator** of Germany. By July 1933, he had banned all other political parties and the trade unions (see Source A). The old Weimar institutions were brought under Nazi control and some new organisations were set up. This was the process that the Nazis called **Gleichschaltung** meaning 'coordination' or bringing into line.

The German Labour Front

While the left-wing parties were broken up, something still needed to be done about trade unions. Most members of trade unions were working class and often left-wing in their politics. Left-wing parties had traditionally enjoyed a close relationship with trade unions. In May 1933, the Nazis set up the DAF (German Labour Front) led by Robert Ley. The new organisation took all the assets of existing unions and brought union members into its organisation.

SOURCE A

Whoever attempts to maintain the organised existence of another political party, or to form a new political party, shall...be punished with hard labour of up to three years or with imprisonment of from six months to three years duration.

From the law against the revival of old or the formation of new parties, 14 July 1933.

The Night of the Long Knives

After taking power, some leading Nazis began to disagree with the way that Hitler was leading Germany. Ernst Rohm, the leader of the SA, was one of these. He began to feel distanced from Hitler and now that the Nazis had taken power, the SA was losing its relevance. Rohm became more and more outspoken, though how far he had thought through some of the things he said, is questionable. Certainly, by the summer of 1934, there were those in the party who were keen to tell Hitler that Rohm was dangerous.

The existence of the SA also made the army feel nervous. With over half a million members in 1934, it was a much larger organisation than the official state army. Rohm's continued insistence that eventually the army would become part of the SA made the generals very nervous. Eventually, Hitler was persuaded to keep the existing army and plans were made to get rid of Rohm and disband the SA.

On the Night of the Long Knives, leading SA men and other Nazi opponents were arrested and

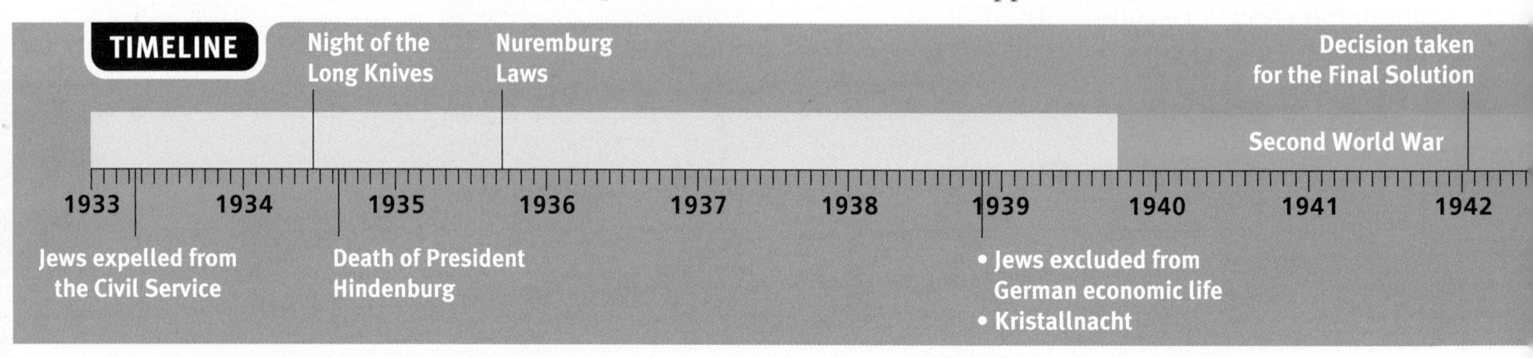

murdered. This had been very carefully planned by Himmler and Goering. The number of those killed is unknown; estimates are as high as 1000, though the figure was probably far less. One of the most important results of this **purge** was that the SA became a part of the SS under the leadership of Heinrich Himmler.

Hindenburg's Death

Soon after the Night of Long Knives, President Hindenburg died at the age of 87. Knowing that Hindenburg's death was imminent, Hitler moved quickly. On 1 August, a law was passed merging the offices of Chancellor and President into a new role; the '**Führer** and Reich Chancellor'. Also part of the law was the agreement that the army would now take a personal oath of loyalty to Adolf Hitler (see Source C). Hindenburg died a day later. Adolf Hitler was now the undisputed dictator of Germany.

SOURCE B

The poster says 'The whole of Germany listens to the Führer on the radio'. The radio was an effective means of taking Hitler's voice to homes and workplaces all over Germany.

ACTIVITIES

1. Briefly describe what the Nazis did to create the one-party state?
2. Explain why the leading Nazis carried out the assassinations during the Night of the Long Knives?
3. Study Source A. Why were the Nazis able to ban other parties? Use the source and your own knowledge to explain your answer.
4. Study Sources B and C. How useful are these sources in understanding how the Nazis kept control of Germany? Use the sources and your own knowledge to explain your answer.

SOURCE 

I swear before God to give my unconditional obedience to Adolf Hitler, Führer of the Reich and of the German people, and I pledge my word as a brave soldier to observe this oath always, even at the peril of my life.

The army's oath of allegiance to Adolf Hitler, taken from August 1934 onwards.

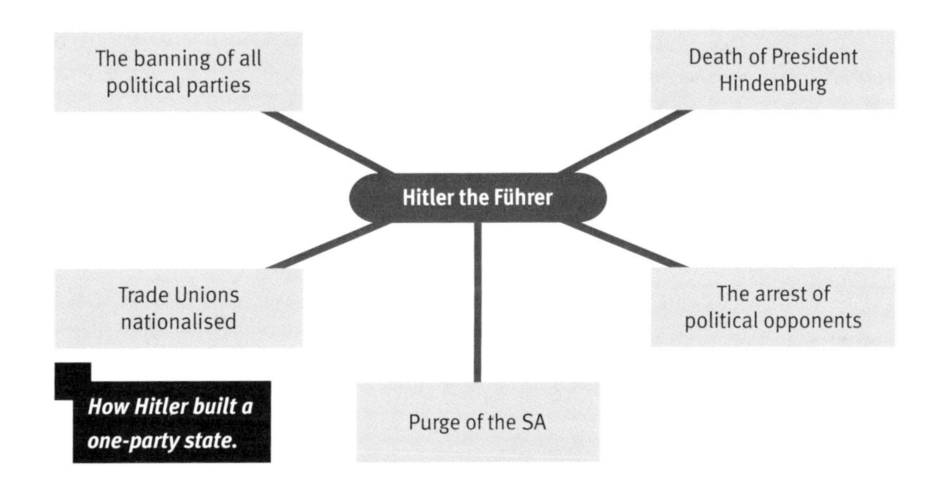

How Hitler built a one-party state.

HISTORY DETECTIVE

Find out which other important people were murdered during the Night of the Long Knives. Were they all friends of Ernst Rohm?

3.3 Get your sources sorted!

Are you surprised by these sources about the Night of the Long Knives?

LEARNING OBJECTIVES

In this lesson you will:

- learn about the relationship between Adolf Hitler and Ernst Rohm
- learn how to answer a source-based question about Hitler and Ernst Rohm.

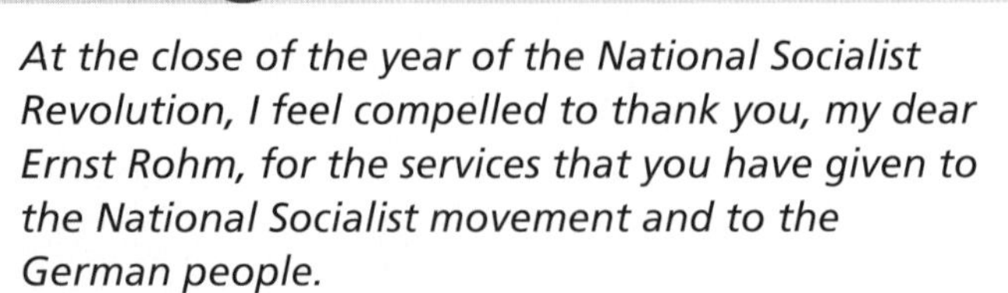

SOURCE A

At the close of the year of the National Socialist Revolution, I feel compelled to thank you, my dear Ernst Rohm, for the services that you have given to the National Socialist movement and to the German people.

Part of a Letter to Ernst Rohm from Adolf Hitler, written on 1 January 1934.

Are you surprised?

Some source-based questions will begin with the phrase 'Are you surprised'. This means whether or not the source presents you with information that fits in with other information you may have come across. In order to answer, you need to say what your expectation might be concerning both the source and other similar sources that are not shown. In order to do this effectively and to fully explain the reasons behind your point, you will need the contextual knowledge that surrounds the source.

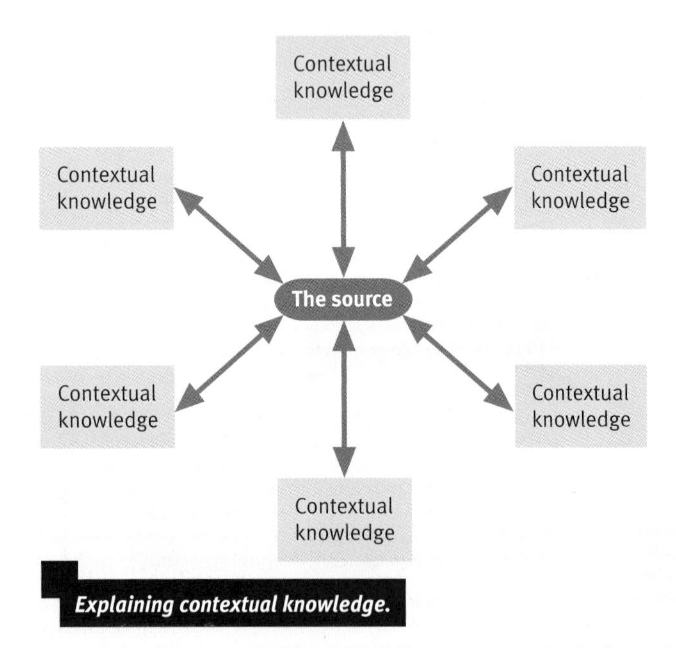

Explaining contextual knowledge.

Look at Source A. The type of question you might be asked could be: 'Are you surprised that Hitler would write to Rohm in this way? Use the source and your knowledge to explain your answer.'

Low-level answers give a straightforward answer, which could be about anybody at any time:

- 'No, I am not. Friends often write to one another at New Year.'

OR

- 'Yes, I am. I would have thought that Hitler had more important things to do.'

Contextual knowledge is the key ingredient needed to make this answer far stronger:

- 'No, I am not. Hitler and Rohm were friends for many years. They were both committed National Socialists. Rohm was the leader of the SA, which played a very important part in the rise of Hitler and the Nazis.'
- 'Yes, I am. In 1934, Rohm was murdered by Hitler during the Night of the Long Knives and I would have thought that Hitler would wish to distance himself from Rohm. By January 1934, Hitler was very secure in power and felt that he did not need the SA or Rohm any longer.'

To get the highest level for this question, both sides of this question need to be considered and answered with contextual knowledge, that is, why you would expect it and why you would not.

- 'In some ways, I would have expected Hitler to write this to Rohm. It was probably his habit to write to prominent Nazis at the beginning of each year to keep their spirits up. Rohm had played a very important part in the Nazi success ("for the services you have given") and Hitler had yet to fall out with him. The problems between them did not really start until later in the year and the Night of the Long Knives was not until the end of June. On the other hand, it is perhaps surprising that Hitler wished to keep up good relations with Rohm, as he would already have known that the SA had served its purpose. Hitler had no intention that the SA would take over from the army and so could have been preparing the ground for the action against the SA leaders that eventually happened in June 1934. In this case, I am surprised that he referred to Rohm as a "friend".'

SOURCE B

Through your decisive intervention and your courageous personal commitment you have nipped all the treasonable plots in the bud. You have saved the German nation from serious danger and for this I express to you my deeply felt gratitude and my sincere appreciation.

Statement issued from the office of President Hindenburg, as a reaction to the Night of the Long Knives.

SOURCE D

If Hitler thinks he can squeeze me for his own ends forever, and some day throw me on the ash heap, he is wrong. The SA can also be an instrument for checking Hitler himself.

Ernst Rohm in conversation with Kurt Ludecke, recalled in Ludecke's book, *I knew Hitler*, published in London in 1938.

ACTIVITIES

1. Study Source B. Are you surprised that Hindenburg should respond in this way to the Night of the Long Knives? Use the source and your own knowledge to explain your answer.
2. Study Source C. Are you surprised that the British should take this view of the Night of the Long Knives? Use the source and your own knowledge to explain your answer.
3. Study Source D. Are you surprised that Rohm would say this? Use the source and your own knowledge to explain your answer.

SOURCE C

British cartoon about the Night of the Long Knives by Sidney Strube, published in the *Daily Express*, 3 July 1934.

3.4 What role did the SS play in controlling the Nazi state?

LEARNING OBJECTIVES

In this lesson you will:

- learn about the role of the SS
- practise using contextual knowledge to improve answers to source-based questions.

KEY WORDS

Concentration camp – *large camp surrounded by barbed wire which housed political prisoners and slave labourers.*

Euthanasia – *killing people in order to prevent suffering.*

Final Solution – *plan to kill all the Jews in Europe.*

The SS in the Community

Himmler quickly took the SS beyond its limited role to protect the Führer. In 1936, Himmler was made the Head of the Police and soon the division between the police and the SS began to blur. This made the SS very powerful at both a national and local level.

Fact file

The SS was originally formed in 1925 as Hitler's personal bodyguard. It was officially part of the SA and was a small elite organisation. After the Night of the Long Knives, the SS under Heinrich Himmler became the most important organisation in Nazi Germany and carried out a wide variety of roles.

SOURCE

We shall recognise the values of blood and selection. We shall keep Germany's internal security. We shall make sure that never again will the Jewish–Bolshevist revolution of sub-humanity be unleashed in Germany, the heart of Europe.

Heinrich Himmler in a speech on 12 November 1935.

Fact file

The Nazis and Race

The Nazis believed that some races, in this case white North Europeans, were superior to other races, for example, Jews. They went to extreme lengths to make sure that 'superior' Germans did not have children with 'inferior' people, so that German blood (meaning DNA) was kept 'pure'. In the later years of the Nazi regime, they removed people they believed to be inferior. Millions were killed in the gas chambers in **concentration camps** (see pages 122–23) and hundreds of thousands in the euthanasia programme.

Himmler believed strongly in racial theory and was anxious to keep German blood pure. Part of this was the **euthanasia** programme, which got rid of people who might have 'bad blood' (see Source A). Those with hereditary illnesses were to be killed under the euthanasia programme, organised by the SS.

The SS was also responsible for getting rid of other 'undesirables'. It was the SS who planned the '**Final Solution**' (see Chapter 4, pages 120–25). Some SS men, like Reinhardt Heydrich or Adolf Eichmann built very successful careers out of their role in organising mass murder.

At the other end of social engineering, women of good German stock were encouraged to have lots of babies. The SS took an active role in this by setting up the 'lebensborn' programme in 1935 (see Source C). This allowed single German women to book themselves into a special 'hotel', where SS men chosen for their Aryan looks and good Nazi ideas, would make them pregnant. By 1944, over 11,000 Nazi babies conceived in this way, had been born.

The SS as an economic empire

The economic activities of the SS originated from its use of political prisoners in concentration camps. The SS found that it was able to charge for the use of their labour and was soon subcontracting services to business. As German-controlled territory expanded in

SOURCE B

The SS selected only Aryan-looking people and gave them uniforms designed and manufactured by top clothing companies.

the early years of the Second World War, the supply of slave labour increased dramatically, as Jews in these new areas and prisoners of war were captured. All of this labour belonged to the SS, and the charges they made for it enabled them to make huge profits, particularly in the middle years of the war.

The fighting SS

In November 1940, Himmler formed the Waffen SS that became a second army that fought alongside the ordinary army. The Waffen SS also allowed non-Germans to fight for Germany, usually because they wanted to fight against Communism. Some of these men joined in such large numbers that they got their own divisions, like the 'Viking' division which was made up of men from Norway, Sweden and Denmark.

SOURCE C

I knew, as everyone did in the SS, about these lebensborn places, but I had never thought of myself as a potential stallion. The whole thing amused me, but at the same time it was rather worrying. I was rather puzzled as to what it would involve. Before I left, the medical officer told me not to mention it to the others in the unit.

Peter Neumann, a SS man writing about his selection for the lebensborn (selective breeding) programme.

SOURCE D

SS guards from Auschwitz relaxing while off duty.

ACTIVITIES

1. Briefly describe the role of the SS in Nazi Germany.
2. Explain why the roles of the SS and the police became similar.
3. Study Source A. How useful is this source in understanding the purpose of the SS in Nazi Germany? Use the source and your own knowledge to explain your answer.
4. Study Source B. Why were looks so important to the SS? Use the source and your own knowledge to explain your answer.
5. Study Source C. Why do you think he was asked not to mention it to his comrades? Use the source and your own knowledge to explain your answer.
6. Study Source D. Are you surprised by this picture? Use the source and your own knowledge to explain your answer.

3.5 What role did the Gestapo play in Nazi Germany?

LEARNING OBJECTIVES

In this lesson you will:

- learn about the importance of the Gestapo
- practise answering source-based questions on utility.

When the Nazis seized power in 1933, there were two kinds of organisations:

- the old government organisations like the Civil Service, the police, the army
- the new Nazi organisations like the SA, the gauleiters and the SS.

Hitler gave power to the Nazi organisations but did not abolish the old ones. This caused a great deal of confusion. The way in which the state was policed was probably the most confusing of all.

The police in Nazi Germany

Part of the confusion was caused by the fact that Heinrich Himmler had two significant but separate roles in Nazi Germany. On the one hand, he was the head of the SS (see pages 74–75) and on the other he was the Chief of Police. The problem was that the SS had a security role through its security service, the SD, which made it a kind of police force, but driven by Nazi ideology. Thus Germany had the normal police force controlled by a fanatical Nazi, Himmler, and the Nazi police.

The Gestapo

The Gestapo was the state secret police force (see Source A). It was part of the official state police but through Heinrich Himmler had very close links with the SS. It had offices in most major centres of population. Statistics reveal that there were not many agents when compared to the number of Germans they were supposed to be watching. For example, in Würzburg there were a million people and only 28 Gestapo agents. At its height, the Gestapo had 30,000 agents; though such were the demands of the paperwork that they spent much of their time behind a desk. Gestapo men relied heavily on informants providing them with the necessary information.

Gestapo raid on Warsaw ghetto.

The Gestapo in action

Given their limited resources, the Gestapo had to be selective about who they watched. Gestapo records show that they were successful at breaking some of the more dangerous resistance groups or rounding up those who took part in the July Bomb Plot. Most of the work undertaken by the Gestapo, however, was at a far lower level (see Source B).

Evidence shows that reports from ordinary Germans were the most common way for the Gestapo to receive information. The effects of this were twofold. Firstly, it meant that no ordinary German was beyond the reach of the Gestapo and that made people afraid and secondly that the task of processing the information, and sometimes following it up, kept Gestapo agents off the streets.

Denunciations were common, though were often inspired by motives other than loyalty to the state or the Nazi Party. Getting rid of people you did not like was possible if you could collect enough 'evidence' against them. Often people who looked different were denounced simply on that basis. There are cases of young people who had been brainwashed by the Hitler Youth or the League of German Girls denouncing their parents for being anti-Nazi.

As the Gestapo got busier, particularly towards the end of the war, they did not have the time to fully investigate allegations and so often Gestapo officers took an easier path. This may have been to ignore the denunciation but more often it meant torture or imprisonment, just in case there was something to the allegations.

Fact file

The July Bomb Plot

There were a group of German nobles, known as the Kreisau Circle, who had opposed Hitler since he was made Chancellor. Towards the end of the war, some of these men began to plot to assassinate Hitler. Along with officers in the army, they devised a plan to leave a bomb in Hitler's headquarters, when he was meeting with the top generals. The bomb was delivered on 29 July 1944 by Colonel von Stauffenburg and left under a table. It went off, killing several important officials but Hitler was only wounded. Afterwards, many people who may have been connected with the plot were executed.

SOURCE A

In these important times an organisation was created with an entirely new set of rules. From the beginning it was a necessary and effective instrument in the hands of the nation's leadership. It proved that it is capable of protecting the people's community against interference with communal life by anti-social elements.

From an article in *The German Police* magazine in 1943.

VOICE YOUR OPINION!

Is there ever a role for a secret police force?

SOURCE B

People were always coming and saying; 'why haven't you hung out a flag for Hitler's birthday' and so on...You almost went to jail. It was very dangerous if you didn't do it... Finally my mother bought a real tiny one.

A woman speaking in 1993 about her childhood in Nazi Germany.

SOURCE C

Protective Custody for Jehovah's Witnesses
If information regarding the impending release of a Jehovah's Witness is received, transfer to a concentration camp can take place immediately. If it is impossible to move them to a concentration camp, they will be retained in prison.

A circular, sent by Heinrich Müller, Head of the Gestapo in 1937.

ACTIVITIES

1. Briefly describe the structure of policing in Nazi Germany.
2. Why was the Gestapo, with its limited resources, able to control people?
3. Study Source A. How useful is this source to a historian studying the control that Nazi leaders had over ordinary Germans? Use the source and your own knowledge to explain your answer.
4. Study Source B. Are you surprised that the mother put out a Nazi flag? Use the source and your own knowledge to explain your answer.
5. Study Source C. How much power did individual Gestapo agents have? Use the source and your own knowledge to explain your answer.

3.6 How did the gauleiters help Hitler rule Germany?

LEARNING OBJECTIVES

In this lesson you will:

- learn about the gauleiters
- practise cross-referencing material in order to improve the quality of answers to source-based questions.

KEY WORDS

Feudal system – *system of regional control with a king and powerful barons.*

The administration of the Party

From its early days, the National Socialist Party had been organised on a national basis, with the country being divided into *gaus* or regions. These were further sub-divided into districts, towns, cells and blocks. There were originally 30 regions in Germany, though these were added to when Austria, parts of Czechoslovakia and Poland were added to the Reich itself. What was important for the government was that the gauleiters had a personal link to Hitler.

Double or triple system?

Germany was governed by the organisations of government left over from the Weimar Republic. The cabinet still issued laws, though often in name only, through decrees or sometimes laws were still passed by the Reichstag. These were then interpreted by civil servants at local and national level. Most of the governmental organisations were not abolished by Hitler. Instead, he governed around them. He used the gauleiters to bypass offices of state, giving the gauleiters special powers to carry out certain functions.

Gauleiters and a 'feudal system'

In the Middle Ages, the **feudal system** worked on the basis of lords being instructed by nobles, who in turn received orders from the king. In Nazi Germany, the gauleiter system functioned in much the same way, with local officials working on orders from gauleiters, who in turn received their orders directly from Hitler. It was this personal contact with Hitler and the fact that their role was not subject to the normal rules concerning government that gave the gauleiters their power (see Source B).

The gauleiter system in practice

In late 1939, two areas of what was then Poland were annexed back into Germany. They both had mixed populations of Poles and Germans. The gauleiters of these regions were told by Hitler to 'Germanise' their areas and that he would ask no questions about their methods. One gauleiter, Artur Greiser, set up a

SOURCE A

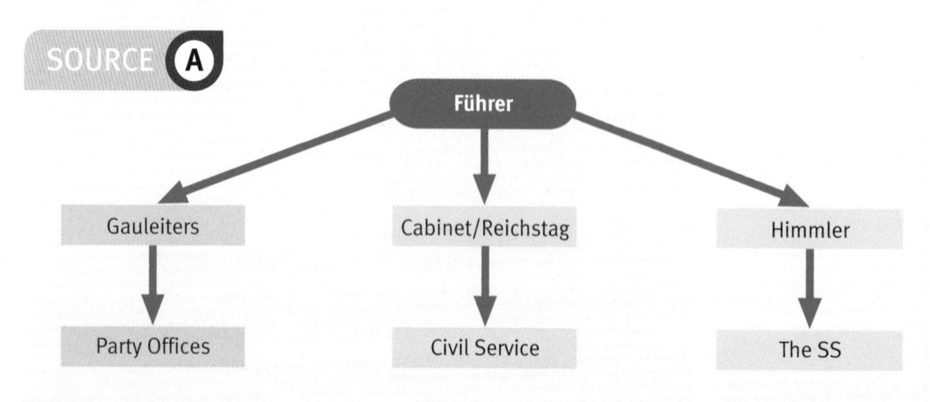

Government in the Nazi State.

SOURCE B

The Gauleiter [district leader] was responsible for all political and economic activities, civil defence, and the mobilisation of workers in his district. Most district leaders were appointed directly by the Führer.

Definition of Gauleiter from the *Encyclopaedia of the Third Reich* by Louis L. Snyder.

complicated programme that meant individuals had to be assessed for their 'Germanness', while another, Albert Forster, simply gave people official pieces of paper stating that they were German. Greiser complained to Himmler about Forster, and Himmler in turn complained to Hitler. Hitler did not intervene and Forster was allowed to carry on (see Source C). Even Himmler could not come between a gauleiter and the Führer.

Hitler as an inactive dictator

In many ways, Nazi Germany was over-governed (see Source D). There were so many people in different positions interpreting orders from above. Hitler himself was able to take a step back from all this. He often spent time away from government at his mountain home in Bavaria. There, he would walk in the mountains and watch films. He did not do the work of a head of state. In Berlin, Hitler was difficult to get hold of and preferred to concentrate on projects that interested him such as new building designs, matters to do with the army or, later on, the war.

SOURCE C

If I looked like Himmler, I would not talk about race.

Albert Forster, speaking in 1940.

SOURCE D

In his twelve years of rule in Germany, Hitler produced the biggest confusion in government that has ever existed in a civilised state. It was not through laziness that he did this, it was deliberate. This way, he disorganised the higher offices of government and made himself more powerful.

Otto Diettrich, Hitler's Press Chief, writing in 1955.

ACTIVITIES

1. Briefly describe how the Nazi Party was organised.
2. Explain why Hitler was more comfortable with the gauleiter system than he was with normal government.
3. Study sources A and B. How do you think that this would lead to a radicalisation of policy? Use the sources and your own knowledge to explain your answer.
4. Study Source C. Why do you think that Forster felt safe enough to make fun of Heinrich Himmler? Use the source and your own knowledge to explain your answer.
5. Study Source D. Explain why Hitler imposed the gauleiter system on German government. Use the source and your own knowledge to explain your answer.

GradeStudio

In the Grade Studio from pages 62 and 63, we looked at part (b) from the structured question. We will now construct an answer to an explanation question.

Question: Explain why Hindenburg and Papen did not stop Hitler.

You need to match the points below with their relevant explanations. You should look to develop these explanations to make sure that the examiner can award you the marks.

Point	Explanation
The Communists were still a danger	Hindenburg referred to Hitler as the 'Bohemian Corporal' and did not think that he was a danger to the 'natural' rulers.
The S.A. were very powerful	This meant that Hindenburg and Papen were prepared to put up with Hitler and hope he got rid of the Communists.
They did not believe that Hitler was a serious danger	The three million men in the SA outnumbered the regular army by thirty to one.

Examiner's tip

Looking for a second phase of explanation can help to take an answer to a higher level. Make a point in a short first sentence and then explain it in a second sentence, which may start with something like, 'This was because...' Some candidates will leave it at that and move on to the next point. Candidates looking for a higher grade should see if they can add another sentence which adds to the explanation. This sentence may begin with phrases like 'Also...', 'In addition...', 'Moreover...', 'Similarly...' or '..., however,...'

3.7 How did the Nazis use the media to exercise control?

LEARNING OBJECTIVES

In this lesson you will:

- learn about Nazi propaganda
- practice answering source-based questions concerning 'purpose'.

GETTING STARTED

Draw a simple picture so that anyone looking at it would know that it symbolised Hitler.

KEY WORDS

Rally – *large meeting, often outdoors, of a political party. Nazi rallies were often held at Nuremburg and were attended by over 100,000 people.*

The 'People's community'

Hitler's idea was to create what he called *Volksgemeinschaft* – a 'People's Community'. This involved capturing the hearts and minds of the German people and convincing them that the Nazi way was correct. In order to achieve this, the Nazis produced a stream of propaganda (see Source A). If anything, after they had gained power, they produced even more propaganda, particularly as they started to use different forms of media to pass on the Nazi message.

Portraying the Führer

Hitler was, of course, central to the Nazi movement and the way that he was portrayed was particularly important. The message continued to be that Hitler was going to save Germany but the focus of the years when the Nazis were fighting elections now changed. Posters, for example, featured more general messages about Hitler's greatness and newsreels focused more on the reactions of supporters when

SOURCE A

The more basic the propaganda message is, the stronger will be the impression it makes on the masses, whose feelings and attitudes are of a similar basic kind. You will not rouse the enthusiasm of the masses with lectures but by presenting them with simple, everyday stories that match their own experiences.

Hans-Joachim Weinbrenner, from the 'Handbook of German Radio', 1939–40.

SOURCE B

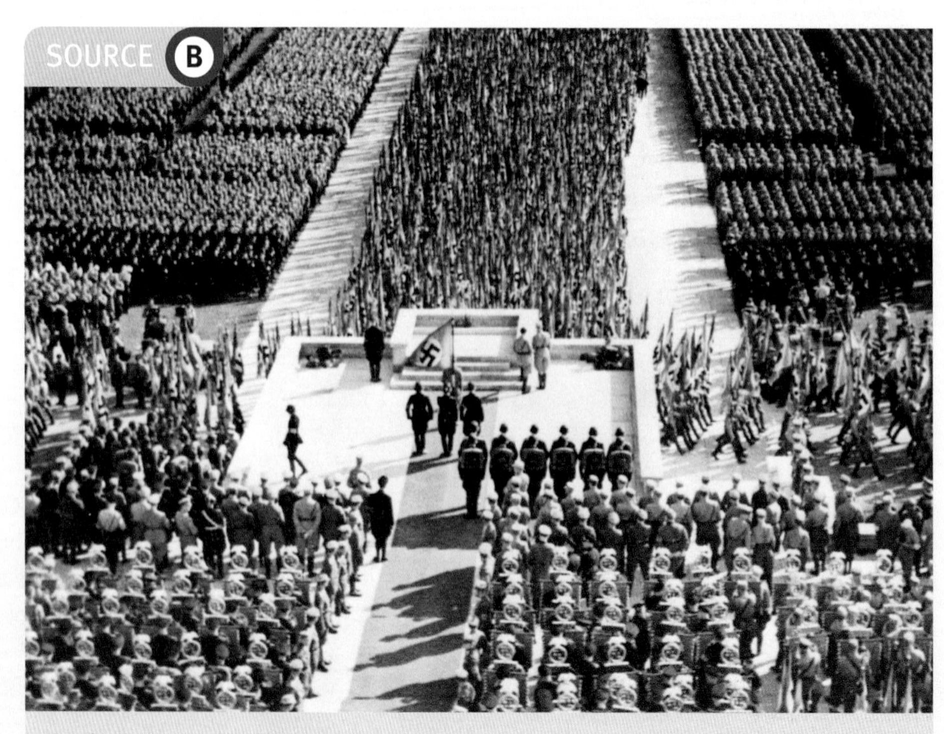

The film, *Triumph of the Will*, showed Hitler as the unchallenged and universally worshipped saviour of Germany.

Hitler was speaking. A full-length documentary film was made in 1934 called *Triumph of the Will,* which showed Hitler speaking to thousands of adoring Nazis at the party **rally** at Nuremburg.

The racial divide

The Nazis had always blamed the Jews for Germany's problems and, once in power, they unleashed a propaganda war against them. Nazi newspapers like *Die Sturmer* were filled with stories, often made up, of horrible things that Jews were supposed to have done. Feature films were made, where 'good' Germans would fight and overcome the 'evil' Jews. *The Eternal Jew,* made in 1940, was cut in such a way that the Jews were shown to be like rats, skulking in the darkness and living on the rubbish that had been thrown away by 'decent' people.

The wellbeing of the people

It was important for the Nazis that people genuinely believed that, under their rule, people's lives had got better. The economy did improve during the 1930s and the Nazis tried to emphasise this through their propaganda (see Source C). The public works that the Nazis organised to reduce unemployment featured heavily in newsreels during the first few years of the Nazi regime, often with Hitler or another leading Nazi visiting the men as they worked. The DAF organised their 'Strength through Joy' programme and this, in itself, was very effective propaganda (see Chapter 4, page 100).

SOURCE C

Germany is the most democratic country in history, by the acid test of the popular vote. Go among our people and ask them. Ask yourselves if they look or act like slaves. I am told nearly every day by some visiting foreigner long acquainted with Germany that he never before saw our people so happy. Germany has shed two unspeakable abominations: an incompetent and cowardly government and the shame of foreign interference. Germany has awakened from the post war nightmare. She is Free!

Adolf Hitler in an interview with Edward Price Bell, printed in *Liberty* magazine in 1938.

VOICE YOUR OPINION!

'People nowadays would still believe in Nazi-style propaganda.' Discuss!

Protectors of German culture

The Nazis portrayed themselves as saving Germany from decadent Weimar culture (see pages 24–25). Popular Weimar figures like Berthold Brecht, George Grosz and Thomas Mann were forced to flee the country and others like Paul Klee and Otto Dix found it hard to make a living. The Nazis put a lot of effort into cultural programming to reinforce Nazi ideas about the 'People's Community'.

SOURCE D

Every speech must first be written but must give the impression of being spontaneous.

The title of a speech must be brief and capable of being whispered as a slogan.

Make your speeches as if you were addressing each member of the audience separately.

Never attack whole professions or occupations.

Address the emotional and sentimental reactions of the audience, not their reason.

The real art of oratory must be to create emotion.

The golden rules for a speaker by Hans Krebs, gauleiter and Nazi activist.

ACTIVITIES

1. Briefly describe the 'People's Community' (*Volksgemeinschaft*).
2. Explain why Hitler started a Ministry for Propaganda and made Goebbels the Minister.
3. How successful was Goebbels' media campaign? Explain your answer.
4. Study Sources A and D. How useful are these sources in showing the Nazis' attitude to propaganda? Use the source and your own knowledge to explain your answer.
5. Study Source B. Why was this film made in 1934? Use the source and your own knowledge to explain your answer.
6. Study Source C. Why would an American magazine print this kind of comment from Adolf Hitler in 1938? Use the source and your own knowledge to explain your answer.
7. Study Source D. Why would Hans Krebs give out advice on public speaking? Use the sources and your own knowledge to explain your answer.

3.8 Why did so many Germans believe in Hitler?

LEARNING OBJECTIVES

In this lesson you will:

- learn about German people and their ideas about Hitler
- practice answering source based-questions on utility.

KEY WORDS

Cult of personality – *movement to portray the leader as all-powerful.*

Führer principle – *the idea that the leader knows best.*

The Führer principle

As early as the mid-1920s, Hitler had organised the Nazi Party along the lines of the **Führer principle**. This concentrated power in the hands of the party leader in order to give it strong and stable leadership. In practice, it made Hitler the absolute dictator of the Nazi Party. When the Nazis took power in 1933, this began to include the state as well (see Source A).

SOURCE A

When I took over power there were more than 6,000,000 unemployed and the farmers seemed doomed to decay. Today you must admit that I have fulfilled my promises. The Four Year Plan will give permanent employment to those workmen who are now being released from the armament industry. It is evidence of the gigantic economic development of our people that there is today a shortage of trained workmen in many industries.

Adolf Hitler from a speech to the Reichstag, 30 January 1937.

SOURCE B

When I first looked into Hitler's eyes they were hot and angry. There was no impression of greatness but he was a spellbinder for his own people. His capacity to be charming was part of his skill as a politician. For me he was sort of a Jekyll and Hyde character.

Sir Neville Henderson, British Ambassador to Berlin during the 1930s.

The cult of personality

Dictators often have a **cult of personality** that is created and kept going by their Chief of Propaganda. The link is made between leader and state and emphasised so that the two become almost inseparable. Large imposing images of the leader, coupled with daily appearances in news reports and radio broadcasts, make people believe that the leader is all-powerful. The personality of the leader becomes a real part of ordinary people's lives (see Source B). An example of this in Nazi Germany is the change in greeting from the standard, 'hello' or 'good day' to that of '*Heil Hitler*'. Subtle perhaps, but simply saying the name several times a day got Hitler into people's minds and kept him there.

Josef Goebbels

In Goebbels, Hitler had both a master of propaganda and someone who was devoted to him. When Hitler came to power, he create a new job for Goebbels in a new ministry, The Ministry of Propaganda, the aim of which was to push the Nazi message so that people could not escape from it or resist it. Goebbels realised that in the person of Hitler, he could personify Nazi ideas and the Nazi state and use him as the vehicle for winning the hearts and minds of the German people.

ACTIVITIES

Work in pairs. One person has to convince the other that Hitler was a good leader, without being racist or offensive.

The Hitler myth

If the Führer principle helped to establish Hitler's control of the party, later the state, and placed him above the influence of normal Germans, the Hitler myth took him above everybody and on his way to god-like status (see Sources C and D). People started to believe that Hitler's instinct was fully in tune with the needs of the nation and that therefore that his will must be done. The good of Germany and the wishes of the Führer became, in many people's opinion, the same thing.

SOURCE 

Hitler was sent to us by providence. It is amazing, but the fact is he never makes a mistake.

Heinrich Himmler, speaking in 1943.

SOURCE 

I read Hitler's book from cover to cover, with extreme excitement. Who is this man? Half ordinary worker, half God! Really the Christ or only John the Baptist?

Josef Goebbels, writing in 1925.

The myth was helped by the Nazis success. Immediately after coming to power, the economy recovered and politics were stabilised. Later on, Germany was able to recover or take over territory without having to go to war. Hitler was able to take the credit for these things. When things went badly, most people blamed the other Nazis and not Hitler.

SOURCE E

A poster produced to be shown in public institutions like schools. The German reads: 'Adolf Hitler is the Victory!'

ACTIVITIES

1. Briefly describe the 'Hitler myth'.
2. Explain why Germans were willing to believe the 'Hitler myth'.
3. How important was propaganda in creating and maintaining the 'Hitler myth'? Explain your answer.
4. Study Source A. In what ways does this source support the ideas of the 'Hitler myth'? Use the source and your own knowledge to explain your answer.
5. Study Source B. How useful is this in explaining Hitler's role in creating and maintaining his own myth? Use the source and your own knowledge to explain your answer.
6. Study Sources C and D. Do these sources help explain the origins of the 'Hitler myth'? Use the sources and your own knowledge to explain your answer.
7. Study Source E. Why did the Nazis produce this poster? Use the source and your own knowledge to explain your answer.

3.9 Why was Hitler so popular?

LEARNING OBJECTIVES

In this lesson you will:

- learn about the reasons why Hitler was popular
- practice using contextual knowledge to improve answers to source-based questions.

KEY WORDS

Munich Agreement – *made between the UK, France, Italy and Germany. It gave Hitler's Germany the parts of Czechoslovakia that Hitler claimed rightfully belonged to Germany.*

SOURCE 

I can only explain this, with the desperation and poverty caused by the mass unemployment, it was really terrible, and in this situation, Hitler seemed like the bringer of salvation.

Jutta Rudiger, party member 1931–45.

Before the war, even though the Nazi regime did things that were unpleasant, it is fair to say that Hitler was the most popular national leader in the world. For people nowadays, this is a very difficult idea to understand. So why was Hitler so popular?

Strong and stable

Many people in Germany yearned for the old days before the First World War. Life was simpler and danger further away. The German economy boomed and poverty was rare. During Weimar, people lived with the uncertainty of revolutions, hyperinflation and unemployment.

The Nazis offered a very simple alternative. Hitler's message was clear. A one-party state based on German racial purity and national pride. Hitler offered a strong government,that was willing to break a few rules and modify a few laws in order to give Germany a stable political system (see Source A).

The economic miracle

Poverty was a key issue towards the end of the Weimar regime and how to solve it a major problem for the government. Chancellor Bruning had resigned because Hindenburg was unwilling to pass the laws that would with the poverty problem. It was only in 1933, that poverty began to get better. This was largely because the Great Depression had reached the bottom of the economic cycle and things were getting better all over the world. Also government spending in Germany had stimulated the economy and provided jobs. This government money had been provided by the Weimar government in 1932 but its effects were only

SOURCE 

Hitler was often presented with flowers by women or children. Sometimes they wore traditional costume.

beginning to be felt in 1933. People believed that it was Hitler who had changed things. He was soon claiming that the 'economic miracle' (see pages 110–111) was down to his leadership.

National pride

With Hitler, it was more important what people believed rather than what the truth was. Reparations had been stopped in 1932 and so had nothing to do with Hitler. It was also in 1932 that during an armaments conference, the major world powers agreed to lift the restrictions on Germany's army, so when Hitler began to re-arm Germany, he was not being the defiant leader that perhaps he claimed that he was. Even in the case of changing Germany's borders, the major powers of Europe were not against Germany. Indeed at Munich in 1938, they seemed to be anxious to help the Germans by signing the **Munich Agreement**. In Nazi propaganda, of course, all these things were attributed to the 'genius' of Adolf Hitler.

Individual self-interest

The Nazis were very good at keeping their appeal broad. Lots of Germans did very well under the Nazis and had reasons, if not to like the regime, then at least to put up with it. Below is a table to explain why certain members of society might have stood to gain from Hitler's government.

Person	Reason for putting up with the Nazis
Manual worker	Under Weimar, it was the workers who were most at risk of losing their jobs. Under the Nazis, they were grateful for the security of work.
Shopkeeper	The elimination of Jewish business meant that non-Jewish businessmen faced less competition and would therefore make more money.
Soldier	Hitler built up the German Armed Forces and made them more important. In 1934, he prevented the SA taking the place of the army.
Industrialist	People who owned large companies could do very well under the Nazis. Re-armament meant that very large contracts were available and the banning of trade unions helped businesses to maximise their profits.
Civil servant	Civil servants wanted to keep their jobs. By impressing the regime, they could do that and even gain promotion.
Farmers	The Nazis passed laws to protect farmers with small farms. This meant that farms would always be under the ownership of the family who farmed the land.

SOURCE 

I got caught in a mob of about ten thousand hysterics who jammed the moat in front of Hitler's hotel, shouting: 'We want our Leader.' I was a little shocked at the faces, especially those of the women, when Hitler finally appeared at the balcony for a moment. They looked up at him as if he were a Messiah, their faces transformed into something positively inhuman. If he remained in sight for more than a few moments, I think many of the women would have swooned from excitement.

Diary of William L. Shirer, an American journalist, September 1935.

ACTIVITIES

1. Briefly describe why Hitler was so popular among Germans in the 1930s?
2. Explain why so many people in Germany put up with the Nazis.
3. Study Source A. How useful is this source in explaining Hitler's popularity? Use the source and your own knowledge to explain your answer.
4. Study Source B. Why do you think that that women and children wearing traditional costume were often chosen to greet Hitler? Use the source and your own knowledge to explain your answer.
5. Study Source C. Are you surprised by this source? Use the source and your own knowledge to explain your answer.

3.10 Why didn't the Nazis destroy the churches?

LEARNING OBJECTIVES

In this lesson you will:

- learn about the relationship between the Nazis and the Churches
- practice cross-referencing material in order to improve the quality of answers to source-based questions.

KEY WORDS

Christian – *follower of Jesus Christ.*

Protestant – *Christian but not a member of the Roman Church.*

Roman Catholic – *member of the Church of Rome.*

The Nazis had an inconsistent relationship with God. At the centre of Hitler's thinking was that fate had destined him to lead Germany to greatness. He stated publicly that **Christianity** was the foundation of the German state and often referred to God and Hell as though they were things that he believed in (see Source A). As a young man, he had thought about becoming a priest.

SOURCE 

Worst of all, however, are the problems caused by people who misuse religious ideas for political gain.

Adolf Hitler in *Mein Kampf*, 1924.

SOURCE 

The Government of the Reich regards Christianity as the unshakable foundation of the moral code of the nation.

Adolf Hitler, speaking in 1933.

SOURCE C

Jesus was almost certainly not a Jew. The Jews would never have handed one of their own people to the Roman courts; they would have condemned Him themselves. It is quite probable that a large number of descendants of the Roman legionaries, mostly Gauls, were living in Galilee and Jesus was probably one of them.

Hitler, speaking in November 1944.

Nazi Church policy

Some Nazis would have preferred to have a state without religion but they knew that banning Churches would not work. Most people if forced to choose between their nation and their religion would choose religion. The Nazis saw that they needed to tread carefully.

The first step was to nationalise the different Protestant Churches and bring them under Nazi control. The Reich Church was launched in July 1933 as an umbrella organisation for all German Protestant Churches.

SOURCE 

If the Christian Church wants to fight me I shall annihilate it as I have crushed and will crush all my other enemies. I don't mind walking over corpses as long as I reach my goal. I need no Christianity. Whoever won't obey will be destroyed, and that goes for you too. You are a deserter, and you know that for desertion there is only one punishment – death.

Pastor Martin Niemoller.

Adolf Hitler in conversation with Pastor Martin Niemoller on 5 January 1934.

The **Roman Catholic** Church posed an even greater problem for the Nazis. Not only are Catholics committed to their spiritual life in the same way as **Protestants**, but their Church is led by a Pope based in Rome. Hitler could not afford to upset the Roman Catholic Church and was very careful in his dealings with their bishops and the Pope.

The Confessing Church

In 1934, many Protestant clergy decided to break away from the Reich Church and form an independent movement. This was called the Confessing Church. Although it was a brave move to make, almost 5,000 clergy took their congregations out of the Reich Church.

Paganism in Nazi Germany

Alfred Rosenburg was an influential Nazi who had been a party member since the earliest days. He believed fanatically in German racial theory and saw a connection between the old pagan myths and the new National Socialist movement. He started the German Faith Movement based on old pagan ritual and it proved very attractive to diehard Nazis, particularly those in the SS. Goebbels was also able to use these paganistic ideas and old German legends as a basis for pageants, which helped to impress the people and reinforce Nazi ideas.

Fact file

Pastor Martin Niemoller was a submarine captain during the First World War and was decorated for bravery. After leaving the Navy, he became a pastor in a Protestant Church. In the early 1930s, he was an enthusiastic supporter of the Nazis and believed in their nationalistic and racial ideas. As Hitler gained power, Niemoller became disillusioned with the Nazis and protested against their Church policies. He was arrested in 1937 and spent the war in concentration camps until set free by the American Army in 1945.

SOURCE E

His Holiness Pope Pius XI and the President of the German Reich, moved by the common desire to consolidate and promote the friendly relations existing between the Holy See and the German Reich, and wishing to regulate lastingly, in a manner satisfying to both parties, the relations between the Catholic Church and the State for the entire territory of the German Reich have decided to conclude a solemn agreement.

Opening to the Concordat between the Vatican and the Third Reich, July 1933.

ACTIVITIES

1. Briefly describe the main Churches during the Third Reich.
2. Briefly describe Nazi policy towards the Churches.
3. Explain why the Nazis felt unable to destroy the Churches in Germany?
4. Study Sources A and B. How far is Hitler consistent in his views? Why might this be? Use the sources and your own knowledge to explain your answer.
5. Study Source C. Are you surprised by this source? Use the source and your own knowledge to explain your answer.
6. Study Source D. Why did Hitler not carry out his threats to either crush the Church or execute Martin Niemoller? Use the source and your own knowledge to explain your answer.
7. Study Source E. Why did the Nazis sign an agreement with the Catholic Church? Use the source and your own knowledge to explain your answer.

BRAIN BOOST

You may need to know the following; **G**erman Christians, **R**eich Church, **C**onfessing Church, German **F**aith Movement, Roman **C**atholic Church. GRCFC could stand for an organisation that may one day combine Scotland's two greatest football teams in Glasgow Rangers Celtic Football Club. This may be far-fetched, but it may also be a useful way of remembering the key religious organisations in Nazi Germany.

3.11 Case study: Who opposed the Nazi regime in Germany?

LEARNING OBJECTIVES

In this lesson you will:

- learn about the people who opposed the Nazis
- use independent research skills.

Opposition to the Nazi State can be divided into three categories:

- ***resistance*** – by those who attempted to overthrow the regime and replace it with something else, for example, trying to kill Hitler
- ***opposition*** – those who criticised the regime, for example, speaking out against Nazi atrocities
- ***non-conformism*** – someone refusing to do what was expected of them, for example, not joining the Hitler Youth.

In this enquiry, you will need to use a wide range of material. Other books are useful, as is the Internet. Be careful and remember to consider the reliability of the sources you use to complete this enquiry. Don't worry too much about the key youth groups as they are dealt with in the next chapter.

Below are the large enquiry questions that you will need to ask of every group you look at.

1. Who were the members of the group in question?
2. How did the group work against the Nazi regime?
3. Did they resist, oppose or not conform?

SOURCE A

Against the advice of experts, Hitler has unscrupulously sacrificed whole armies for his desire for glory. To maintain his power, he has established an unbridled reign of terror, banishing decency, and destroying the happiness of millions.

General Ludwig Beck, part of a declaration written just before the bomb plot to kill Hitler of 20 July 1944.

Political opposition

The Nazis banned all other political parties in July 1933. Most members of the right-wing and centre parties, either joined the Nazis or gave up politics. Some members of the left-wing parties, the Socialists and the Communists continued with their active political lives. Some of them fled abroad in order to continue the struggle. The following questions will help to frame your investigation about these people:

1. Where did the Social Democrats base their continued opposition?
2. What tactics did the Communist resistance use?
3. What was the Kreisau Circle?
4. How did people in the army oppose Hitler?

Religious opposition

Some members of Churches felt it their duty to criticise the Nazi regime. Some of the things that the Nazis were doing went against Christian beliefs:

1. What did Dietrich Bonhoffer do?
2. How was Heinrich Gruber's story similar to that of Bonhoffer?
3. Why did the Nazis change their policy on euthanasia?
4. Why was Bishop Galen not arrested for his criticism of the Nazis?

SOURCE B

Damage caused by the bomb plot of July 1944.

SOURCE  C

I am reliably informed that in hospitals and homes in the province of Westphalia lists are being prepared of inmates who are classified as 'unproductive members of the national community' and are to be removed from these establishments and shortly thereafter killed. Article 211 of the German Penal Code is still in force, in these terms: 'Whoever kills a man of deliberate intent is guilty of murder and punishable with death.'

From a sermon given by Bishop Galen of the Catholic Church on 3 August 1941.

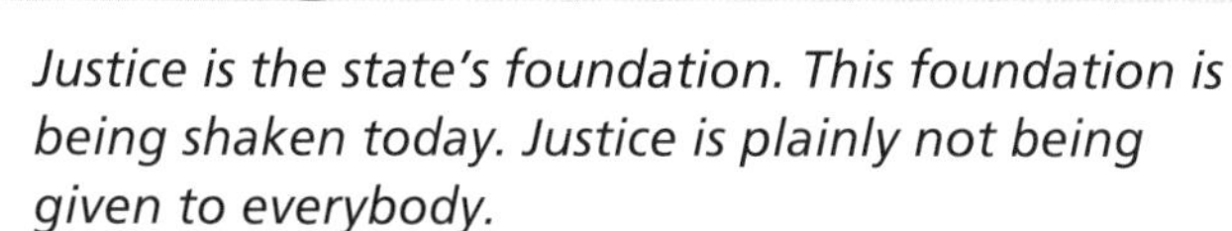

SOURCE D

Justice is the state's foundation. This foundation is being shaken today. Justice is plainly not being given to everybody.

The regular courts have no say over what the Secret Police do – its arrests, its imprisonment of fellow Germans in concentration camps – large groups Germans have a feeling of being without rights against the actions of the Gestapo.

Bishop Clemens von Galen, from a sermon delivered on 13 July 1941.

SOURCE F

Despite being an outspoken critic of the Nazis, Bishop von Galen was never arrested.

SOURCE  E

Of course, there are those for whom joining the SA was the only way out. And there are those who the Nazis believe they have converted but who really wear the brown shirt because they have been threatened and forced to do so. Finally, there are the volunteers we have sent in ourselves. They could be shot at any moment, but they are doing fantastic work from the inside.

A Communist activist in conversation with French traveller, Daniel Guerin, in 1934.

GradeStudio

It is important to know where a source comes from and that can often add material to an answer. Below are some sources from elsewhere in the book. The origins of the sources have been mixed up. Sort them out and write a couple of sentences that relate to the origins of the sources in a way that will help to answer the questions that have been asked of the sources.

Source	Origin
Source C, page 83	German politician. Politicians always criticise their political opponents.
Source C, page 15	A Nazi newspaper. Official party newspapers are not going to criticise their own members.
Source C, page 49	American journalist living in Germany. Journalists often look for the sensational aspect of an event.
Source B, page 36.	German priest. Priests often seek to sympathise with the unfortunate and try to make them feel better about their situation.

3.12 Youth groups: Serious resistance or youthful rebellion?

LEARNING OBJECTIVES

In this lesson you will:

- learn about three different youth groups who opposed the Nazis
- arrive at a judgement about the purpose of these groups.

KEY WORDS

Totalitarian – *state ruled by one party, often with harsh rules and restrictions on freedom.*

During the process of growing up, teenagers often go through a rebellious phase. At times, they may become surly or disagreeable. At school, they may not do their tie up properly as a little act of rebellion. Learning how to deal with authority is a difficult part of becoming an adult.

In all societies there are people who disagree with the government. In a democracy, they can voice their opinions openly, even using the mass media if they wish. In totalitarian states, people who oppose the regimes have no outlet for their opposition and may take other forms of action, often at great personal danger.

Nazi Germany certainly had teenagers. It also had, as we have seen previously, young people who were opposed to the Nazi regime and who took direct action to fight against it. In these two pages, there is information on three of the major youth opposition groups. Having reviewed it all, you should be able to arrive at a judgement as to whether young people constituted a serious political threat to the Nazi regime (see Source A) or whether they were just rebelling against authority.

SOURCE A

The Purpose of all National Socialist mass organisations is the same. Whether it is The Labour Front (DAF) or the 'Strength through Joy' programme or the Hitler Youth, overall the organisations serve the same purpose: to 'assess' or to 'care' for citizens of the Volk, not to let them go their own way and possibly never arrive at the truth.

From a report for the Social Democratic Party in Exile in 1935.

The Edelweiss Pirates

In different cities, different groups of Edelweiss pirates had different names; 'The Travelling Dudes' in Essen or 'The Navajos' in Cologne but they all wore the edelweiss, a symbol of resistance to the Nazis. The activities of these groups were no different to most teenage groups. They hung around street corners and socialised with their peers. At weekends, they took themselves off on hikes or went camping, not unlike people in the Nazi groups. They wore their hair long and wore scruffy clothes, clearly opposing the regimented smartness of the Hitler Youth and League of German Girls.

As the war progressed, they became a much greater problem for the authorities. Membership of Nazi youth organisations had become law by 1939 and from that point had dropped away. Membership of unofficial groups began to rise and their opposition began to get more and more extreme. At first, the Nazis organised patrols of special street police, usually boys just out of the Hitler Youth. This led to fights, ones which the Nazi boys did not always win.

Towards the end of the war, some of the Edelweiss Pirates began to act against the Nazi state itself rather than the local Hitler Youth. Stealing arms and explosives, attacks on leading Nazi figures and acts of sabotage were carried out. Against this the authorities launched a major initiative to combat this, the result of which was the hanging of several Edelweiss leaders (see Source B).

The 'Swing Youth'

The rebellion of the Swing Youth centred on culture. The deliberately went out of their way to wear clothes with English or American connections. Items like sports jackets, crepe soled shoes, shirts

SOURCE B

Edelweiss Pirates hanged in Cologne, 1944 for crimes against the Reich. By the end of the war, the Nazis were extremely intolerant of youth rebellion.

SOURCE C

Typical outsiders, the condemned persons shamelessly committed offences against the armed security of the nation and the will to fight of the German People by defacing houses with slogans attacking the state and by distributing treasonous leaflets. At this time of heroic struggle on the part of the German people, these despicable criminals deserve a speedy and dishonourable death.

From the death sentence passed on Sophie Scholl, Hans Scholl and Christoph Probst on 22 February 1943.

SOURCE 

It is a sad fact that our people's community is infested with traitors. If they succeed, 1918–1919 will be child's play by comparison. They will have to be weeded out now without any thought of mercy.

Dr Roland Freisler, Nazi judge speaking on 1 August 1944.

with high collars were popular with the boys or shorter lighter skirts and shirt type blouses for the girls. They all wore their hair long, 'up to 27 cm' according to one Gestapo report.

The main activity of this group was organising parties at which would be played American style' swing' music. The energy of this music and the nature of the dancing to it scandalised the strict morals of the Nazis. They saw the wiggling of hips as something decadent and the fact that boys and girls danced with each other in close proximity, further offended the prudish Nazis. In time, the authorities acted against the Swing Youth which led to the same kind of clashes as with the Edelweiss Pirates.

The White Rose Group

This was a movement based at the University of Munich and consisted of a group of students and their Philosophy professor. One of the students, a 21-year-old called Sophie Scholl became the most famous member of the group. Between June 1942 and February 1943, the group produced and distributed leaflets calling for people to oppose the Nazi regime. They accused the Nazis of war crimes and claimed that the war was lost. In the end they were picked up by the Gestapo and interrogated. Many of the group including the professor and Sophie Scholl were executed for treason (See Source C).

SOURCE 

Do you know that our armies have been smashed on the Russian Front?

Do you know that millions of soldiers are being sacrificed by the mad Austrian corporal named Hitler, to satisfy his lust for power?

Do you know that his co-conspirator Mussolini is finished? The Italian people have had enough of him.

SABOTAGE THE WAR EFFORT

ORGANISE ARMED RESISTANCE!

From a leaflet produced by a Youth Resistance Group in Berlin in 1943.

ACTIVITIES

1 For each of the groups copy and complete the table below. Use other sources of information to help you:

Group	Evidence for rebellion	Evidence for resistance
Edelweiss Pirates		
Swing Youth		
White Rose Group		

2 Study Source A. How far does this explain why some young people did not join the Nazi youth groups? Use the source and your own knowledge to explain your answer.

3 Study Sources B and C. How far do these sources support the view that the Nazi reaction indicates that youth groups were a threat? Use the source and your own knowledge to explain your answer.

4 Study Sources D and E. How far do these sources indicate that these groups were a genuine resistance movement? Use the source and your own knowledge to explain your answer.

3.13 Why did the Nazis intimidate groups outside the 'People's Community'?

LEARNING OBJECTIVES

In this lesson you will:

- learn about the groups that the Nazis thought of as enemies
- practise answering source-based questions on 'purpose'.

KEY WORDS

Asocials – *people who belong outside normal society.*

Racial theory – *idea that different racial groups are superior or inferior.*

The Nazis had very well-defined enemies. From the earliest days, Hitler's ideas about who could and who could not be members of the 'People's Community' were well developed. These people were referred to as **asocials** and were targeted by the Nazis from the earliest days of the movement.

Eugenics – the 'science' of racial differences

The Nazis believed that different people could be categorised 'scientifically' into sub-species (see Source A). This **racial theory** put forward that, of these sub-species, some were superior and others were inferior. The Germans were classed as Aryans, who were the superior human species. Aryans became known as the 'master race'. Slavs in Eastern Europe were seen as inferior humans, while Jews and Blacks were sub-humans. This pseudo-science was taught in Nazi schools and Nazi universities, although it was also believed by some scientists in other countries.

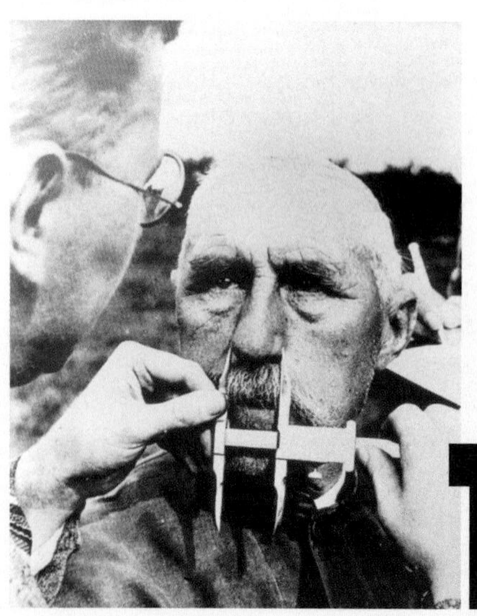

The nose of a German villager being measured by an anthropologist in 1932.

SOURCE A

The Third Reich under the guidance of racially conscious men has established a comprehensive race policy of population development and race improvement based on the knowledge of eugenic science.

Clarence Campbell, an American admirer of Hitler's race policies, quoted in the Nazi newspaper, *Volkischer Beobachter*, in August 1935.

Social problems

The Nazis believed that the Weimar Republic had encouraged social problems through a large and effective system of welfare. They accused many people of being work-shy or of being poor parents (see Source B). They felt that the decadent aspects of Weimar culture had encouraged people to live immoral lives. The Nazis felt that to create the perfect 'People's Community', they needed to deal with these social problems. The Nazis often made a link between social problems and racial inferiority and conditions like alcoholism were seen as 'social' problems.

Imperfect humans

The Nazis did not feel the need, as many other societies do, to care for the weak and those who cannot look after themselves. They saw the 'People's Community' as the important part of society and that individuals were important only if they could give something to that community. Those who were born with hereditary illnesses were seen as not contributing and their care was seen as a drain on society.

Ideas

Those with ideas that did not match the Nazi ideas were considered outside the 'People's Community'. Communists were one example of a political set of ideas that did not fit into the Nazi pattern. Often, Communists were portrayed as Jews and regarded as mentally ill. In the early days, the Nazis thought of the Communists as the most dangerous threat.

Hitler's view

A lot of Nazi ideas, particularly racial ones, came from Hitler (see Source D). He made clear the difference between 'emotional' racism, where people simply hate other people but can't really explain why and 'rational' racism, where the hate grows out of a logical (in his mind) development of ideas. To describe racism as 'rational' makes the unreasonable sound reasonable and it is perhaps this that made Hitler so dangerous and perhaps begins to explain why the Nazis were able to carry out such terrible crimes (see pages 120–25 for information about the Holocaust).

Fact file

Anti-Semitism has been in Europe since the time of the Roman Empire. At one time or another every European country has persecute the Jews. In the nineteenth and early twentieth century, Jews were very badly persecuted in Russia and Eastern Europe, with many of them emigrating to America. It is ironic that in the years before the First World War, Germany was one of the most tolerant societies towards Jewish people.

SOURCE 

According to information from the welfare office here, C. is to be classified as a work-shy person. He does not care for his wife and his 2 children, so that these have to be supported from the public purse. He has never taken up the work duty assigned to him. He has given himself over to drink.

Gestapo report from June 1938. The man was sent to Sachsenhausen concentration camp where he died 18 months later.

SOURCE C

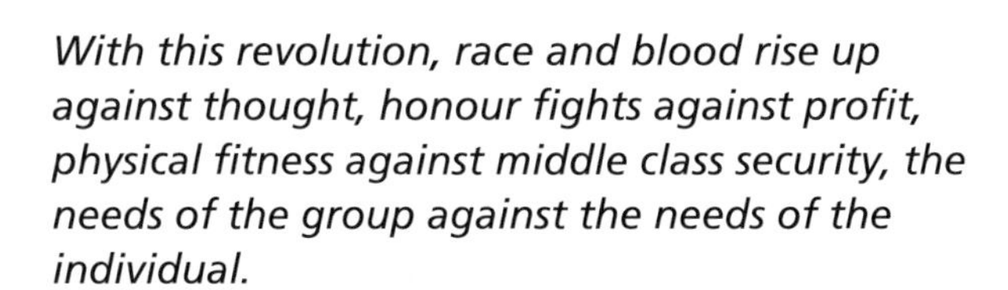

With this revolution, race and blood rise up against thought, honour fights against profit, physical fitness against middle class security, the needs of the group against the needs of the individual.

From a book by Ernst Krieck, an academic and Nazi sympathiser, written in 1932.

VOICE YOUR OPINION!

Can euthanasia ever be justified? How does your view on this alter your opinion of the Nazis?

SOURCE 

Purely emotional anti-Semitism finds its final expression in the form of violence. Rational anti-Semitism must lead to taking away all the privileges that Jews enjoy in our country. Its final objective, however, must be the total removal of all Jews from our midst. Both objectives can only be achieved by a government of national strength.

Part of a letter written by Adolf Hitler in 1919.

ACTIVITIES

1. Briefly describe the groups that the Nazis thought of as being asocial?
2. Explain why the Nazis chose to intimidate these groups?
3. Study Source A. Why would a Nazi newspaper publish the thoughts of an American? Use the source and your own knowledge to explain your answer.
4. Study Source B. How far did the Gestapo carry out Hitler's policy? Use the sources and your own knowledge to explain your answer.
5. Study Source C. Why did the Nazis seek to intimidate certain groups of people? Use the source and your own knowledge to explain your answer.
6. Study Source D. Explain the differences that Hitler gives between emotional and rational anti-Semitism. Why is this idea dangerous? Use the source and your own knowledge to explain your answer.

3.14 How did the Nazis isolate their enemies?

LEARNING OBJECTIVES

In this lesson you will:

- learn about the methods used by the Nazis to isolate their enemies
- practise using contextual knowledge to improve answers to source-based questions.

KEY WORDS

Sterilisation – *biologically removing people's ability to reproduce.*

The Nazis used their power to change the law in order to undermine, isolate and eventually remove those that they regarded as enemies.

Laws against the Jews

The following were the laws that gradually removed the Jews from normal life. Alongside these legal measures were thousands of local initiatives and schemes to persecute Jews:

- April 1933. **The Law for the Restoration of the Civil Service.** Jews could no longer work in the Civil Service.
- September 1935. **The Nuremberg Laws.** Marriages and sexual relations between Aryans and Jews were made illegal. Jews were deprived of their German citizenship. Aryans who wished to marry could be medically examined in order to obtain a 'certificate of fitness to marry' proving that they were fully Aryan.
- April 1938. **Decree on the Registering of Jewish Property.** All Jewish property worth over 5,000 RM had to be registered.

SOURCE A

And the aim remains the complete removal of the Jews from our nation. Not because we would begrudge them existence but because the existence of our own nation is a thousand times more important than that of an alien race.

Adolf Hitler, in a speech in the 1920s.

- June 1938. **Laws on the Jewish Professions.** Jewish lawyers, dentists and doctor were forbidden to have Aryan clients.
- October 1938. **Laws on Jewish Identification.** All Jews had to add the names 'Israel' or 'Sarah' to their names and have a large red 'J' stamped in their passport.
- November 1938. **Decree on the Economic Life of Jews.** Jews banned from shops, businesses, schools, universities and leisure facilities. Jews could not belong to trade organisations or bid for public contracts.

Sterilisation and euthanasia

Very early on in the regime, the Nazis passed a law to **sterilise** those with hereditary illnesses, such as blindness, deafness or mental illness. At the discretion of doctors, this law could also include alcoholism, drug addiction or male homosexuality. By the end of the Nazi period, it is estimated that over 350,000 people had been sterilised under this programme.

By the late 1930s, a more radical solution was adopted by the Nazis. This involved 'mercy' killings of those identified as being 'useless' to the 'People's Community'. The victims were people kept in special homes – they would die of neglect, be starved to death or given lethal injections. Later on, experiments with mobile gas chambers were carried out. In total, it is estimated that 200,000 people were killed as a result of the euthanasia programme.

In 1941, Bishop Galen spoke out against the euthanasia programme. The Nazis countered by releasing a film. It was called 'I Accuse' and told the story of a woman with multiple sclerosis who begged her husband to kill her. In the final scene, he makes a passionate speech during his trial about the right to die a noble death. Disquiet about the programme faded slightly and the Nazis took more careful steps to hide what they were doing.

Isolation

Physical isolation of certain groups (for example, Communists, Socialists, Jews, homosexuals) began with the detaining of political enemies in concentration camps in the spring of 1933. They were either arrested for some form of 'crime' or were taken into 'protective custody'. Some of those jailed for a 'crime' found themselves being released and then immediately taken into 'protective custody'. For the Nazis, the important thing was that these people were out of the way.

Isolation of those with hereditary illnesses was a far simpler affair. Homes were already in operation to care for these people and so the Nazis only needed to modify the way that people were chosen for these homes and the way in which they were treated once they were there. Being isolated already, it is not surprising that the Nazis' campaign of systematic murder began with this group.

SOURCE C

Jews were often humiliated in public by the Nazis. A boy is forced to cut his father's beard while German soldiers watch and jeer.

SOURCE B

A propaganda poster for euthanasia which reads: 'This person suffering from hereditary defects costs the community 60,000 Reichsmark during his lifetime. Fellow Germans, that is your money, too.'

At first, the isolation of the Jews in Germany was carried out through a series of laws, which were mainly concerned with the spheres of work and society. These laws prevented them from doing things like taking certain jobs or belonging to certain organisations. It was in the autumn of 1941 that plans were made for the physical relocation of German Jews.

HISTORY DETECTIVE

Try to find out about some of the other laws passed against Jews that are not mentioned here. Why might the Nazis have passed them?

ACTIVITIES

1. Briefly describe how the Nazis removed German Jews from everyday life during the 1930s.
2. Explain why the Nazis decided to carry out a programme of euthanasia.
3. Study Source A. How useful is this source in explaining Hitler's policy towards the Jews in the 1930s? Use the source and your own knowledge to explain your answer.
4. Study Source B. Why would the Nazis make a poster showing mentally disabled people in this way? Use the source and your own knowledge to explain your answer.
5. Study Source C. How did humiliation of this type help the Nazis to isolate the Jews? Use the source and your own knowledge to explain your answer.

3.15 How far was *Kristallnacht* a turning point in the Nazi treatment of the Jews?

LEARNING OBJECTIVES

In this lesson you will:

- learn about the events of *Kristallnacht*
- practise answering source-based questions on utility.

KEY WORDS

Genocide – *attempt to murder a whole race of people.*

Pogrom – *large-scale act of violence usually against Jews.*

SOURCE 

The instructions from Goebbels were understood by the party leaders to mean that the Party should not be seen to have organised the attacks but in reality should have done so.

From a secret report by the Nazi Party Supreme Court.

By 1938, Germans had been subjected to five years of constant and extreme anti-Jewish propaganda. The Nazis had passed laws to try to keep the Jews out of the economy and social life of Germany. Violence against Jews took place regularly and humiliating people was something that was often seen but there was no sustained campaign against them.

On the night of 9–10 November, a massive nationwide attack took place against Jewish people and property (see Source A). This was called *Kristallnacht* (the night of broken glass). The official excuse was the murder of Ernst von Rath, a German diplomat, by a French Jew in Paris. Nazis wanted revenge.

Hitler and Goebbels met early in the evening of the 9 November and receive reports that some unofficial demonstrations against Jews had taken place. Goebbels persuaded Hitler that they should encourage further demonstrations and to not intervene when these demonstrations descended into violence. At ten o'clock Goebbels made a radio speech calling for vengeance against the Jews and Nazis listening to that speech were soon attacking synagogues and Jewish businesses. At one o'clock, Himmler's deputy Reinhardt Heydrich instructed the police to observe the attacks but not to intervene unless non-Jews were threatened or non-Jewish property was in danger.

The Aftermath of *Kristallnacht*

It is estimated that over 500 synagogues were destroyed and over 1,000 shops. Twenty-thousand Jews were arrested and sent to concentration camps. Some historians suggest that around 100 Jews were murdered and many hundreds more committed suicide.

The backlash against the violence could not have been expected by the Nazi leaders. Prominent individuals within Christian Churches spoke out against the violence, which may have been expected, but the feelings of many middle-class people were also strongly and publicly expressed against Nazi violence. Some were even encouraged to actively help Jewish people who were in danger of being targeted. Even some leading Nazis were irritated by the violence – Hermann Goering complained that it was harmful to the economy.

After *Kristallnacht*, violence against Jews got worse. It took the form of unofficial initiatives, often carried out by local Nazis for their own profit or to settle old scores. The government in Berlin did nothing to encourage these attacks and went back to their more legally based persecution of the Jews, though they did nothing to discourage them either. It was much to Hitler's benefit for ordinary Germans to believe that he was unaware of the violence being inflicted on the Jews.

Kristallnacht as a turning point

There was certainly a shift in Nazi ideas about the Jews between the years 1933 and 1945. Though Hitler was openly anti-Semitic from the earliest days, there is nothing to suggest that mass murder was a possibility even as late as 1938 or 1939.

SOURCE B

Millions of marks worth of damage was caused to Jewish property during the attacks of *Kristallnacht*.

SOURCE D

After November 10th, 1938, those Jews still in Germany and Austria were filled with nightmarish fears about the future might hold for them. But even someone gifted with the most fertile fantasy could not have imagined anything like the Holocaust. And yet, the dam had cracked.

Werner Weinberg, in his book, *Self Portrait of a Holocaust Survivor* written in the 1960s.

The disapproval of Jews that had found expression in several laws and public humiliation had, by *Kristallnacht*, developed into full-scale state-sponsored violence. This in itself was not uniquely Nazi. Large scale **pogroms** against Jews had been a fact of life in Tsarist Russia in the years before the First World War. What was uniquely Nazi were the concentration camps and the gas chambers and the policy of exterminating entire minority groups.

While violence got worse after *Kristallnacht*, the decision for **genocide** (see pages 120–25) was taken much later. In some ways, *Kristallnacht* ended the nervousness that some Nazi leaders felt about a radical policy towards the Jews and may have given them the confidence to move towards a policy of genocide. It may also have given a message to the masses of ordinary Germans that a more violent approach was coming into force and that they would be advised not to get involved (see Source C).

SOURCE C

The SA man wants to fight, and he also has a right to be led into battle. Without a fighting tendency the SA is absurd and pointless.

Josef Goebbels writing in 1936.

ACTIVITIES

1. Briefly describe the events of *Kristallnacht*.
2. Explain why the Nazi leaders did nothing to stop the attacks.
3. How far was *Kristallnacht* a turning point in the Nazi treatment of the Jews? Explain your answer.
4. Study Source A. Are you surprised by this source? Use the source and your own knowledge to explain your answer.
5. Study Source B. Why might the Nazis want to restrict photographs like this in the foreign press but encourage them at home? Use the source and your own knowledge to explain your answer.
6. Study Source C. How useful is this in helping to explain the causes of *Kristallnacht*? Use the source and your own knowledge to explain your answer.
7. Study Source D. What can we learn about the consequences of *Kristallnacht* from this source? Use the source and your own knowledge to explain your answer.

Putting it all together

You have now completed this unit, which has focused on the Nazi regime and how effectively the Nazis controlled Germany between 1933 and 1945. You have also had practice in answering questions designed to prepare you for your exam. Below is an example of one type of exam question, with some hints to help you write a top-level answer.

c Who were more important in the Nazi Party, the SA or the SS? Explain your answer. **[8 marks]**

Fact file

In the exam, you will be asked to answer two questions from Section B, the Depth Study: a source-based question and a structured question. The structured question is divided into three parts – **a**, **b** and **c**. In this Grade Studio, we'll be looking at how to produce a top-level answer for the **c** type of question, which asks you to evaluate something. The **c** question has 8 marks.

Examiner's tip

The part **c** question requires some evaluation and sometimes judgement. We can divide these questions into those that require a definite choice to be made between two or three alternatives and those that deal with the idea of 'extent'. This Grade Studio will deal with the questions that require a clear choice to be made, that is, 'evaluation' questions. These questions may start with phrases like 'Which was more important...?' or 'Was X more important than Y....?' They may ask an either/or question and introduce notions like 'better or worse' or 'easier or more difficult'.

Look at the sample answer below and the simplified mark scheme that follows.

Candidate's answer

'The SS were more important because they lasted longer. This meant that they were the ones responsible for the death camps that murdered the Jews, Also, SS men fought for the German Army during the war. The SA became part of the SS after the Night of the Long Knives. Even Hitler knew that once he had gained power, the SA were no longer needed. The role of the SA had been to help Hitler gain power. They organised the Nazi effort to win elections during the early 1930s, demonstrating, handing out leaflets and breaking up opposition meetings. As soon as the Enabling Act was passed and Hitler secured power, the SA became irrelevant. The SS on the other hand were needed for Hitler to keep power and to control Germany. In 1933, for example when the Nazis arrested thousands of their enemies, it was the SS who built and ran the concentration camps to hold all the prisoners. Without the SS, Hitler could not have run Germany as he wanted or exterminated the Jews, which was one of his key policies. Therefore the SS were more important than the SA.'

Examiner's comment

The first part of the answer (in red) gets the candidate into Level 1. By identifying specific reasons, and then explaining them, the candidate is able to build on their answer and move up through the levels. At the end the answer arrived at a judgement (in light blue).

Simplified mark scheme

Level 1 (1 to 2 marks): General assertions A statement regarding one or other of the factors. No personal knowledge is shown here. A simple statement is often needed to show the examiner a clear answer to the question, i.e. that 'the SS were more important'.
Level 2 (2 to 3 marks): Identifies reasons why one or other is important/not important In the answer above, two points of own knowledge are given to show why the SS were important.
Level 3 (4 marks): Identifies reasons why one is important and why the other is not important The other factor, the SA, is introduced. A brief description is given as to why the SA were not as important as the SS.
Level 4 (5 to 6 marks): Explains reasons why one or the other is important/not important Here the reasons why the SA was not as important as the SS is explained.
Level 5 (6 to 7 marks): Explains reasons why one is important and the other is not as important Here the answer is extended to clearly explain why the SS was important. Giving full explanations for both points in the question will get the answers into the higher levels.
Level 6 (8 marks): As for Level 5 but in addition explains why one side of the argument is stronger than the other or how they are connected.

It is important to remember that you need to make a clear choice and tell the examiner what it is. There is no right or wrong answer. You need to explain why you have chosen one of the things and why have not chosen the other one(s). Ask yourself why one is important and why the others are less important. Remember the examiner is marking you on your ability to argue, not simply on your ability to recall information.

Try out these evaluation questions for yourself, using Chapter 3 to help you:

1. Was economic prosperity or Goebbels' propaganda more important for the Nazis in winning the hearts and minds of ordinary Germans? Explain your answer.
2. Were Himmler's agencies (The SS, the Gestapo and the police) more effective in keeping control of Nazi Germany than the gauleiters? Explain your answer.
3. Which was more important in giving Hitler power, the Enabling Act or the Night of the Long Knives? Explain your answer.
4. Which was a bigger threat to the Nazi regime, the Christian Churches or the army? Explain your answer.

Chapter 4

What was it like to live in Nazi Germany?

This chapter is about ordinary life in Nazi Germany. The experiences of people under Hitler's regime were more extreme than people's lives today due to the problems in the world, and in Germany in particular. For some, there was great joy that Hitler had solved some of the most pressing problems. Those who were natural enemies of the Nazis lived their lives in fear. The Second World War brought fear, even to those who had previously only experienced joy under the Nazis. This chapter will give you an understanding of how different people experienced Nazi rule.

The 'People's Community'

The Nazis had very clear ideas about who they wanted to be part of their 'People's Community' and who they did not. For those they did want, they had very clear ideas about their role. They saw workers, administrators, soldiers, women and children working together towards a series of common goals. What was expected from people was communicated often through propaganda, lessons in schools and the activities of various Nazi groups.

The future belongs only to a nation which is united, strong and healthy, a nation which is joyous and positive in its attitude to life. We must therefore give every individual strength and joy to develop his capacities to the utmost. For this purpose we need not only physically strong people but also happy people who face life in a joyful spirit of acceptance.

Dr Robert Ley, the Nazi Minister in charge of the German Labour Front and the 'Strength through Joy' programme.

Young people were attracted to the youth groups run by the Nazis. These provided fun activities for young people like camping, sport and singing, while constantly reminding them of the key messages of National Socialism. Women also had their own organisations that were enjoyable and yet prepared women for the very restricted role, that of wives and mothers, that they were intended to play in the 'People's Community'.

Joy

Ordinary people benefited from Nazi rule in the early years as the economy improved. Jobs were created through public works, wages went up and so did the standard of living. The Nazis banned trade unions and they were replaced by the German Labour Front (DAF), which supposedly represented the workers. The 'Strength through Joy' programme run by the DAF was meant to ensure that the workers enjoyed their leisure time in order for them not to have time to think for themselves (see Source A).

The Nazis made sure that young people enjoyed themselves in their youth organisations.

Fear

The fear of being reported to the authorities was real and got worse throughout the period. The Gestapo was not a large organisation but it often relied on the public to help it track down people who were not behaving 'correctly'.

Some groups were already earmarked for special treatment. Those, such as the Communists, who had politically opposed the Nazis in the early 1930s, were arrested very soon after the seizure of power and sent to concentration camps. The campaign of terror against potential political opponents went on throughout the period.

Non-Aryan groups lived in constant fear. Jews and the Sinti and Roma (often referred to as Gypsies) were particular targets of Nazi violence, which grew ever more extreme during this period (see Source C). The mass relocations and systematic murder in the later years of the Second World War caused millions of people to live in constant fear of the Nazi regime.

The Second World War

The war changed the way in which the Nazis could rule Germany. In some ways, their possibilities were restricted. Industry, for example, could not be used to improve standards of living because everything was moved over to war production. Luxury items were difficult to get as the British Navy prevented large-scale imports by sea. This meant that they increasingly began to use fear to keep control rather than joy. The problem of Jews living in Germany could no longer be solved by mass migration as the war situation made this impractical.

SOURCE C

Under proper guidance, in the course of the final solution the Jews are to be allocated for appropriate labour in the East. Able-bodied Jews, separated according to sex, will be taken in large work columns to these areas for work on roads, in the course of which action doubtless a large number will be eliminated by natural causes.

From the Wannsee Protocol, the plan for the 'Final Solution', January 1942.

SOURCE D

Political prisoners arriving at Oranienburg concentration camp.

SOURCE E

Living in German cities was extremely difficult during the last years of the war.

4.1 What did children learn in Nazi schools?

LEARNING OBJECTIVES

In this lesson you will:

- learn about the Nazi school curriculum and its purpose
- practise answering source-based questions about 'purpose'.

KEY WORDS

Curriculum – *subjects learned in school.*

SOURCE A

In my great educative work I am beginning with the young. We older ones are used up...we are rotten to the marrow. But my magnificent youngsters! Are there any finer ones in the world? With them I can make a new world.

Adolf Hitler, speaking in the 1930s.

SOURCE B

Jewish students would be used by teachers in class as live examples in race study lessons.

The Nazis, and particularly Adolf Hitler, felt that young people were the most important part of their 'People's Community'. They saw that the young had yet to be fully influenced and realised that if they surrounded the young with Nazi ideas, they could potentially make a whole generation of fully committed National Socialists. They wasted no time in altering the school **curriculum** to match the needs of Nazi propaganda (see Source A).

Obedience and discipline

Intellectual freedom suffered under the Nazis. They did not want young people to think for themselves. They wanted a generation who were fully obedient to the wishes of the Nazi government. They needed iron discipline and physical strength. Teaching became very didactic, which meant that the teacher spoke and the children copied down. Questioning anything was discouraged.

Subjects

The Nazis altered old subjects to fit their needs and invented new subjects altogether. There was a clear focus on teaching based on Germany, physical fitness and preparation for clearly defined roles.

The most significant of the new subjects was racial theory. This was a simplified version of the pseudo-science of eugenics (see page 92). Students were taught how to categorise people by race including the significance of hair and eye colour and the shape and size of the skull and nose. Often, Jewish children in the class would be used to provide real life examples of 'racial inferiority' – they would stand in front of the class while the teacher pointed out the features that according to Nazi theories made them racially inferior.

Traditional subjects were modified to give a Nazi view of the world. They centred around Germany and put

German matters before a world view, reinforcing Hitler's ideas that the Jews were plotting to overthrow Western Civilisation. History and geography lent themselves to this (see Source C) and mathematics problems were also given a Nazi aspect.

Teachers

Initiative and individuality among teachers were discouraged. In order to remain employed, teachers were forced to join the German Teachers' League, which made sure that they only taught Nazi ideas.

Special Nazi schools

Nazi organisations began to open their own schools to fast-track those who they thought would make particularly good Nazis. Initially, cooperation between the German Labour Front under Robert Ley and the Hitler Youth under Baldur von Shirach led to the formation of NAPOLA schools. When these were taken over by the SS, Ley and Shirach started Adolf Hitler schools – different name, same purpose.

SOURCE C

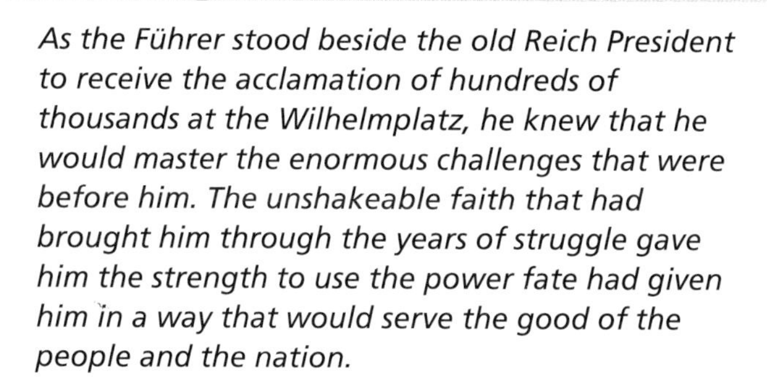
As the Führer stood beside the old Reich President to receive the acclamation of hundreds of thousands at the Wilhelmplatz, he knew that he would master the enormous challenges that were before him. The unshakeable faith that had brought him through the years of struggle gave him the strength to use the power fate had given him in a way that would serve the good of the people and the nation.

From the Nazi history book, *The Battle for Germany*, by Phillip Bouhler, published in 1938.

ACTIVITIES

1. Briefly describe the average school day for children under the Nazis.
2. Explain why the Nazis were so eager to change the school curriculum.
3. Was the altered school day more or less enjoyable for children under the Nazis? Explain your answer.
4. Study Source A. Why would Hitler wish to concentrate on young people? Use the source and your own knowledge to explain your answer.
5. Study Sources B and D. How useful are these sources in explaining how the Nazis used education to get their message across? Use the source and your own knowledge to explain your answer.
6. Study Source C. Why would Bouhler write the book in this way? Use the source and your own knowledge to explain your answer.

SOURCE D

PERIODS	Monday	Tuesday	Wednesday	Thursday	Friday	Saturday
1 8:00–8:45	German	German	German	German	German	German
2 8:50–9:35	Geography	History	Singing	Geography	History	Singing
3 9:40–10:25	Race Study	Race Study	Race Study	Race Study	Party Beliefs	Party Beliefs
4 1025:11:00	Break – with sports and special announcements.					
5 11:00–12:05	Domestic Science with Mathematics – Every day.					
6 12:10–12:55	The science of breeding (Eugenics) – Health Biology.					
	2:00–6:00 Sport each day.					

4.2 How did children spend their time outside school?

LEARNING OBJECTIVES

In this lesson you will:

- learn about the key Nazi youth groups
- practise using contextual knowledge to improve answers to source-based questions.

KEY WORDS

Landjahr – *a year of national service for young adults.*

As far as the Nazis were concerned, the training of young people did not finish when school stopped (see Source A). Even though German children went to school on Saturday and were there until 6 p.m., they were expected to be out in the evening attending activities run by the various Nazi youth organisations. From ages 6 to 18, German children were provided with things to fill their 'free' time.

Nazi youth groups

Age	Boys	Girls
6 to 10	Cubs	
10 to 14	Young German Boys	Young German Girls
14 to 18	Hitler Youth (HJ)	League of German Girls (BDM)
18 to 21		Faith and Beauty

Boys were targeted early. From the age of six, they could join the cubs and begin the semi-military training that would extend up through the movement. Sports, camping, outdoor survival skills, long cross-country marches and weapons training all formed part of the activities put on by the boys' organisations. As the boys got older the demands on them became greater and the activities more closely resembled the kind of training that new recruits were given in the army (see Source C). By the age of 18, boys were expected either to be working full-time or in the army.

Girls' training started and ended later. They were being prepared for motherhood and as family carers and so home-craft skills such as cooking and sewing were common activities for girls belonging to the Nazi organisations. Sport and fitness activities were also popular. After the age of 18, many girls had not yet begun to produce a family and so they were encouraged to remain in the Nazi Youth movement to prepare themselves for the task of raising a healthy National Socialist family (see Source D).

Both girls and boys were also given work to do for the good of the nation. One such type of work was the ***landjahr*** programme. Members of the Hitler Youth and League of German Girls would volunteer to spend eight months working on farms to help the nation's economy. This work was mixed with a programme of activities of the type that they would have experienced in the youth groups where they lived.

Youth groups and war work

When the war broke out, youth groups were given tasks to help with the war effort. These involved running messages for officials and helping organise civil defence. When the allied bombing offensive began to get heavy in 1942, boys from the Hitler Youth helped fire fighters and air raid wardens. They would also help clear up the bomb damage. Both girls and boys could do extra farm work and

SOURCE A

In our eyes the German boy of the future must be slender and supple, swift as greyhounds, tough as leather and hard as Krupp steel. We must bring a new type of human being, men and girls who are disciplined and healthy to the core. We have undertaken to give the German people an education that begins already in youth and will never come to an end. It starts with the child and will end with the 'old fighter'. Nobody will be able to say that he has a time in which he is left entirely alone to himself.

Adolf Hitler, speaking in 1935.

SOURCE B

Fun was at the heart of the Nazi youth experience though the purpose was indoctrination.

VOICE YOUR OPINION!

Would you have joined a Nazi youth group?

girls particularly could help fill the shortage of factory workers caused by men being recruited into the army. Towards the end of the war, the SS formed its own 'Hitler Youth' tank division and Hitler Youth members found themselves fighting in the Volkssturm (the German equivalent of the British Home Guard) once the Allies had invaded Germany in 1944.

SOURCE 

Every boy should learn how to shoot and obey orders otherwise when war breaks out he will be no more use than an old woman.

Robert Baden Powell in his book, *Scouting for Boys*. Baden Powell was the founder of the Scouting movement.

Fact file

Baldur von Shirach was born in 1907 to a German father and an American mother. He joined the Nazi Party in 1925 and rose to become the head of the Hitler Youth in 1933. During the war, he was made the gauleiter of Vienna and was responsible for the deportation of nearly 200,000 Jews to camps in Poland. One of only two men to criticise Hitler at the Nuremburg trials (the other was Albert Speer), he was found guilty of war crimes and served twenty years in prison.

SOURCE 

As I travel through Germany, I see in the millions of children nothing less than what gives meaning to all of our work. I see children who in obeying their mothers also obey me. When I see this wonderful growing youth, my work becomes easy.

Gertrude Scholz-Klinck, leader of the Nazi Women's Organisation, speaking in 1936.

ACTIVITIES

1. Briefly describe the things that young Germans did in the youth organisations.
2. Explain why the Nazis put so much effort into their youth organisations.
3. Study Source A. What can we learn about Hitler's attitude to youth organisations? Use the source and your own knowledge to explain your answer.
4. Study Source B. Why would the Nazis wish to circulate this kind of image to a wide audience? Use the source and your own knowledge to explain your answer.
5. Study Source C. Are you surprised by this source? Use the source and your own knowledge to explain your answer.
6. Study Sources C and D. How similar are these sources? Use the sources and your own knowledge to explain your answer.

4.3 How successful was Nazi youth policy?

LEARNING OBJECTIVES

In this lesson you will:

- learn about Nazi youth policy
- practise coming to a judgement on a key issue.

Hitler did not want any young person to be alone for even a moment. He needed people occupied as much of the time as possible. As a result, young people were pressured to join the relevant Nazi youth group. By the end of the 1930s, 82 per cent of eligible young people were voluntary members of Nazi youth groups. It would seem that Hitler had succeeded in building his generation of Nazis.

Arguments against success

- It is true that 82 per cent is a high figure for membership of any organisation or group of organisations, but how many of those were enthusiastic members and how many joined for a quiet life?
- There is also an argument that young people joined youth groups for the activities and took little notice of the group's political aspects. There was a strong tradition in Germany for young people to belong to organisations like the Boy Scouts, *Wandervogel* and the Catholic Youth Organisation.
- If we take into account what we know about the youth groups who resisted Hitler, like the Edelweiss Pirates and Swing Youth, it is clear that the Nazis failed to win over all young people to National Socialism.

SOURCE A

We believed in Hitler. We believed in the whole system, the entire leadership. There we were, already half dead, still believing in victory. We could not do anything else. That was our generation and he was our idol.

A member of the Hitler Youth, speaking after the war.

SOURCE B

The son of a Social Democrat comrade in my house is 13 years old and in the Hitler Youth. Recently he came home from a training evening and asked his father, 'Why didn't you defend yourselves then? I despise you because you didn't possess a shred of heroism. Your social democracy is worthy of nothing more than to be beaten to a pulp because you didn't have a single hero!' His father said to him, 'You don't understand any of that.' But the boy laughed and believed what his leader had told him.

An incident reported by a Social Democrat agent in 1934.

Arguments for success

- There is strong anecdotal evidence of young people worshipping Hitler like a pop star (see Source A).
- The actions of German people throughout the war and their apparent willingness in some cases to fight to the death would suggest that Hitler and the Nazis had won over vast numbers of young people.
- Gestapo records indicate that young people were quite prepared to report their parents for acting against the Nazi Party. Some of this may be down to teenage rebellion but still represents success for the Nazis (see Source B).

Fact file

There were some smaller organisations of young people who resisted the Nazis, like the Edelweiss Pirates or the Swing Youth. They wore special uniforms that made them stand out from the Hitler Youth and took part in activities that showed their non-conformity. This ranged from listening to American swing music or jazz to handing out anti-Nazi leaflets or even helping Allied prisoners of war to escape. When arrested, they often had their heads shaved or were given short prison sentences. Towards the end of the war, some of the leaders of the Edelweiss Pirates were hung.

SOURCE C

A drummer of the Hitler Youth, from the film *Triumph of the Will*.

ACTIVITIES

1. Briefly describe how the Nazi youth movements helped the Nazis.
2. Explain why some young people may not have wanted to join the Nazi youth movements.
3. Study Sources A and C. How far does this show that Hitler's youth policy was successful? Use the sources and your own knowledge to explain your answer.
4. Study Source B. To what extent can this attitude be blamed on Nazi youth policy? Use the source and your own knowledge to explain your answer.
5. Copy the table below onto a large sheet of paper. Complete the second and third columns, judging whether against each criterion, the Nazis enjoyed success, partial success and partial failure, or failure. In the third column, explain your choice with examples where possible. When you have completed the table use it to write a discursive (where you argue both sides) essay. The Grade Studio on pages 126–27 may help you.

Success criteria	**Success or failure**	**Notes**
Young people would join the Nazi youth organisations.		
Young people would successfully become good adult Nazis.		
Young people would follow Adolf Hitler, if necessary to the death.		
Young people would listen to Adolf Hitler first and all others second.		
Young people would not take part in anti-Nazi activities.		
In peacetime, young people would volunteer to take part in programmes to help the state.		
During wartime, young people would do tasks that aided the war effort.		

4.4 What role did women play in the Nazi state?

LEARNING OBJECTIVES

In this lesson you will:

- learn about the role of women in the Nazi State
- practise answering source-based questions about 'purpose'.

Hitler was very clear about what women should or should not do. His ideas were very traditional. He saw women as home-builders and mothers, nurturing and raising the young. The skills they should learn revolved around the needs of the home, such as cooking and sewing. He preferred women to dress modestly, in traditional clothing. In National Socialist Germany, everybody should know their place and their duty (see Source A).

Like many other Nazi ideas, the traditional view of the role of women was nothing new. Many conservative organisations, looking back to a different era, stressed the role of women as home-builders. Many churches, particularly the Catholic Church, were concerned with promoting the Christian family group as the basis of society.

Women and propaganda

Women were subjected to the same propaganda as men in Nazi Germany but they were also given some specific advice about what they should do (see Sources B and C). The Propaganda Ministry made sure that all representations of women fitted the Nazi ideal and produced a lot of posters showing the ideal Nazi family and the woman's place within that family.

SOURCE A

I detest women who dabble in politics. And if their dabbling extends to military matters it becomes utterly unendurable. In no section of the party has a woman ever had the right to hold even the smallest post. Gallantry forbids one to give women an opportunity of putting themselves in situations that do not suit them.

Adolf Hitler, from a speech made in 1942.

SOURCE B

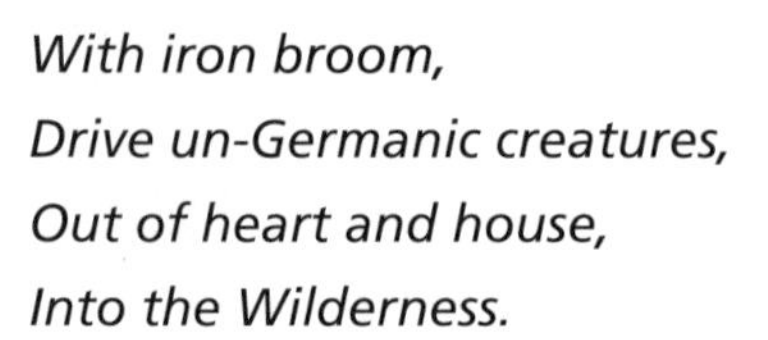

With iron broom,
Drive un-Germanic creatures,
Out of heart and house,
Into the Wilderness.

Poem by Guida Diehl, a campaigner for women to take on their 'traditional' role (from Claudia Koonz's book, *Mothers in the Fatherland*, 1986).

Women and the economy

Hitler did not want women going to work, particularly in the factories. He felt this kind of employment sent out the wrong messages and would damage the 'People's Community'.

However, the German economy, towards the end of the 1930s, was short of workers. Hermann Goering, with Hitler's agreement, tried to get women back into employment. Many women did not want to go, particularly as they could receive in child benefit more money than they could make working. A 'duty year' was introduced where women who were coming to the age where they could look for work

SOURCE 

The woman, besides caring for her own children, should first care for those who need her help as mothers of the nation.

Gertrude Scholz-Klinck, Head of the Nazi Women's Organisation, speaking in 1936.

VOICE YOUR OPINION!

Today, we tend to see the Nazi attitude to women as 'sexist' and the emancipated woman of the 1920s as 'good'. Is it fair to impose our attitudes on different periods of history?

would do a year's work for the good of the state. This was usually on a farm or in domestic service. Women on this scheme did not get paid but got bed and board in return.

SOURCE D

I was proud. When I got the gold Mother's Cross, also when I got the silver, there was a big celebration in a school, where the mothers were all invited for coffee and cake.

Wilhemine Haferkamp, speaking in an interview after the war.

Fact file

Gertrude Scholtz-Klinck joined the Nazi Party in 1929 and was promoted to the head of the Women's Bureau of the German Labour Front in 1934. As a mother of six and having blonde hair and blue eyes, she was everything that the Nazis wanted in a woman. She was a good organiser and an excellent public speaker and worked very hard to get women to contribute to the Nazi state.

SOURCE E

Gertrude Scholtz-Klinck was the female public face of the Nazi Party.

SOURCE F

A Nazi poster showing the 'ideal' German family.

ACTIVITIES

1. Briefly describe the role of women according to the Nazis.
2. Explain why Nazis wanted women to fulfil this role.
3. Study Source A. Why do you think Adolf Hitler uses the word 'gallantry'? Use the source and your own knowledge to explain your answer.
4. Study Source B. Guida Diehl began campaigning just after the First World War, then she discovered Hitler and became an admirer. What does this tell us about Nazi policy towards women? Use the source and your own knowledge to explain your answer.
5. Study Source C. Why would Gertrude Scholtz-Klinck have made this speech? Use the source and your own knowledge to explain your answer.
6. Study Source D. How useful is this in explaining the rise in the birth rate during the time of the Nazi regime? Use the source and your own knowledge to explain your answer.
7. Study Sources C, E and F. Why do you think Gertrud Scholtz-Klinck became the head of the Nazi Women's Organisation? Use the sources and your own knowledge to explain your answer.

4.5 Did the Nazis improve the German economy?

LEARNING OBJECTIVES

In this lesson you will:

- learn about how the economy improved under the Nazis
- practise answering questions that require evaluation.

The economic situation at the end of the Weimar Republic had played a major part in the rise of the Nazis. The change in the world economic situation in 1933 and 1934 had helped Hitler to consolidate power. In 1934, Hjalmar Schacht, the man who had helped solve hyperinflation was made Minister for the Economy and helped Hitler with the economic recovery (see Source A). By the end of the decade, however, people began to ask: 'Have things really improved? Was this the miracle that Hitler talked about?'

The programme of public works

A key policy of Hitler and the Nazis was the scheme to build things for the benefit of society. Central to this was the German network of motorways and public swimming pools. These schemes reduced unemployment and also improved morale.

Trade unions and the German Labour Front

In May 1933, trade unions were banned and their assets given to a new Nazi organisation, the German

SOURCE **A**

In July 1934, Hitler asked me whether I would take over the Ministry of Economics as well as my work as President of the National Bank. I was not frightened by the great difficulties involved. We had succeeded in reducing unemployment considerably with the aid of National Bank credits.

Hjalmar Schacht, from his book *Account Settled*, written in 1948.

SOURCE **B**

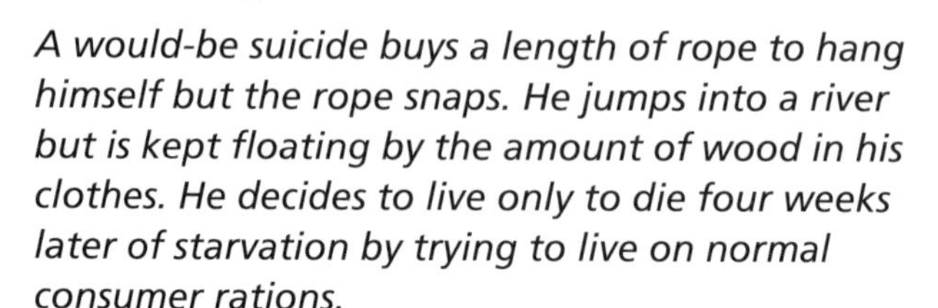

A would-be suicide buys a length of rope to hang himself but the rope snaps. He jumps into a river but is kept floating by the amount of wood in his clothes. He decides to live only to die four weeks later of starvation by trying to live on normal consumer rations.

A popular joke in the late 1930s.

Labour Front (DAF). The aim of the DAF was to promote goodwill between the workers and the government and it was therefore a very important organisation in the Nazi 'People's Community'. By 1939, it had 22 million members.

SOURCE **C**

Between them Schacht and Hitler oversaw a significant improvement in the state of the German economy.

One of the key aspects of the DAF was the 'Strength through Joy' programme. This arranged subsidised leisure activities for workers. These ranged from film shows, theatre visits and sports events to holidays in the Alps or on cruise ships and there was even a 'Strength through Joy' band, which toured the country. Evening classes were also organised to help people to learn new skills.

GradeStudio

In the Grade Studio on pages 98–99, we looked at how to answer a part (c) question, where a clear choice has to be made. An example of that kind of question is:

Did life get better or worse for workers in Nazi Germany, 1933–1939?

Copy the table below and decide whether the explanation is 'better' or 'worse'. Then use the completed table to put together a Level 5 answer.

Examiner's tip

Remember, to achieve the highest level you need to explain the reasons why it might be better and why it might be worse. This could be set out in two paragraphs, one which deals with 'better' and one which deals with 'worse'. In order to achieve the highest level, you will need to add a third paragraph answering the question by saying whether you think it was either better or worse and explaining your choice.

Explanation	Better or worse?
The Nazi government banned trade unions. This meant that workers did not have independent representatives.	
Ordinary Germans ate cheaper food under the Nazis. Consumption of cheaper foodstuffs like potatoes and rye bread replaced food like meat and milk.	
The 'Strength through Joy' programme gave German workers new opportunities. People who had never been to the theatre were able to experience this for the first time.	
Work was abundant under the Nazis. Unemployment was lower than it had been for most of the time of the Weimar Republic.	
'Strength through Joy' was a myth for most German workers. Few German workers actually experienced the subsidised holidays.	
Life improved because people did not have to worry anymore. In a managed economy, there would always be work.	

ACTIVITIES

1. Briefly describe the change that happened to the economy under the Nazis.
2. Explain why the economic improvement helped Hitler to consolidate power.
3. Study Source A. Are you surprised that Schacht might think this about the German economy? Use the source and your own knowledge to explain your answer.
4. Study Source B. How useful is this source in understanding the priorities of German economic policy in the late 1930s? Use the source and your own knowledge to explain your answer.
5. Study Source C. How far was Hitler responsible for the improvement in the German economy? Use the source and your own knowledge to explain your answer.

4.6 Get your sources sorted!

What was the economic impact of the Nazis?

LEARNING OBJECTIVES

In this lesson you will:

- learn how to answer questions that require you to evaluate sources for reliability.

Evaluating for reliability

Two types of questions asking you to evaluate sources are used in the examination papers.

Firstly, there are questions requiring you to evaluate sources for their utility – you will be asked to explain how useful particular sources are (see page 26).

However, we are going to focus on questions requiring you to evaluate sources for reliability. This basically means 'do you trust what the source is telling you?' These questions can be asked in several ways e.g. 'How reliable is this source?', 'Do you trust this account of the Munich Putsch?', 'Does this source prove that all Germans supported Hitler?'

There are several different methods that can be used to evaluate sources for reliability. They do not all work well with all sources. You need to study the source you are being asked about and decide which method works best with that particular source.

Using your knowledge to check what a source says

This is a good, straightforward way to evaluate sources and will work with most sources. However, you do need to know something about the topic. You need to use your knowledge to check what the source says. You can use your knowledge to support or challenge what the source says.

Commenting on the tone or language of the source

This method can work well but it needs to be used with the right sources. It only works with sources that contain language that shows us that the author was biased. This is usually very strong language. Or it might be that the whole tone of the source e.g. a sarcastic tone, suggests that the author is not trying to write an accurate account of events. Instead, he has a purpose and wants us to accept his point of view.

Making good use of the information you are given about the source

In exam papers you are usually told something about where a source has come from e.g. who wrote it, the date, or whether it came from a newspaper or a memoir. These can be used to evaluate sources but you need to be careful with this approach. Do not try and say whether a source can be trusted just because of its type e.g. 'I do not trust this source because it was written by someone who was there.' This will not get many marks. You need to think about the person who has written or drawn the source. It might be someone you know something about. Ask yourself what are they up to, are they trying to argue a case, are they trying to persuade us about something?

Look at Source A. You have to answer the question, 'How far do you trust what Hitler is saying?' How many of the methods for evaluating sources that are considered above, can be used with this source?

SOURCE A

What we have achieved in two and a half years in the way of planning jobs and controlling prices and wages, was thought, only a few years ago, to be impossible. We only succeeded because we had the whole nation behind us. The destruction of the Trade Unions and the political parties were necessary for this success.

Hitler speaking to the Reichstag in 1935.

SOURCE B

Would you rather have butter or guns? Shall we bring in lard or iron ore? I tell you, guns make us powerful. Butter only makes us fat.

Hermann Goering, speaking in 1935.

SOURCE C

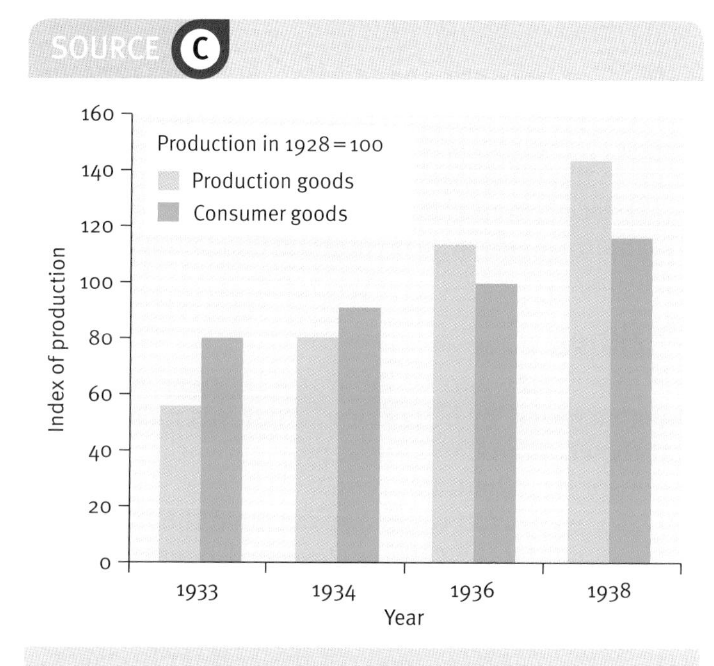

Industrial production in Germany 1933 to 1938.

SOURCE E

There is only one interest, the interest of the nation; only one view, the bringing of Germany to the point of political and economic self-sufficiency... I thus set the following tasks:

1 The German armed forces must be operational within four years.

2 The German economy must be fit for war in four years.

Adolf Hitler, from the declaration of the four-year plan in 1936.

ACTIVITIES

1. Study Source A. Why did people believe that Hitler had brought about an economic miracle? Use the source and your own knowledge to explain your answer.
2. Study Sources A and D. How far does Source D support the ideas in Source A? Use the sources and your own knowledge to explain your answer.
3. Study Source C. How far did Germany move towards a war economy in the years up to 1938? Use the source and your own knowledge to explain your answer.
4. Study Sources B and E. How similar are these two sources? Use the sources and your own knowledge to explain your answer.

SOURCE D

German working-class tourists giving the Hitler salute on one of the 'Strength through Joy' cruiseships.

4.7 How did war change the economy?

LEARNING OBJECTIVES

In this lesson you will:

- learn about the impact of the war on the German economy
- extract material from sources to answer questions requiring evaluation and judgement.

KEY WORDS

Autarky – *national self-sufficiency – when a country is able to produce everything that it needs.*

Blitzkrieg – *lightning war. A modern style of warfare used very successfully by the German Army in the first three years of the war.*

Mobilisation – *putting things on a war footing (particularly armies or armaments industries).*

Self-sufficiency

Hitler switched the direction of the economy in 1936 with the announcement of a four-year plan. The aim of this was **autarky** – national self-sufficiency. This involved increasing the production of certain things like food or steel and developing substitute products for things that Germany could not produce, like rubber. This was particularly important once Germany was at war as the size of the British Navy caused problems for the German merchant fleet.

The drive for autarky did not work and by the time the war started, Germany was still heavily reliant on foreign imports. Iron ore from Sweden, oil from Russia and wood from Norway were all crucial for the German economy. German chemists had developed a method of producing oil from coal but it took six tons of coal to make one ton of oil and so was not very efficient.

Expanding Germany, expanding economy

From 1938 onwards, Greater Germany started to expand. First, in March 1938, German troops entered Austria and it became part of the Third Reich. In the Munich Agreement of September 1938, part of Czechoslovakia was given to Germany and, in March 1939, German troops invaded the rest of the country. The Czechs did not resist.

These new territories were very good news for the German economy. Austria gave Germany a new supply of iron ore and Czechoslovakia contained some of the most modern heavy industry in the world. Of particular use to the Nazis were the armaments plant at Brno and the Skoda tank factory at Pilsen.

Blitzkrieg

The first three years of the war were filled with quick victories, or **blitzkrieg**. What this meant was that the economy and the supply network were not seriously stretched. Between campaigns, the war industry was given time to make good the losses in equipment and the Germans were also quick to mobilise the captured armaments industry for their own uses. Supplies captured from opposing armies were used by the Germans in their later campaigns.

SOURCE 

It seems to me that in earlier times the thing was simpler. In earlier times, you pillaged. If you conquered a country you disposed of the riches of that country. At present, things are done in a more humane way. As for myself, I still think of pillage comprehensively.

Hermann Goering, Nazi leader responsible for the war economy, speaking in August 1942.

SOURCE 

From the first I was certain of the one system that could possibly achieve success in the armaments industry. Of course I had a certain advantage, for during my two years of construction work for the armaments industry, I had seen many fundamental errors which would have remained hidden from me if I had been at the top.

Albert Speer, writing in 1969.

The move to a war economy

The relative ease with which the Germans conducted the first years of the war meant that there was no pressure within Germany from the government for a rapid **mobilisation** of industry. In Britain, and later in Russia and America, the move towards a total war economy began with the declaration of war but with Germany this was different. It seemed that Hitler and the Nazis had found a different approach to autarky and the question of guns or butter. By conquering foreign territory, they were able to put off the move to a total war economy and maintain normality for the ordinary German consumer.

ACTIVITIES

1. Briefly describe how Germany gained more territory from 1938 onwards.
2. Explain why the Nazis believed that self-sufficiency was so important.
3. 'The Second World War came out of Germany's inability to gain self-sufficiency.' How far do you agree with this statement? Explain your answer.
4. Study Source A. How did the conquest of foreign land help Germany's economic position? Use the source and your own knowledge to explain your answer.
5. Study Source B. How far do you think Albert Speer was satisfied with the efficiency of the Germany war economy when he became Minister for Armaments in 1942? Use the source and your own knowledge to explain your answer.

GradeStudio

You have learnt about four of the most common source-based questions. Below are four questions, one of each. Can you identify which is which and use the sources indicated, and the material on pages 26, 54, 72 and 112, to help you to construct an answer?

1. Study Source C on page 75. What can we learn from this source about the way in which Hitler ruled Germany? Use the source and your own knowledge to explain your answer.
2. Study Source B on page 63. Are you surprised by the harsh terms of this decree? Use the source and your own knowledge to explain your answer.
3. Study Source D on page 105. Why would Gertrude Scholz-Klinck talk about children in this way? Use the source and your own knowledge to explain your answer.
4. Study Source A on page 100 and Source A on page 102. How similar are these two sources? Use the sources and your own knowledge to explain your answer.

Examiner's tip

Remember, when answering source-based questions contextual knowledge is very important. This means information that relates to the source but is not contained within the source.

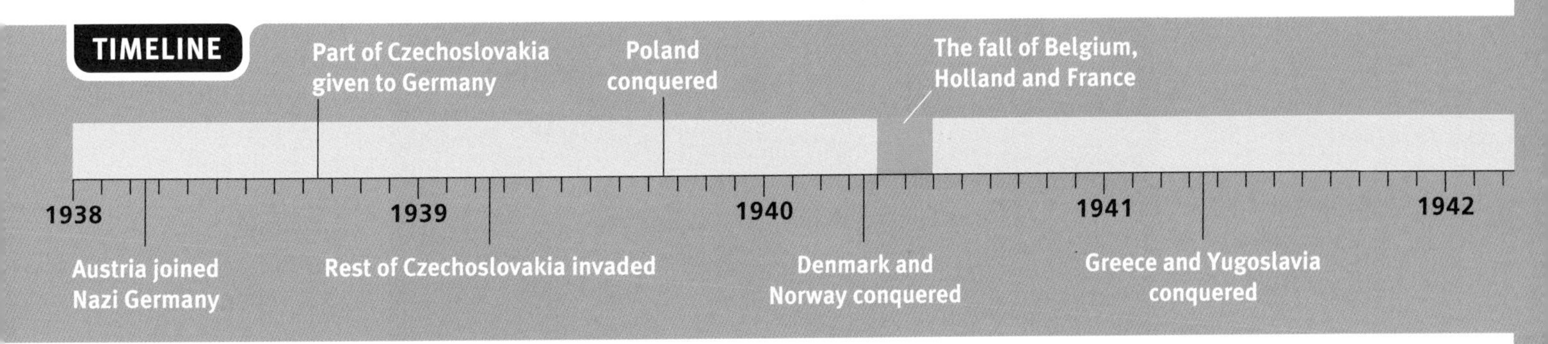

4.8 How did the Second World War affect life for ordinary Germans?

LEARNING OBJECTIVES

In this lesson you will:

- learn how the war changed the lives of ordinary Germans
- practise answering questions on utility and typicality.

KEY WORDS

Black market – *unofficial buying and selling in order to get round the rules of rationing.*

Rationing – *limiting the amount of food and goods available to civilians during wartime.*

Refugees – *people who have to leave their homes due to some catastrophe.*

Germany victorious!

German victories in the early campaigns allowed the Nazis to avoid putting too many restrictions on the ordinary German. Some **rationing** measures were introduced but these were more like changes in the allocations as much as being limitations on the amounts people could obtain. Extra rations were given to key workers and to expectant mothers and it is estimated that 40 per cent of Germans actually ate better as a result of rationing.

The victories also made German people more enthusiastic about the war. The success of the blitzkrieg meant that people no longer feared the terror of trench warfare, and the relatively short periods of actual fighting meant that casualties were not coming home in a steady stream. German propaganda made much of the triumphs, particularly the defeat of France, and German morale was high.

The air raids

Perhaps the most striking effect of the war on Germany was from the air raids carried out by the British and American Air Forces on German cities (see Source B). The Germans had already started bombing British cities in 1940 and so it was a logical response for the British to do the same and bomb German cities. The difference was that the British had much bigger bombers and more of them. When the US Air Force began to arrive in 1942, a sustained and terrifying campaign was unleashed against the larger German cities.

The pattern was that the British would bomb at night and the Americans by day. They used incendiary bombs designed to set fire to things and cause damage that way. Occasionally, the British gathered all their strength and launched 'thousand bomber raids' against a particular city. These raids caused firestorms that destroyed everything in their path. Some casualty estimates are as high as 30,000 people killed in a single attack. Often, people would suffocate as the fires burned up all the oxygen in the air around them.

SOURCE A

Ordinary people were willing to show their support for the Nazis as long as the Nazis were successful.

SOURCE B

Speer claims that production in the armament industry is not too badly affected after an enemy air raid. The fact is that workers often stay away from their workbenches for weeks after an attack. Thus, for instance, the Lanz works at Mannheim have been completely open for production for a fortnight, yet only 60 percent of the workforce has thus far returned.

Josef Goebbels, diary entry for 21 September 1943.

The collapse of the Nazi State

By the beginning of 1945, ordinary Germans were experiencing the beginning of the breakdown of Nazi control. Millions of German **refugees** were moving west, fleeing the advancing Russian Army which was taking revenge for the horrors that the Nazis had brought to their country. Stories of murder and rape were commonplace and captured German males were sent to Russian concentration camps where they would probably die.

The rationing system broke down completely and Germans relied on the **black market** simply to stay alive. People scavenged for dead animals killed in air raids as a source of meat and looted from bombed-out buildings. As the Allied soldiers approached, ordinary Germans destroyed any evidence that they had supported the Nazis in an attempt to win favour and thereby survive. It is estimated that 3.5 million German civilians died as a result of the Second World War – many of them died of starvation in 1945.

ACTIVITIES

1. Briefly describe the changes in the way in which ordinary Germans experienced the war.
2. Explain why so many German civilians died during the war.
3. Study Source A. How far does this show that the German experience of the early war was a positive one? Use the source and your own knowledge to explain your answer.
4. Study Source B. Are you surprised that Goebbels wrote this in his diary? Use the source and your own knowledge to explain your answer.
5. Study Source C. How useful is this source in understanding the problems caused by the Allied bombing campaign? Use the source and your own knowledge to explain your answer.

SOURCE C

Allied forces entering the bombed out city of Cologne in 1945.

4.9 What did total war mean for Nazi Germany?

LEARNING OBJECTIVES

In this lesson you will:

- learn how total war affected Nazi Germany
- practise cross-referencing material from sources.

GETTING STARTED

What do you think total war is?

KEY WORDS

Total war – *government takes special powers to focus all the country's effort on the war.*

Total war was proclaimed by Josef Goebbels, Nazi leader responsible for total war, in a speech in February 1943. This represented a change in attitude among the Nazi leaders that had started with the failure to defeat Russia in 1941. Following the death of Fritz Todt, the architect Albert Speer was appointed as the Minister for Armaments and Munitions (see Source A).

The efficiency of the war economy

Speer improved the way that information was gathered, and prioritised production of certain key items, such as tanks and aeroplanes. He stopped the waste of raw materials on items that did not directly aid the war effort and closed down some research projects. He made factories work round the clock rather than closing down at night and as a result German war production reached its highest output in 1944, despite the air offensive by Britain and America (see Source B).

SOURCE A

Hitler had already appointed a wine salesman as his Foreign Minister, his party philosopher as his Minister for Eastern Affairs, and a fighter pilot as the overseer of the whole economy. Now he was appointing an architect as Minister for Armaments. Undoubtedly Hitler preferred non-specialists. All his life, he respected but distrusted professionals like, for example, Schacht.

Albert Speer, writing in 1969.

SOURCE B

Everything was dark and the house seemed dead as if forsaken by God. Sometimes I shivered with fright that I could hardly pray. Up there everything sounded threatening and I was always thinking: now the house will start to burn.

A Jewish man, Moritz Mandelkern, writing about his experience of air raids, while hiding in the attic of the Schwarz family in Berlin.

Foreign labour

One of the cornerstones of the German war economy was the use of foreign labour. This consisted of volunteers from the conquered territories in the west who had moved to the Reich, and press-ganged prisoners from the east. Speer began to realise that volunteer foreign labour worked better in its own country rather than living in poor barracks in Germany and so contracts were increasingly given to firms in the conquered territories.

Slave labour became an increasingly important part of the German war effort. Slave labourers came from two groups, either Russian prisoners of war or Jews. They were held in concentration 'work' camps like Plasov or Sachsenhausen, where they were given starvation rations, the idea being that they should work while they were useful and then be replaced when they died.

Big business

Rather than bringing big business under the control of the government, the Nazis gave large industrial firms a great deal of independence. Some of the larger German companies made huge profits during the war years because of this. Not only were they able to keep down the wages of German workers but they also benefited from slave labour from the work camps. They had to pay the SS for these workers but even with this taken into account, the workers were far cheaper than free labour.

SOURCE C

Slave labour was an important part of Germany's war production.

Fighting the total war

The total-war mentality led to an escalation in brutality. Hitler identified that the war against Russia would be a struggle of two ideologies and would be a fight to the death. German soldiers on the Eastern Front were told to terrorise the local population and often whole villages were burned to the ground as the Germans advanced.

SOURCE D

Total war removed any last legal or moral obstacles in the Nazis' treatment of people they thought of as undesirable.

ACTIVITIES

1 Briefly describe what total war means.

2 Explain why Germany did not declare a state of total war until so late.

3 Study Source A. Does this mean that Hitler's ministers were less efficient? Use the source and your own knowledge to explain your answer.

4 Study Source B. How useful is this source in understanding the impact of total war on ordinary Germans? Use the source and your own knowledge to explain your answer.

5 Study Sources C and D. How similar are these sources? Use the sources and your own knowledge to explain your answer.

HISTORY DETECTIVE

How did German companies do under the Nazis? Find out about some of them. As a starter, find out about I.G. Farben, Krupp Thyssen, Volkswagen, Porsche, Bayer, Akso.

4.10 Case study: How did people survive the Holocaust?

LEARNING OBJECTIVES

In this lesson you will:

- learn the story of a Holocaust survivor
- use independent research skills to find out more about people who experienced the Holocaust.

KEY WORDS

Auschwitz – *village in southern Poland where two important camps were built. The work camp called Auschwitz 1 and the death camp at Auschwitz Birkenau.*

Holocaust – *attempt by the Nazis to kill all the Jews in Europe during the Second World War.*

This case study is based around the book *Self Portrait of a* ***Holocaust*** *Survivor* by Werner Weinberg.

Early life

Werner Weinberg grew up in the small German town of Rheda, in the state of Westphalia. As a child, he was conscious enough of his Jewishness for it to be special, though he mixed readily enough with non-Jewish children. As a gifted scholar, he was sent to the high school in the nearby city of Bielefeld and finished his studies at the Hebrew Teaching College in Würzburg. His first job was as the Jewish teacher at the synagogue in Rheda.

Werner's experience of the 1930s was one of increasing intimidation. At first, the Nazis in the town amounted to a powerful minority but slowly their influence grew and those non-Jews who would openly show their distaste for Nazi anti-Semitism grew fewer and fewer. The size of the Jewish population dwindled as some emigrated and others were arrested.

The persecution in Rheda amounted to threats and name-calling, with the odd stone or paint pot launched in the direction of someone as they walked down the street. Gangs of Nazis, often drunk, would congregate in front of houses banging on the doors and windows and shouting at those inside. Sometimes they would break down the doors, ransack the house and drag the terrified inhabitants outside and chase them round the streets.

Marriage and emigration

Werner married his fiancée, Lisl, in December 1938 and they made great efforts to emigrate from Nazi Germany. Their task was a difficult one as other countries were not keen to take Jewish refugees. Without any relatives abroad or the money to buy their way out, things seemed desperate for the newly married couple. In March 1939, however, they were both offered teaching jobs in Holland and were able to escape the horrors of Nazi Germany. Unfortunately, in May 1940, the German Army invaded Holland and it became an occupied territory until May 1945.

SOURCE A

Werner Weinberg, author and Holocaust survivor.

Bergen Belsen

Werner and his wife were taken to the concentration camp at Bergen Belsen in 1944. Unusually, they were housed together in the 'Dutch' compound (normally camps were segregated by gender). Bergen Belsen was not a death camp like **Auschwitz** Birkenau or Treblinka. It was a camp where inmates died of 'natural' causes, usually disease or starvation. Many of them had worked in German industry but had become too weak to be useful and were sent to the camp to die. There was a crematorium in the camp but no gas chamber.

In the three months before it was liberated by the British, Bergen Belsen suffered from chronic overcrowding. Inmates from camps in the east had been moved there to prevent them being liberated by the advancing Russian Army. There was no longer enough food or space for all the inmates in the camp and it became difficult for the guards to organise them. Latrines overflowed, food was scarce and there was an epidemic of typhus. What had been an awful existence became a nightmare moment-to-moment struggle for survival, surrounded by the dead and the dying.

Werner relates an interesting incident concerning a former inmate of Auschwitz who boasted that the scenes of degradation at Bergen Belsen would never have happened at a more efficient camp like Auschwitz. Werner was ashamed of Bergen Belsen. It is difficult to decide what is stranger: the other inmate's pride at the efficiency of Auschwitz or Werner's embarrassment at the inefficiency of Bergen Belsen.

The train and freedom

A month before the end of the war, Werner and his wife were selected. They were to be cleaned up and put on a train. Werner as an inmate had no idea of the destination of the journey and from the behaviour of the SS guards, it is debatable whether they had any better idea. The journey lasted over two weeks and ended when the train was found by Allied soldiers near the small town of Trobitz, 25 miles east of Torgau. Eventually, Werner settled in the USA, where he was able to resume his teaching career.

HISTORY DETECTIVE

There is a good deal of information about individual Holocaust survivors in books, on film and on the Internet. They can form an interesting subject for a piece of independent research.

SOURCE B

The photographs and newsreel films of Bergen Belsen showed people in the west the true horrors of the Holocaust.

4.11 How far was Hitler responsible for the Holocaust?

LEARNING OBJECTIVES

In this lesson you will:

- learn about Hitler and his role in the Holocaust
- extract material from sources to answer questions requiring evaluation and judgement.

KEY WORDS

Einsatzgruppen – *groups of SS whose job was to dispose of undesirable people.*

The problem for historians is that Hitler neither planned nor ordered the Holocaust. A very small and misguided minority have used this technicality to argue that Hitler was not responsible for the Holocaust. Germans at the time often felt that had Hitler known about the violence towards the Jews or to the occupied people, he would not have approved. There is enough documentary evidence to suggest that he did approve and in many instances encouraged it.

State racism

Hitler started the Nazi Party on the basis of anti-Semitism. The 25 points of 1920 show this (see page 36). Once in power, these ideas began to take shape as policy. Laws against the Jews originated with Hitler and the Reich Chancellery and though the detail was often left to minor officials, Hitler would have checked and approved the final drafts. With violent acts like *Kristallnacht*, Hitler showed his approval through doing nothing. By the start of the Second World War, people accepted that National Socialism was racist and that persecution based on race was going to escalate (see Source A).

SOURCE A

If the international Jewish financiers in and outside of Europe should succeed in plunging the nations once more into a world war, then the result will not be the Bolshevising of the Earth, and thus the victory of Jewry, but the annihilation of the Jewish race in Europe!

Adolf Hitler from a speech to the Reichstag, 30 January 1939.

Hitler's war

Many people make the link between the way the First World War ended (with the Treaty of Versailles and reparations) and the inevitability of the start of the Second but this should not take anything away from the role that Hitler played. It was his policy to equip the German nation for war and his foreign policy that provoked war. It was his decision to invade Poland and his decision to continue with the invasion after the ultimatum given by France and Britain (see Source B).

The invasions of territory in the east brought more Jews under German control and the cruel conduct of the campaign largely rested with Hitler's directing of it (see Source C). The ***Einsatzgruppen*** were an attempt to match the aims of a racist policy with the problems of millions of Jews under Nazi control.

SOURCE B

Minister-President General Goering will do what is necessary. He has the power to make new laws and to give orders to all, including those in the government and the party.

From the decree on the execution of the four-year plan, October 1936.

SOURCE C

I am a true German soldier and I do not approve of what is happening on the Eastern Front. Decent young people are forced, by gangster methods, to participate in what amounts to mass murder.

George Keppler, Commander of the 1st SS Panzer Corps, writing in January 1943.

The villa at 56–58 Am Grossen Wannsee, where the Wannsee Conference was held. This photograph was taken in 2006.

It was Hitler who constantly talked about the Jewish problem and it should have been no surprise when a group of high-ranking SS men came up with a solution to the problem.

The Wannsee Conference

A meeting was called by the SS for January 1942 to try to find a solution to the Jewish problem. At the meeting, the idea of the 'Final Solution' was arrived at. The plan involved rounding up all the Jews in German-occupied Europe and placing them in concentration camps, some to work until they died, others to be killed immediately. New purpose-built camps were to be built, death camps like Sobibor, Treblinka and Auschwitz Birkenau. Hitler was not present at the Wannsee Conference. Himmler, Heydrich and Eichmann were (see Source D).

SOURCE D

It has often been said that Hitler knows nothing of the atrocities committed in the concentration camps. This is untrue. He knows everything about them. Films have been made of life at Dachau and Buchenwald and they have found an appreciative audience in Hitler. Indescribable scenes have been flashed on the screen for his enjoyment.

Pauline Kohler, Hitler's former maid, speaking in 1940 for an article in *Liberty* magazine.

Fact file

Industrialised mass murder

At first, the Nazis murdered Jews using special death squads called *Einsatzgruppen* but this proved inefficient and stressful for those carrying out the murders. As existing concentration camps had already been built for political prisoners, usually by surrounding old army camps with barbed wire, these were now used for some of the Jews who were arrested. In these camps, they would work as slave labour until they died. After the Wannsee Conference, special camps were built with large gas chambers, the purpose of which was to murder as many people as efficiently as possible.

ACTIVITIES

1. Briefly describe how state racism developed under the Nazis.
2. Explain why Hitler could be held responsible for the Holocaust.
3. Study Source A. What can we learn about Hitler's role in the Holocaust from this source? Use the source and your own knowledge to explain your answer.
4. Study Source B. How far did Hitler rule Germany? Use the source and your own knowledge to explain your answer.
5. Study Sources C and D. How similar are these sources? Use the sources and your own knowledge to explain your answer.

4.12 What was different about the Holocaust?

LEARNING OBJECTIVES

In this lesson you will:

- learn to explain why people think the Holocaust is unique
- practise cross-referencing material from sources.

The genocide of the Jews by National Socialist Germany is not the only example of genocide in history. In terms of the proportion of the target group killed, it was not the most successful. It is, however, by far the best known. In British schools, it is one of the few things from history that teachers are obliged by law to teach. So what is different about the Holocaust?

The progress towards genocide

Genocides start with an emotional response. One group commits violence against another group, which then retaliates. The first group retaliates in turn. The emotional responses drive a situation until one group becomes committed to the total destruction of the other. This kind of sequence happened in 1994 in Rwanda and between 1992 and 1995 in the former Yugoslavia. Hate comes out of immediate emotions.

Fact file

The victims of the Nazis

The Second World War is unique because in addition to those killed as a consequence of the fighting, the Nazis systematically murdered those they saw as inferior. Estimates put the number of those murdered by the Nazis at 6 million – it may have been more than this. Most of these people were Jewish, though a significant proportion of the Roma and Sinta populations were also murdered and other minorities were affected also (see page 101). To put this into context, the Nazis murdered more people in this way than the combined total of people killed from Britain, France and Germany during the First World War.

SOURCE A

No Jew can be a countryman... The party as such represents the point of view of a positive Christianity without binding itself to any one particular confession. It fights against the Jewish materialist spirit within and without.

From the 25-point programme of the National Socialist Party, written by Adolf Hitler and Anton Drexler in 1920.

The Holocaust was not immediate. In many ways, it had been brewing for centuries. Anti-Semitism had been a reality of life for many Jews since the time of the Romans. Hitler did not invent anti-Semitism, but what is unique is the way that he manipulated it and the results of this manipulation (see Source A).

The logic of the Holocaust

Each stage towards the genocide seemed to lack a clear plan, though overall there seems to be a logical escalation. Part of the issue is that Hitler constantly referred to 'the Jewish problem'. Problems need solving. They need solving by rational thinking. Once the Second World War made mass emigration impossible, the possibility of murder became a possible solution.

SOURCE 

As regards the gas chambers, he said that Himmler, a very kind-hearted man, was most anxious that prisoners should be exterminated in a manner which caused them the least anxiety and suffering.

From *The Venlo Incident* by Sigismund Payne Best. The conversation was with an SS doctor called Dr Rascher, while they were both held in Buchenwald concentration camp.

Systematic murder

The Jewish problem became more difficult for the Nazis when they started conquering territory in the east. The conquest of Poland added two million Jews to the 330,000 in Germany and when the Nazis took over large areas of the Soviet Union, the number grew even higher. As a result, the Germans deployed battalions of *Einsatzgruppen* whose job was to go around occupied territory disposing of undesirable people, most of whom were Jewish, but not all. The *Einsatzgruppen* found many locals willing to help them in their activities and they found that they could cover greater distances by splitting up into smaller groups and getting locals to murder the Jews for them. Anti-Semitism was not only a German prejudice.

SOURCE C

New arrivals being sorted at Auschwitz Birkenau. Some would be murdered immediately in the gas chambers, others would be slowly worked to death.

SOURCE D

A crematorium building in a Nazi concentration camp. A major component of the most effective industrialised killing in history.

Different?

The Holocaust was carried out as policy of a state government. It was undertaken by people who believed that what they were doing was the right thing to do. They took modern technology and used it in the most evil and destructive way thinkable. As human beings, we might believe ourselves capable of striking out as an emotional response to deep pain. It is far more disturbing to consider humans as willing agents to the largest state-sponsored crime in history.

ACTIVITIES

1. Briefly described what happened during the Holocaust.
2. Explain why the Nazis were able to carry out such terrible crimes.
3. How far was the Holocaust unique? Explain your answer.
4. Study Source A. How was the Holocaust a logical continuation of Nazi policy? Use the source and your own knowledge to explain your answer.
5. Study Source B. How useful is this in explaining why the Holocaust developed as it did? Use the source and your own knowledge to explain your answer.
6. Study Sources C and D. How similar are these sources? Use the sources and your own knowledge to explain your answer.

Putting it all together

You have now completed this unit, which has focused on the Nazi regime and what it was like to live in Nazi Germany. You have also had practice in answering questions designed to prepare you for your exam. Below is an example of one type of exam question, with some hints to help you write a top-level answer.

c 'It was Hitler who was mainly responsible for the Holocaust.' How far do you agree with this view? Explain your answer.

In the Grade Studio at the end of Chapter 3 (pages 98–99), we looked at **c** questions that require you to make a clear choice and then justify it. In this Grade Studio we will deal with questions that require answers that deal with the extent to which something may or may not be true, that is, 'judgement' questions.

Examiner's tip

Historical judgements are tentative. This is largely because all the evidence about any given issue cannot be known and so historians don't make sweeping or definitive statements. Therefore, the answer to a question like 'To what extent....' is always 'to a certain extent...' Clearly, this is only a starting point and the quality of the explanation will be the key factor in determining the mark that the answer gains.

Look at the sample answer below and the simplified mark scheme that follows.

Candidate's answer

The Holocaust was mainly Hitler's fault. He was the dictator and everybody had to do as he wished. Also, when the Nazi Party started he wrote the 25 points. However, he did not organise the death camps or come up with the idea, so maybe he was not completely responsible. As the leader, it was Hitler who set the policy for the government. He was the one who started the anti-Semitic feelings of the Nazis. As early as 1919, he was outlining his feelings about the Jews in writing and then the 25 points contain reference to the Jews. Also, in the late 1930s and early 1940s, Hitler made speeches talking about the destruction of the Jewish race in Europe. On the other hand, Hitler often spoke in ideas. He did not give people under him specific instructions. A lot of Nazi policy came about when people at lower levels interpreted orders from above. Without Heydrich and Eichmann's interpretation of Hitler's ideas, the Holocaust would not have happened as it did. In the end, Hitler set the agenda. Although he was not present at the Wannsee Conference, he would have had to approve of the plans that were made there. On balance, that makes him mainly responsible.

Examiner's comment

The first part of the answer (in red) gets the candidate into Level 1. By identifying specific reasons, and then explaining them, the candidate is able to build on their answer so that it reaches the top level.

Simplified mark scheme

Simplified mark scheme
Level 1 (1 to 2 marks): General assertions A statement regarding the question. No personal knowledge is shown here. A simple statement is often needed to show the examiner a clear answer to the question, in this case, that Hitler was mainly responsible for the Holocaust.
Level 2 (2 to 3 marks): Identifies reasons why you agree or why you do not These points have been identified in this example to show agreement but they have not been taken any further.
Level 3 (4 to 5 marks): Identifies reasons why you agree and why you do not More points have been identified to show the other side, that is, that Hitler was perhaps not 'mainly responsible'.
Level 4 (6 to 7 marks): Explains reasons why you agree or do not agree The reasons why Hitler could be seen as mainly responsible have been explained here using contextual knowledge.
Level 5 (8 marks): Explains reasons why you agree and reasons why you may not The other side of the argument is explained here, naming the people who perhaps shaped the Holocaust.
Level 6: Fully explains an overall reason why you agree or do not Here the answer arrives at an overall judgement and explains it, gaining the highest level for this type of question.

Try out these judgement questions for yourself, using this book to help you:

1. How far were the Nazi youth groups able to control the young population? Explain your answer.
2. To what extent was the Munich Putsch a threat to the Weimar Republic? Explain your answer.
3. To what extent was Hitler able to keep his promises to the German people?
4. How far was life for ordinary Germans better under the Nazis?
5. 'The Gestapo were in total control of German people from 1933 to 1945.' How far do you agree with this statement?

Examiner's tip

You need to start your answer with a statement that answers the questions. Judgement questions require partial answers so that you agree/disagree with the statement to a certain extent. You then need to explain the reasons why you might agree and also the reasons why you don't. At the end of your answer, you need to make it very clear which set of arguments you most agree with and explain why. The conclusion should be an extension of your opening statement.

Exam**Café**

Welcome

Following the completion of the Depth Study, you will need to make sure that the material and skills you have covered are learned fully. This involves a revision programme to make sure that when you go through to the exam you are as well prepared as possible to recall the required material and have the skill to use it effectively to answer the set questions. Revision, therefore, is not simply the repetition of the facts that you have learned but the last part of a complex training programme. This Exam Café is designed to help you through the last phase and to help you to be as well prepared as possible for the big event.

Revision

REVISION TIPS

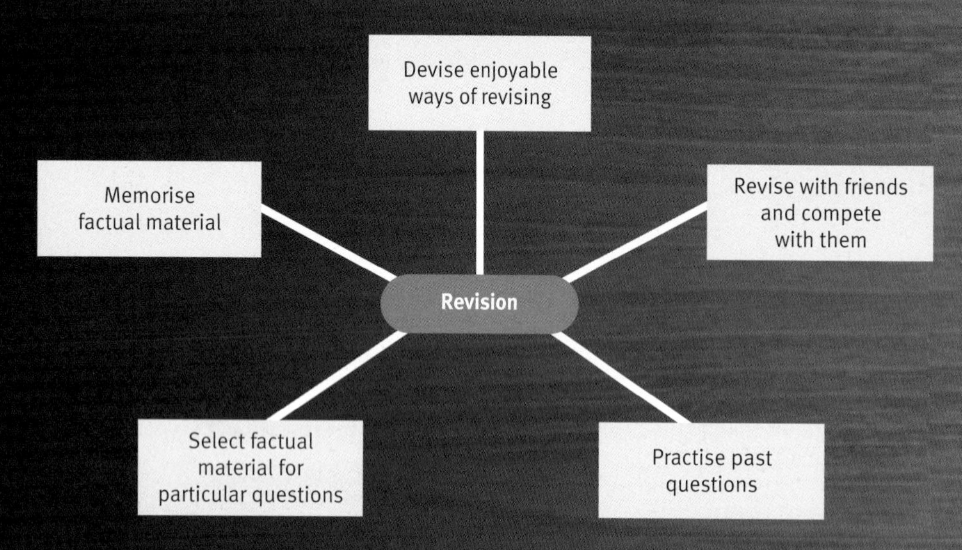

Revision should be hard work up to a point because you will be trying your best to pass your exam. However, if you are stressed and tired and if the types of revision exercises you choose to do are longwinded and dull, you will not be getting the best out of your revision programme. The best tip is to do 'little and often', and mixing up the different tasks will keep it fresh. Try to do the more difficult tasks like answering past questions for when you have energy and do the more fun things for when you feel tired.

Revision lists and mnemonics

The temptation with content revision is to read and write. Students who simply re-read the textbook or their exercise books could be spending that time in a far more useful way. Similarly, copying out large passages of material is an inefficient use of time. Revise smarter, not harder.

Consider the two examples below. The student is trying to revise the issue of whether people benefited from Nazi rule. The student has used the textbook to put together the following.

Example 1

Many people enjoyed better living conditions because the Nazis cut unemployment. The programmes that the Nazis started helped many thousands back to work. These people were also happier at the more stable political situation. As a leader, Hitler had restored their pride in their country. They felt that the government was working towards building a great Germany and was attacking the natural enemies of the Germans, namely the Jews and the Communists. On the other hand, some people suffered greatly under the Nazis. Many millions were sent to concentration camps and most of them died there. Ordinary people lived in fear and were unable to speak their minds. At the end of the war, Germany was a broken nation and the people in it had suffered greatly.

Example 2

Jobs, stability, pride, camps, fear, war.

Of the two the first one has some merit if it is to answer a specific question; however, the second one is a far better method of revising. Firstly, it will physically take less time but it also needs explaining to be useful. This means that the thinking process that put it together in the first place will have to be repeated when the list is revisited. Explaining it to a friend will also serve to reinforce the learning. Remember, what is important is what is in your head, not what you can get down on the paper, at least at the revision stage.

Another advantage of lists is that you can make mnemonics and/ or words from them. Look at the list below. Can you work out what it is for?

Rhineland, borders, empire, army, reparations, blame.

You may have noticed that if you take the beginning letter of each word that you can make the word b-a-r-b-e-r. 'Barber' could be a useful way to remember the key clauses of the Treaty of Versailles.

Similarly, if a friend said to you: 'My mum went round every newsagent', you may feel that, pleasant though it is to have a conversation, you are not really interested in their mother's shopping habits. If you consider that it is a mnemonic for the key events in the Nazis seizure of power, then perhaps it becomes more interesting: **M**unich Putsch, ***M**ein Kampf*, **W**all Street Crash, **R**eichstag fire, **E**nabling Act and **N**ight of the Long Knives.

Short quizzes

Quizzes with a few questions, requiring short answers, are a very good way of testing factual recall and can be fun. Using the resources from your course and the textbook, it is easy to construct very simple quizzes to share with your friends. One way of doing it is to start each quiz with the same question word, for example, 'Who? Why? When? Where?', and so on. Below are some examples of short quizzes:

'Who' quiz

1. Who was the Nazi Minister of Propaganda?
2. Who was the leading Nazi murdered during the Night of the Long Knives?
3. Who were the two Presidents of the Weimar Republic?
4. Who was responsible for the production of armaments after 1942?
5. Who were the SS leaders who devised the 'Final Solution'?
6. Who was the leading Nazi who was a fighter pilot during the First World War?

'When' quiz

1. When did Hitler and Drexler write the 25-point programme of the Nazi Party?
2. When was the worst month of hyperinflation?
3. When was the Reichstag fire?
4. When did Germany invade Poland to begin the Second World War?
5. When did Gustav Stresemann die? Why is this year significant?
6. When did the Nazis pass the Nuremburg Laws against the Jews?

Spider diagrams

Ideas-mapping is a good way to structure an answer even before you begin to write. It is acceptable to draw a spider diagram in the exam to help you, though you should put a line through it to show the examiner that it should not be marked as part of the answer. Below is a spider diagram constructed to help with a part **b** question.

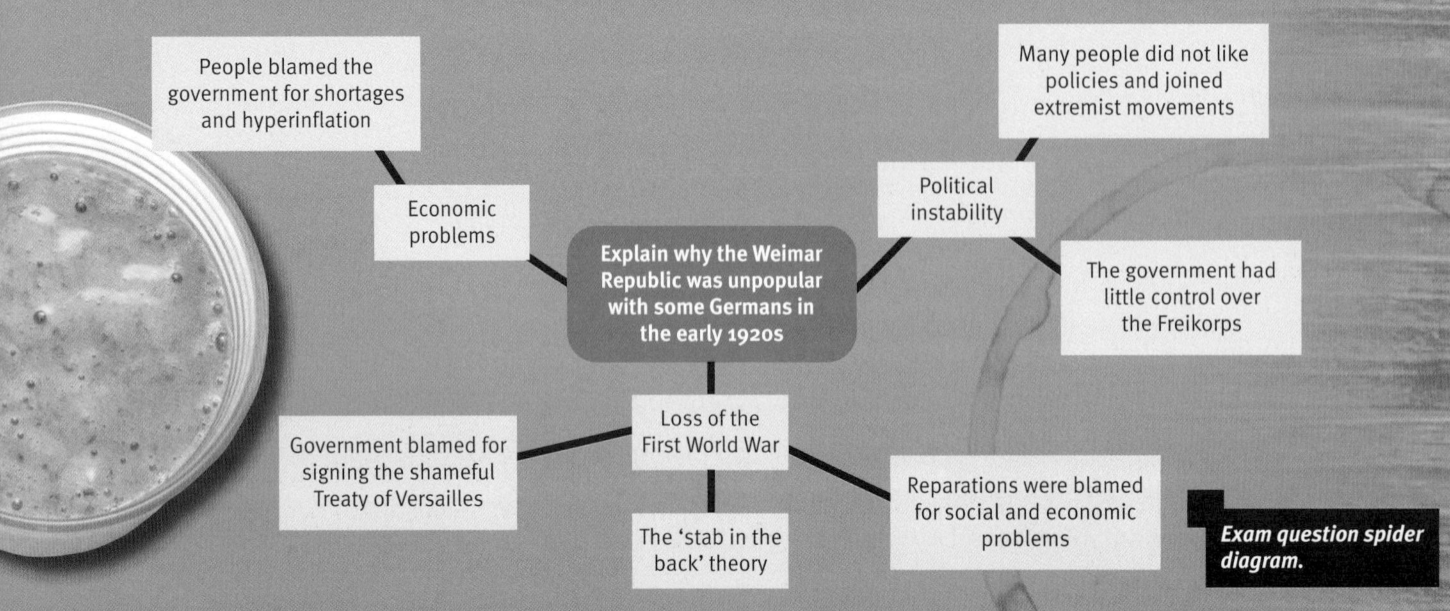

Exam question spider diagram.

Revision activities with cards

It would be useful to make a set of cards to use for a variety of revision exercises. They should be approximately 7 cm by 4 cm and each group below will need to be on different coloured card:

- Group 1: Adolf Hitler, Gustav Stresemann, Paul von Hindenburg, Heinrich Himmler, Hermann Goering, Josef Goebbels
- Group 2: Franz von Papen, Hjalmar Schacht, Ernst Rohm, Albert Speer, Friedrich Ebert, Reinhardt Heydrich
- Group 3: hyperinflation, reparations, Great Depression, motorways and swimming pools, rearmament, slave labour
- Group 4: Weimar Constitution, Treaty of Versailles, Dawes Plan, decree of the 28 February 1933, the Enabling Act, law combining the offices of President and Chancellor
- Group 5: sterilisation, Nuremburg Laws, *Kristallnacht*, euthanasia, Wansee Conference, Holocaust
- Group 6: Weimar nightclubs, modern art, Nazi propaganda, 'Strength through Joy', Hitler Youth, education.

Card-sort activities are a very good way of productively using information in new and creative ways, reinforcing previously learned material without necessarily repeating the activities. The tasks below are a selection of examples but you can easily invent other exercises. You might even wish to take the individuals and construct your own trump game.

Chronology

Putting events into chronological order is a useful exercise. You do not always need to use all the cards but can take a random selection each time. You may need to give the individuals some criteria, like when they first get a mention, or when they achieved power or when they died. If you do this in pairs, the criteria themselves can provide a useful point for debate.

Ranking order

Putting people and events in ranking order is a very good way of stimulating thinking about the material. It could be simply a question of putting things in order of importance at the time, or in order of lasting significance. You could construct a rank of reasonable behaviour or a rank of charismatic individuals. There are two basic ways of doing ranking exercises. Either start with all the cards in the selection face up and work through or have a small pack face down and turn them over one at a time.

Doing ranking exercises in groups or pairs is a good idea because it stimulates discussion about the material in question. Using material in creative ways is far better than bland repetition and has been shown to be a far more effective way of retaining information.

Grouping

This is similar to ranking but takes out the comparative element and deals with the material on its own terms. Groups can be as simple as 'Things I know a lot about', 'Things I know a little about' and 'Things I know nothing about'. They can also be linked to some aspect of the material like 'Helpful to Hitler', 'Not helpful to Hitler' and 'Not relevant'.

In some cases, you can create Venn diagrams by having groups with some overlap. A simple example may be 'To do with the Weimar government', and 'To do with the Nazi government'. There will be some cards that fit both, like Paul von Hindenburg, for example.

As with the ranking exercises, what is important is not simply making the choice but justifying it. That is why doing revision with friends is so useful, someone arguing back makes the discussion real and forces you to come up with points that you can defend. In a way, this mirrors the demands of the examination.

Card games

There is no limit to the number of games you can devise with the cards; the only requirement is that it involves some factual recall linked to the cards.

One game is where each player is dealt a hand of seven cards and holds them so that the other players can see the backs of the cards they hold. In turn, they then have to guess what cards the other players are holding by indicating which of the other players' cards they have nominated and then guessing what is on it. If they guess correctly, they get the card from the player. When they have got the six in the group, they place them on the table and that group is out of the game. If the player does not guess correctly, they must take a card from the pack and give it to another player of their choice.

A variation of this is where the cards are shuffled and placed face down. Players then take it in turns to guess which card is next. If they guess correctly, they get the card.

For both these games, a variation could be that a player can only retain cards if he or she can provide a piece of relevant contextual knowledge to the satisfaction of the other players. Also, the level of support can be reduced as the games are played. At the beginning, each player may have a list of the groups or the textbook to help and these aids can be removed as players get more familiar with the cards.

COMMON MISTAKES

- **Topic-related answers**. In the heat of the exam, students can read the question and get the topic area stuck in their minds. Often, they write what they know about that topic and do not answer the question. For example, a question like: 'Explain why the Jews were attacked so violently on *Kristallnacht*' is a question that may mislead students who do not read it carefully. A student producing an answer that describes the events of that night may know a lot about it but will not really be answering the question. The question requires the student to explain the causes of it, not focus on the event itself.
- **Having a poor understanding of the big picture**. This is still important in the depth study. Understanding the order of events and the years that they occurred is something that is always shown as a weakness by students attempting the exam. The use and/or construction of timelines and using the card exercises can help.
- **Writing too little**. If you don't write it, the examiner cannot give you credit for it. Exams are marked positively so giving the examiner enough possibilities to award marks is the way to give yourself the best chance.
- **Running out of time**. Discipline with time is very important. If you get stuck, don't waste time. It is better to move on to the next question. You can always go back and add more at the end as long as you make it clear to the examiner that you have continued an answer at the end of the exam script.

REVISION CHECKLIST

Look at the revision checklist below to see where you can make some lists of key factors and then create a mnemonic or word to remember them by. You could then give this to a friend, tell them the theme and see whether they can work out what the letters stand for.

The table below outlines the key content of the course. It is not necessary to be able to tick the final column for every row but a good spread of expertise should hold you in good stead for the examination. If you keep going back to this, you will be able to see where your weaknesses lie.

Area	Details	I have little knowledge of this	I have some knowledge of this	I have a lot of knowledge of this
The First World War and its settlement	Spring offensive, Russia and the United States, The 'stab in the back', main clauses of the Treaty of Versailles			
The birth of Weimar	Spartacist Uprising, role of the Freikorps, Kapp Putsch, hyperinflation, Munich Putsch			
The Golden Age of Weimar	Art, music and theatre, standards of living, foreign policy			
Germany and the Great Depression	Wall Street Crash, consequences of Great Depression for Germany, rise of the Communists and the Nazis, move to government by decree, role of Schleicher and Papen			
The rise of the Nazis	Early life of Adolf Hitler, Drexler and the founding of the party, the 25-point programme, the Munich Putsch, *Mein Kampf*, the SA and the SS, success in elections			
The Nazi seizure of power	Reichstag fire, Enabling Act, banning other parties, banning trade unions, anti-Jewish laws, Night of the Long Knives, death of Hindenburg and the combining of the role of President and Chancellor and the new title, 'Führer'.			
Impact of the Nazis on ordinary Germans	Public works projects, freedom of big business, Hjalmar Schacht, the four-year plan, 'Strength through Joy', national pride			
Nazis keeping control	Concentration camps, Gestapo, propaganda, 'Hitler myth', policies with young people and women			
Impact of the Second World War	Blitzkrieg and victories, total war, British and American bombing campaign, shortages, invasion of Germany			
Nazis and the Jews	Anti-Semitism, Nuremburg Laws, *Kristallnacht*, *Einsatzgruppen*, Wansee Conference, 'Final Solution', Holocaust			

Revision checklist.

EXAM PREPARATION

'Without the support of the young, Hitler could not have controlled Germany.' How far do you agree with this statement?

Sample student answer

Response 1

The young were very important to Hitler. Lots of them joined the Hitler Youth and learned to be like good soldiers. Girls could join the League of German Girls and learn skills that would help them at home. The Hitler Youth met nearly every evening and weekend. They would learn how to survive outdoors and play lots of sport. They would learn about German history. Girls would learn how to cook traditional German recipes and to make and repair clothes.

Examiner says
A straight answer to the question is a good way to begin.

Examiner says
Here the candidate identifies reasons why they agree.

Examiner says
This is description and does not really answer the question. Be careful not to just write what you know about the subject. You must answer the question.

Response 2

Young people were important to Hitler because they were easily brainwashed. This meant that sometimes they would listen to Hitler or the Nazis rather than their parents. There are examples of children informing the police when their parents said something against the Nazis. This helped Hitler keep control because people were afraid. When the children grew up, they would become soldiers and fight in the war. Germany was successful in the early years of the Second World War because so many young people had learned soldiering in the Hitler Youth.

Examiner says
The candidate has used evidence to back up their argument.

Examiner says
Up to here, the candidate has explained one side of the argument.

Examiner says
Here, the candidate is starting to explain the reasons.

Examiner says
This is other side of the argument.

Response 3

It was not just the young who helped Hitler take control. When he was made Chancellor in 1933, it was Papen who thought that the rich and powerful could control him. As time went on and Hitler got more powerful, rich people realised they could do well from the Nazis and did not want to upset things. In 1934, even the army generals were on Hitler's side after the Night of the Long Knives. Having support in lots of areas helped Hitler to control Germany, not just from the young.

Examiner says
The candidate has explained and then supported with evidence.

Examiner says
The answer finishes with a short statement that directly answers the question.

Understanding exam language

The key to exam success is being able to recall the material and use it to *effectively construct an answer* to a given question. Understanding the requirements of the question is a very important part of the process and decoding it is something that could be worked on.

Question words	Type of question	Tips
Briefly describe...	(a)	Remember the 'power of five'. In the mark scheme, the examiner will be looking to reward each relevant point with a mark. If you provide a good explanation, the examiner can reward that with a mark. If you are not sure that all your points are relevant, you may make some extra ones or add further explanation. Remember that the examiner can only give you five marks for this question, so do not waste too much time on it. A quick answer that gets four will serve better than a drawn-out answer that gets five but leaves you with less time to answer the other questions.
Explain why...	(b)	Explanation is key here. At least two reasons must be identified to have a chance of achieving the highest level. Providing three factors with three substantial arguments may give you insurance against one of your factors or explanations being wide of the mark. Again, do not waste time looking for a perfect answer, be satisfied with a good one.
Which was more important...	(c)	You need to make a choice here and justify it. Find reasons why one is more important and then explain it. Then, find reasons why the other is less important. There is no right or wrong here, it is a test of whether you can argue.
'How far...' or 'To what extent...'	(c)	Explain reasons why it is and also explain reasons why it is not. If you can arrive at a final judgement, you will be in with a chance of achieving the highest level.
Study source...	Source-based	The source-based questions are looking for a mix of explanation of the source with explanation of contextual knowledge.

Decoding the question.

Time management

As a rough guide, allow ten minutes' reading time. Then take the remainder of the time and divide it by the number of marks available on the whole paper. This will give you the time per mark. You can then times this by the number of marks available for each question. This is the approximate time that you should spend on each question. If you can produce a reasonable description answer, that will also give you more time for thinking about the more complex 'explain and evaluate' questions.

Glossary

Allies – *countries that fight together against a common enemy.*

Anti-Semitism – *hatred of Jews.*

Asocials – *people who belong outside normal society.*

Auschwitz – *village in southern Poland where two important camps were built. The work camp called Auschwitz 1 and the death camp at Auschwitz Birkenau.*

Autarky – *national self-sufficiency – when a country is able to produce everything that it needs.*

Black Market – *unofficial buying and selling in order to get round the rules of rationing.*

Blitzkrieg – *lightning war. A modern style of warfare used very successfully by the German Army in the first three years of the war.*

Bolsheviks – *Russian Communists.*

Christian – *follower of Jesus Christ.*

Civil liberties – *rights enjoyed by ordinary people.*

Coalition government – *government formed by more than one party.*

Communists – *supporters of a system of politics where everybody owns things collectively and gets an equal share.*

Concentration camp – *large camp surrounded by barbed wire which housed political prisoners and slave labourers.*

Cult of personality – *movement to portray the leader as all-powerful.*

Curriculum – *subjects learned in school.*

Decree – *law made by the leader, not the parliament.*

Dictator – *someone who has absolute control of a country.*

Dictatorship – *state that is ruled by a single individual who has total power.*

Economic depression – *period where confidence in business is low and unemployment is high.*

Economy – *the interaction of everything connected with money.*

Einsatzgruppen – *groups of SS whose job was to dispose of undesirable people.*

Empire – *group of territories ruled by another country.*

Euthanasia – *killing people in order to prevent suffering.*

Feudal system – *system of regional control with a king and powerful barons.*

'Final Solution' – *plan to kill all the Jews in Europe.*

Freedom of speech – *the right to express your opinion.*

Freikorps – *groups of ex-soldiers who remained armed.*

Führer – *German word for leader, adopted by Hitler as his title in place of 'Chancellor'.*

Führer principle – *the idea that the leader knows best.*

Gauleiters – *regional Nazi Party leaders.*

Genocide – *attempt to murder a whole race of people.*

Gestapo – *Nazi secret police.*

Gleichschaltung – *coordination of all state institutions under Nazi control.*

Holocaust – *attempt by the Nazis to kill all the Jews in Europe during the Second World War.*

Hyperinflation – *out-of-control inflation, causing a country's currency to become worthless in a short period of time.*

Landjahr – *a year of national service for young adults.*

League of Nations – *international organisation of countries devised to aid cooperation and to prevent war.*

Lieutenant – *an assistant to the leader.*

Manifesto – *document produced by a political party showing its policies.*

Manual workers – *a person who may, for example, work in a factory or outdoors and who performs physical work.*

Mark – *German currency.*

Martyrdom – *dying for a cause.*

Mobilisation – *putting things on a war footing (particularly armies or armaments industries).*

Munich Agreement – *made between the UK, France, Italy and Germany. It gave Hitler's Germany the parts of Czechoslovakia that Hitler claimed rightfully belonged to Germany.*

National self-determination – *the right of people of the same nationality to live in their own country.*

National Socialism – *idea that a strong leader and cooperation would benefit Germany.*

Nationalisation – *where the state takes control of important industries.*

Nationalists – *people who support their country, often to excess.*

Nazis – *slang term for Hitler's political party, the NSDAP.*

Paramilitary – *amateur soldiers working for a political party.*

Pogrom – *large-scale act of violence usually against Jews.*

Power vacuum – *situation without any clear group in control.*

Propaganda – *the use of information to make people think in a certain way.*

Protestant – *Christian but not a member of the Roman Church.*

Purge – *getting rid of unwanted people, usually by murdering them.*

Purpose – *the reason why something is made.*

Putsch – *revolution.*

Racial theory – *idea that different racial groups are superior or inferior.*

Rally – *large meeting, often outdoors, of a political party. Nazi rallies were often held at Nuremburg and were attended by over 100,000 people.*

Rationing – *limiting the amount of food and goods available to civilians during wartime.*

Refugees – *people who have to leave their homes due to some catastrophe.*

Reich – *German word for empire.*

Reichstag – *German parliament.*

Reparations – *money paid by Germany to France and Britain to compensate them for their losses from the First World War.*

Retrojection – *judging historical figures with the use of unreasonable hindsight.*

Right of assembly – *the right to organise meetings.*

Roman Catholic – *member of the Church of Rome.*

Rural – *in the countryside.*

Schutz Staffeln (SS) – *a large organisation within the Nazi Party run by Heinrich Himmler.*

Shares – *documents giving part-ownership of companies.*

Significance – *importance.*

Social Darwinism – *application of Darwin's idea about the survival of the fittest to different groups of people.*

Spartacists – *communist revolutionary group.*

Standard of living – *the quality of food and goods you are able to buy.*

Sterilisation – *biologically removing people's ability to reproduce.*

***Sturm Abteilung* (SA)** – *the paramilitary wing of the Nazi Party.*

Total war – *government takes special powers to focus all the country's effort on the war.*

Totalitarian – *state ruled by one party, often with harsh rules and restrictions on freedom.*

Totalitarian dictatorship – *government by a small unelected minority, with one man having absolute power.*

Treason – *crime against the state.*

Treaty – *agreement between nations.*

Utility – *how useful a source is.*

Welfare – *state support for the very poor.*

Workers – *people who work with their hands.*

Zeitgeist – *the spirit of the times; things that symbolise those times to people in future generations.*

Index